Computer Aided Design with Unigraphics V18

*Engineering Design in Computer
Integrated Design and Manufacturing*

Second Edition

H. Felix Lee
and
David W. Fulton

Southern Illinois University--Edwardsville

 KENDALL/HUNT PUBLISHING COMPANY
4050 Westmark Drive   Dubuque, Iowa 52002

Book Team

Chairman and Chief Executive Officer   Mark C. Falb
Vice President, Director of National Book Program   Alfred C. Grisanti
Editorial Development Supervisor   Georgia Botsford
Developmental Editor   Angela Willenbring
Prepress Project Coordinator   Sheri Hosek
Prepress Editor   Victoria D. Noel
Design Manager   Jodi Splinter

Dedication

To my parents and wife, Guim, and children, Jake and Joshua

- HFL

For my wife, Barbara, our grown up, married children and children-in-law, Keith and Emmanuelle, Kyle and Ginger, and Kara and Cris, and our precious grandchildren, Matthew, Elizabeth, Natasha, Nicholas, and Stella.

- DWF

TABLE OF CONTENTS

Chapter 4.　　　Primitives

Chapter 5.　　　Basic Form Features

Chapter 6.   Querying and Editing Models

Chapter 7.   Feature Operations on Edge and Face

Chapter 8.   Reference Features

Chapter 9.   Boolean Operations and Swept Features

Chapter 10. Introduction to Sketch

Chapter 11. Instance, Trim Body, and Thread Features

Chapter 12.   Introduction to Assembly Modeling

Chapter 13.   Master Model

Chapter 14.　　Introduction to Drafting

Appendix A. Guided Student Assembly Project: Geneva CAM Assembly Model

About the Authors

H. Felix Lee

H. Felix Lee is Professor of Department of Mechanical and Industrial Engineering at Southern Illinois University at Edwardsville. He holds a Ph.D. in Industrial and Operations Engineering from the University of Michigan, an M.S. in Industrial Engineering and Management from Oklahoma State University, and a B.S. in Industrial Engineering from Hanyang University in S. Korea. His area of interest is in computer integrated design and manufacturing. He renovated Manufacturing Engineering curriculum and courses with introduction of Unigraphics CAD/CAM/CAE/PDM, and has taught students and Boeing engineers with these courses. He was a recipient of a NSF research grant on developing an integrated design-aid tool for flexible manufacturing systems. Dr. Lee is a member of SME, IIE, INFORMS, Tau Beta Pi, and Phi Kappa Phi. His papers appear in numerous refereed journals, books, and proceedings.

David W. Fulton

David W. Fulton holds a B.S. in Mechanical Engineering from University of Missouri-Columbia. He has many years of industry experience as a design engineer and has taken various roles in computer engineering application customer support. The application support includes 15 years experience in computer aided design engineering in McDonnell Douglas and 12 years with Unigraphics Solutions (UGS) as a Unigraphics trainer, courseware development, curriculum development, and training manager.

Preface

The twenty-first century manufacturing environment can be characterized by the paradigm of delivering products of increasing variety, lower demand and higher quality in the context of expanding global competition. In order to realize this manufacturing paradigm and facilitate coordinated efforts across different departments, more and more companies are moving into computer-integrated production systems where computer technology is widely used to support design, manufacturing, and business operation in an integrated fashion. The core of this computer technology includes computer-aided design (CAD), computer-aided manufacturing (CAM), and computer-aided analysis (CAE).

This book is intended to introduce CAD using Unigraphics in order to support the design process. Unigraphics is a software product of UGS, Inc., headquartered in St. Louis, MO. Unigraphics is 3D solid modeling CAD/CAM/CAE software used by thousands of companies worldwide in diverse industries. They include automobiles, aircraft and spacecraft, and various consumer products including shavers, phones, appliances, motorbikes etc. Unigraphics is considered one of the top 3 mechanical design systems in the world. According to an independent study (Business Week Magazine) conducted in 1999, UGS was selected as one of the top-10 software companies in the world.

While the intent of this book is to introduce CAD with usage of Unigraphics, the focus of the book is on 3-D solid and assembly modeling to support various engineering design projects. We also introduce parametric and associative modeling to facilitate capturing the design intent and easy changes of designs.

This book can serve as a stand-alone text for Engineering Design or entry-level CAD/CAM courses in colleges and universities. Also this book can be used for Engineering Drawing courses that cover 3D modeling. No prerequisite is required. Instead of presenting all available functionalities and options of Unigraphics CAD like a look-up dictionary format, this book coherently organizes the key features and functionalities of Unigraphics CAD that are most commonly used in engineering design modeling. Thus, this book is suitable for one-semester usage for a 3 or 4 credit course.

This book is application-oriented and design-project based rather than involved in theories and mathematical derivations. It provides many projects to which students can apply the design and modeling concepts. This book can also serve as a supplement to upper-level CAD/CAM theory-oriented books by supplying applications to real design problems in industries. From our past teaching experience, we find these applications to motivate students to learn more about the subject.

The book consists of 14 chapters and 3 appendixes. Most chapters follow a common format. First, concepts of a modeling feature are presented, which is followed by activities, which demonstrates step-by-step how to carry out the concepts in Unigraphics. And then design projects are presented with brief guidelines so that students can further practice and solidify the concepts in the context of engineering design. These design projects can be used as classroom homework or test. There is usually more than one modeling approach to design projects. We find it very educational to compare different modeling approaches. Each chapter concludes with exercise problems to help students review what they learn in each chapter.

In Chapter 1 we give an overview of computer integrated design and manufacturing. We describe a product-life cycle, a product design process and CAD, and three geometric modeling methods for CAD to represent objects with a focus on solid modeling. We also present steps necessary to get started with Unigraphics.

In Chapter 2 we present a case study on CAD/CAM/CAE using Unigraphics. A simple part is used to take you though step-by-step from design, analysis, then to manufacturing of the part. The objective is to demonstrate how Unigraphics can support computer integrated design and manufacturing. Chapter 2 can be skipped if desired without losing any continuity. Alternatively, Chapter 2 can be covered after Chapter 13, since the case study of Chapter 2 uses the Master Modeling concept addressed in Chapter 13.

The rest of chapters deal with Unigraphics CAD. In Chapter 3 we present fundamental UG essentials that will be frequently used during a session with Unigraphics. In Chapters 4 to 11 we discuss different features used to build a 3D solid part. We suggest covering Chapters 3 to 11 in sequence since later chapters build on the previous chapter materials. In Chapter 12 we introduce different approaches to assembly modeling, putting together more than one part into an assembly. In Chapter 13 we discuss the concept of Master Model, which enables different engineering departments to concurrently work together with use of 3D solid models. In Chapter 14, we introduce Drafting, which is one application of the Master Model concept, showing how to create 2D drawings and dimensions from 3D solid models.

In Appendixes A and B, we provide extra design and assembly projects. Students use 2D drawings to build 3D solid models for individual parts from a scratch and then assemble them. In Appendix A, we provide detail steps for students to easily follow to build a Geneva Cam assembly model. These projects will serve as good opportunities to practice textbook materials in total and real setting. In Appendix C, we provide glossary of terms used in this book.

We use V18 throughout the book. In Appendix D, we present a summary of user interface changes between Unigraphics V16, 17, and 18 for those features used in this book. Unigraphics V16 or later version is fully Windows compliant and uses native Windows user interface technology.   For all V16, 17, and 18, the user interface is near identical for all the features used in this book, and thus this book is directly applicable for V16 and 17.   In this book we present a set of essential features most commonly used in solid modeling for engineering design. We do not expect a drastic change in these essential features (user interface or functionality) in future versions.

In order to assist instructors who use this book for their class teaching, we prepare the following items: (a) the solution WORD file for chapter review questions, (b) the Unigraphics part files for completed chapter activities and projects, (c) the Unigraphics part files for completed Appendix A and B projects. These items are available upon request to the book publisher by the instructors.

We are grateful to Hulas King of UGS for his constant support and encouragement, which made it possible to complete this book, and to UGS for providing an excellent source of reference material through various training documentations. Sean Kenney, who is a Boeing engineer, deserves a special mention for his significant contribution to Chapters 3 and 6. Discussions with him at the early phase of this book were valuable. Thanks also go to several students at our program, Kyle Knowlson, Matthew Grainger, Bryon Belter, Sam Hall, and Steve Arana for testing out design projects in Appendixes A and B, and to many Boeing Engineers who took classes on this subject and provided useful feedback on course material. Lastly we always remember our spouses and children for generously giving in their special time with us for our work toward this book.

H. Felix Lee

David W. Fulton

Chapter 1. Introduction

This chapter consists of three sections. In section 1.1, we give an overview of computer integrated design and manufacturing. We describe a product-life cycle, a product design process, and computer-aided design (CAD) and three geometric modeling methods for CAD to represent objects with a focus on solid modeling. We also give a brief introduction to computer-aided engineering analysis, and computer-aided manufacturing. In section 1.2 we give an introduction to Unigraphics to support computer integrated design and manufacturing. In section 1.3, we give a description and steps necessary to get started with Unigraphics.

1.1 Overview of Computer Integrated Design and Manufacturing

Traditional view of manufacturing is just the transformation of raw materials into value-added products meeting specifications. Present-day's view of manufacturing takes a much broader meaning. According to the CAM-I definition, manufacturing is defined as a series of interrelated activities and operations involving design, material selection, planning, production, quality assurance, management, and marketing of discrete consumer and durable goods. This broader view puts more emphasis on coordinated efforts across different departments within manufacturing companies.

The twenty-first century manufacturing environment can be characterized by the paradigm of delivering products of increasing variety, lower demand and higher quality in the context of expanding global competition. This implies manufacturing products for mass market in such a way that products are customized for each individual in that market. In order to realize this manufacturing paradigm and facilitate coordinated efforts across different departments, more and more companies are moving into computer-integrated production systems where computer technology is widely used to support design, manufacturing, and business operation in an integrated fashion. The core of this computer technology includes computer-aided design (CAD) and computer-aided manufacturing (CAM), and computer-aided analysis (CAE).

In order for a manufacturing company to succeed, it must deliver products to customers at the minimum possible cost, the best possible quality, and the minimum lead time starting from the product conception stage to final delivery, service, and disposal. As a result, a product has to be understood in a much broader context and the overall performance of the product during its life cycle becomes important. The product life cycle includes the following four phases: design phase, manufacturing phase, product usage phase, and disposal phase. Opportunities for reduction in cost and leadtime and improvements in product quality must be sought from all the areas of a product-life cycle. However, the design phase is most critical, determining the product success or failure in the market place. This is because it has a direct impact on product cost, quality, and manufacturing process yields, future maintenance costs, and cost to dispose of the product after its usage. According to Dransfield (1994), about 80% of the product cost is fixed at the design stage, and it is easier and less costly to change the design at the early design phase.

Product Design Process

Product design is a complex process. It requires a cross-functional team consisting of not only design engineers but also various individuals from manufacturing, financing, marketing, and etc. There are different approaches to product design but we give one adopted by Earle (1992). This approach consists of the following six steps.

1. Problem Identification. This step is to identify the attributes of the need for which the product is being designed (what customers want). This involves collection of field data via field surveys, personal observations, and physical measurements.

2. Preliminary Ideas. With the product attributes of specific need identified from the previous step, this step is to generate preliminary ideas with

respect to technical choices, materials, design complexities, and so on. Usually brain storming sessions among the cross-functional team members are needed in this step.

3. Refinement Process. This step is to refine product ideas using geometric models. Among the preliminary ideas from step 2, several good ideas are pursued in this step in terms of space requirements and critical measurement and dimensions. The use of geometric modeling is useful in visualizing and determining the identity of the product.

4. Analysis Process. This step is to analyze product designs from the point of view of many criteria such as cost, weight, functional requirements, and marketability. Engineering analysis tools such as finite-element methods (for strength, stress, deformation analyses) and assembly analysis tools (for tolerance and weight analyses) can be used to evaluate alternative designs.

5. Decision Process. This step is to select a design that has all the desirable characteristics including ease of assembly, manufacturability, maintainability, etc. A decision matrix approach can be adopted to make a best trade-off solution by using proper weighting schemes for various attributes among design alternatives.

6. Implementation Process. This step is to provide a detailed design providing detailed specifications with respect to materials, dimensions, tolerances, surface roughness, and so on. This involves creating the drawings to be used directly for developing process plans so that the product can be manufactured.

The above design process is an iterative process, usually engaging these six steps several times before the final design is selected that best meets design criteria.

Computer-Aided Design (CAD)

CAD refers to the design process with the aid of computers. Thus, computers do not change the nature of the design process. Design engineers provide knowledge and creativity and control the entire design process from the problem identification step to the implementation step. Computers contribute to improving the efficiency and productivity of the design process. This is because computers can accurately generate easily modifiable geometry models of products, perform complex design analysis at fast speed, and manage information and design knowledge with consistency and speed.

CAD technology has evolved over the last three decades. The development of the SKETCHPAD system by Ivan Sutherland at MIT in 1962 could be considered the beginning of CAD. This system allowed a user to interact graphically with the computer, via a visual display and light pen. CAD in the early 1960s was mainly a two-dimensional (2D) drafting system. Then it was extended to three-dimensional (3D) models with development of wireframe-based modeling systems. It was not possible, however, to represent a higher-order geometry data such as surface data. As a result, surface-based models were developed in the early 1970s. These surface-based models had also limitations. They could not represent solid or volume enclosure information. The need for solid modeling grew with increasing demand of numerical control (NC) code generation for manufacturing and mesh generation for engineering analysis. A volume representation of parts was also necessary to perform topological validity checks. The solid modeling technology has evolved since the mid-1970s.

In the 1980s, assembly modeling was introduced in response to the need of automobile and aircraft industries. Assembly modeling allows putting together various parts of 3-D solid models into an assembly, and managing and performing analyses for an assembly. Soon after, parametric modeling was introduced to make it easy to modify designs and geometric models. At the early design phase, product requirements and product designs are prone to change, which leads to frequent changes in product geometries. Parametric modeling allows dimension-driven capability. This means that an object is defined by a set of dimensions (parameters) for which designers can change their values at any time during the design process. The latest development has been knowledge-based engineering systems that can capture both geometric and non-geometric product information such as engineering rules, part dependences, and manufacturing constraints, which result in more complete product definitions. CAD is becoming more popular as computer technology with higher speed, larger memory, and smaller size is more available and affordable.

Geometric Modeling

We discussed earlier that the third step of the product design process is the refinement process, which involves developing geometric models of a product from the conceptual ideas. Geometric modeling refers to a set of techniques concerned mainly with developing efficient representations of geometric aspects of a design. The geometric information about a part includes types of surfaces and edges and their dimensions and tolerances. Thus, geometry modeling is a heart of CAD. Traditionally, the geometric information about a part was provided on blueprints by a drafter. Today, such information is directly transferred from the CAD files to the CAM files to perform subsequent manufacturing of the part or to the CAE files to conduct subsequent analyses of the part. Clearly this helps to significantly reduce product development and manufacturing leadtime. In Chapter 2, we will present a case study to demonstrate this notion.

There are three basic geometric modeling approaches available in CAD. They are wireframe, surface, and solid modeling. Wireframe modeling is one of the most basic methods among these. It uses points and curves (lines, circles, arcs, conics, and spline curves) to define objects. For example, a user may enter 3D vertices, say (x, y, z)'s, and then join the vertices to form a 3D object. Figure 1.1 shows a wireframe model of a part.

Part A

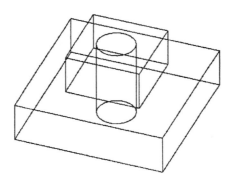

Figure 1.1 Wireframe model of Part A

This is simple and straightforward in concept but has limitations such as:

a. With wireframe modeling, it is not possible to calculate volume and mass properties of a design. It cannot support numeric control (NC) path generation, cross-sections, and interference detection since wireframe modeling contains only low-level information such as points and lines.

b. It can create ambiguous representations of real objects. For example, it is not clear if the wireframe model of Figure 1.2 represents a block or an inward corner. A similar problem occurs between a boss and a hole.

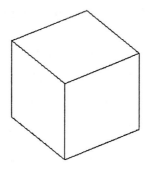

Figure 1.2 Ambiguous representation: block or inward corner

c. Wireframe modeling usually requires more user input to create models than solid modeling. For example, a 3D wireframe model of a simple cube requires12 lines while a 3D solid model of the same cube requires positions of only 3 corner points.

In wireframe modeling, we take advantage of the simplicity of certain surfaces. For example, a plane is represented by its boundaries. Nothing is said about the middle of the plane. Shapes of cars, airplanes, ships and so forth do not simply consist of standard geometry such as planes and cylinders but curved surfaces. Surface modeling contains definitions of surfaces, edges and vertices. Parametric techniques popularized by Coons were adopted as a way of precisely describing the curvature of a surface in all three dimensions. The Bezier, B-spline, and NURBS surfaces are three types of surfaces based on third-degree parametric curves. Precise, mathematically defined curved surfaces are a must in the aerospace, automotive, and shipbuilding industries. In many cases, information about the surface of the object is the most critical element in manufacturing the product, and can be used directly by analysis and manufacturing software tools.

One general weakness of surface modelers is their inability to handle topology. For example, if you have a series of patches that form a closed-volume model and you drill a hole in the model, you will pass through an infinitely thin surface into a void, for which no information is available. To handle this situation, the user or the system must cover over the inside of the hole. Some surface models simply do not have the flexibility to make this sort of topological modification easily. Surface modeling does not provide information on the component's inside and outside. As a result, a surface modeling system may not guarantee that the user has designed a realizable object. That is, the collection of surfaces may not define a physical part.

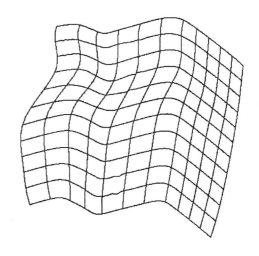

Figure 1.3 Example of a curved surface: shaded and wireframe views

Solid modeling becomes more popular because it has many advantages over wireframe modeling and surface modeling. Solid modeling can support applications to manufacturing and engineering analysis such as finite-element analysis, NC part programming, and generation of CAPP (computer aided process planning. It can be used to evaluate size, shape, and weight of products early during the conceptual design phase. It can give complete and unambiguous representation of objects. There are several solid modeling techniques available, but here we will introduce two common ones. These two are boundary representation (BREP) and constructive solid geometry (CSG).

BREP describes the geometry of an object in terms of its boundaries, namely vertices, edges and surfaces, and direction of the face normal to indicate inside or outside the material. A real object is formed and bounded. For example, three planes do not form a solid object. Euler's equations are used to ensure validity of BREP models.

CSG constructs a model by simple solid objects, called primitives or entities such as blocks, cylinder, cone, and sphere. These solid entities are not simply objects by lines and vertices but objects that occupy space. Thus, intersection of two solid entities creates a more complex object. These primitives are arranged using Boolean operators. There are three types of Boolean operations: Union (U), difference (—), and intersection (∩). For example, CSG models the part of Figure 1.1 consisting of three primitives: a large block A, a small block B, and a cylinder C. CSG constructs the part as {A U B} — C.

The structure is concise and relatively less storage but slow in displaying the objects. It is usually converted internally into BREP to display the model or generate the wireframe drawing. CSG provides easier input and BREP provides faster display and line drawing. CSG serves as an underlying modeling method that will be used to create various models throughout this book.

Computer-Aided Engineering (CAE)Analysis

Engineering analysis is concerned with analysis and evaluation of engineering product designs. There are a number of computer-aided engineering analysis techniques available for this purpose. They include finite-element analysis (FEA), tolerance analysis, design optimization, mechanism analysis, and mass property analysis. Mass information of 3-D solid models helps calculate the forces acting on a part. A real-world object is a continuous mass that responds in a very complex manner to forces acting on it. FEA is one of the most frequently used analysis techniques in engineering applications. FEA is a powerful numerical analysis. It divides an object into a number of small building blocks, called finite elements in order to evaluate the functional performances of the object such as stresses and deflections. This division process is called meshing. Each element is a simple shape such as a triangle, a square, or cube, etc. These elements are connected at node points. The unknowns for each element are the displacements at the node points. The finite-element program develops governing equations in the form of a matrix such that it assembles the matrices for these simple elements to form the global matrix for the entire model. This matrix is solved for the unknown displacements, given the known forces and boundary conditions. From the displacement at the nodes, the functional performances in each element are then calculated.

FEA usually employs the following steps.
1. Meshing
2. Selection of the solution approximation
3. Development of element matrices and equations
4. Assembly of the element equations
5. Solutions for the unknown at the nodes
6. Interpretation of the result

Instead of having real forces exerted on real models, hypothetical forces can be applied to a solid model in FEA. This helps to avoid the often-destructive results for physical prototypes and to reduce costs and lead times for design and manufacturing. We give a case study in Chapter 2 for demonstration of CAE and FEA.

Computer-Aided Manufacturing (CAM)

Solid modeling techniques can be combined with CAM capabilities to ensure that a product design satisfies the desired manufacturability requirement as closely as possible. In addition, these techniques speed the transition from design to manufacturing by reducing or eliminating the need for traditional working or production drawings. Solid models can be made to what each part will look like at each stage of the manufacturing process. These models provide information used to determine how much time, material, and labor would be required to manufacture the product as modeled. If special types of tooling (e.g., cutters, jigs, etc.) are required, solid models can also be made for them.

More and more, the machinery used for fabrication is programmed using the computer models of each part. The information related to the model is translated into manufacturing operations by specialized programs. These programs control the machine tools through a process called numeric control (NC). Originally, information was provided NC machines by punched tapes. Improvements in technology have led to the full-scale integration of CAD and CAM. This means less translation and less chance for error. Simulations of the tool cutting action is created and tested on solid models before actual materials and equipment are used. This cuts down on material waste and reduces troubleshooting time, freeing up the equipment for greater use in production.

1. 2 Introduction to Unigraphics

Unigraphics is an interactive CAD/CAM/CAE system. The CAD functions automate the normal engineering, design, and drafting capabilities found in today's manufacturing companies. The CAM functions provide NC programming for modern machine tools using the Unigraphics design model to describe the finished part. The CAE functions provide the analyses of the design model to check if the part can satisfy design requirements in mechanical, thermal, or dynamic aspects.

Unigraphics functions are divided into "applications" of common capabilities. These applications are supported by a prerequisite application called Unigraphics Gateway. Every Unigraphics user must have Unigraphics Gateway; however, the other applications are optional and may be configured to meet the needs of each individual user.

Unigraphics is a fully three-dimensional, double precision system that can accurately describe almost any geometric shape. By combining these shapes, you can design, analyze, and create drawings of your products.

Once the design is complete and analyzed, the Manufacturing application allows you to select the geometry describing the part, enter manufacturing information such as cutter diameter, and automatically generate a *cutter location source file* (CLSF), which can be used to drive most NC machines.

1.3 Getting Started with Unigraphics (UG)

On starting Unigraphics, you first find yourself in the **Gateway** environment. This is like standing in the entrance lobby of an office building; you are within the realm of Unigraphics, but no part file is loaded and no application has started. You are only just within the front door.

The menu bar is the horizontal menu of options displayed at the top of the main window directly below the title bar. Menu bar options are called menu titles and each corresponds to a Unigraphics functional category. Each menu title provides access to a pull-down menu of menu choices. When a command on a pulldown menu, or a series of submenus is selected, the path is often expressed by arrows. For example: **Insert →Form Feature→Extrude.** To begin work you must first load a part file. To load a part file, you can either create a new part file or retrieve one that already exists. Both options are available from **File** on the menu bar. The most frequently used **File** options are:

- Create a new part (**File → New**)
- Retrieve an existing part (**File →Open**)
- Saves the file (**File → Save**)
- Exit from Unigraphics without saving parts (**File → Exit**)

After you create or retrieve a part and it has been loaded, choose **Application** from the menu bar. Then you can start the application you wish to use, such as Modeling, Manufacturing, or Structure by picking the respective application.

Certain applications are not available on all platforms that run Unigraphics. If an application is not supported on the platform, it will not display on the Application pull-down menu. The application you choose determines which toolbars are available. For example, if you choose Modeling, the following toolbars are available to you: Curve, Edit Curve, Form Feature, Feature Operation, Edit Feature, Free Form Feature, Edit Free Form Feature, Die Engineering, and Sheet Metal Feature. Choosing an icon from the Form Feature toolbar lets you generate 3D solid models.

The Form Feature Toolbar

Note that the minimum screen resolution to display Unigraphics on PC and MAC are 1024 x 768. (For the PC you must also be running in Super VGA mode.) If this minimum resolution is not met, dialogs may not fit entirely on the screen.

Pull-down Menu

Pull-down menus appear below the menu bar when you select their title. They remain open without further action until you either choose a menu option or click somewhere outside of the menu. You can open a pull-down menu by pointing at its menu title and clicking mouse button 1 (MB1). Once a pull-down menu is displayed, you can move the focus to individual options by dragging the mouse pointer down the menu (if the menu was displayed with a mouse press), or by using the keyboard arrow keys (if the menu was displayed with a mouse click). A three-dimensional shadow is displayed around the menu option that has focus.

Keyboard mnemonics can also be used as shortcuts for menu bar navigation and selection. You can use a menu's mnemonic to display the menu by holding down the ALT key and pressing the mnemonic letter key for the menu. The mnemonic letter for each menu is underlined in the menu title. Once the menu is displayed, pressing another mnemonic key selects the menu item associated with that key.

Keyboard accelerators (**shortcut keys**) can also be used to make menu selections. Accelerator keys for menu selections are displayed on the menu. Pressing the accelerator keys together, such as <**Ctrl + N**> for **File** → **New**, will cause the selected command to be executed directly. Pull-down menu options fall into three categories:

When a menu option name is followed by three periods (**...**), it indicates that the option will display a dialog. A small triangle to the right of an option name indicates that a cascade menu will be displayed.

Toolbars

Toolbars are a row of icons you can use to launch standard Unigraphics menu items. Unigraphics comes with a large selection of toolbars, several of which are displayed when you start Unigraphics. Most toolbars are initially docked in the container area along the border of main Unigraphics window. To undock a toolbar, position the cursor over the grip handle of the docked toolbar and use MB1 to drag it. An undocked toolbar has its name displayed in its title area. When you remove your finger from MB1, the toolbar becomes a free-floating icon palette that you can move anywhere on the desktop. When a toolbar is undocked on Windows NT, you can also turn it OFF by choosing the "x" in the upper right corner.

Undocked toolbar

If the toolbar extends beyond the window frame, the toolbar will be clipped. Any adjustments that you make to the toolbars' location, visibility, and docked state will be remembered and restored the next time Unigraphics is invoked. You can customize a toolbar's visibility and content. Please refer to **View →Toolbars → Customize** or **Tools → Customize** for further details.

Cue/Status Line

The Cue/Status line appears at the bottom of the main Unigraphics window. The Cue area displays prompt messages on input expected by the current option. These messages indicate the next action you need to take. The Status area, located to the right of the Cue area, displays information messages about the current option or the most recently completed function. These messages do not require a response.

View Popup Menu

Certain **View** options are also available from a special **View Popup** menu; which can be opened from the graphics window by pressing **MB3**. The location of the cursor at the time you initiate the popup menu determines the view in which certain options are performed. Other options are either automatically applied to all views, or can be made active in any view by moving the cursor. To activate an option, drag the cursor down the menu with MB3 held down, releasing it when the desired option is covered.

View Popup Options	
Apply	Apply changes made in the current dialog. **Apply** on the View Popup menu is synchronized with the **Apply** option on the current dialog, so that it has the same status on both dialogs and menus (e.g., either active on both or grayed out on both).
Back	Goes back to a previous dialog. **Back** option on the View Popup menu is synchronized with the **Back** option on the current dialog.
Cancel	Cancels the current operation and dismisses the dialog. This option is synchronized with its counterpart on the current dialog.
Refresh	Cleans up the entire graphics screen by eliminating any holes in the graphics display left by blanked or deleted objects, and to display the results of some modification functions. **Refresh** removes temporarily displayed items such as asterisks, conehead vectors.
Fit	Calculates the extents of the model in the view where the cursor is positioned. The fit percentage you have set (found under **Preferences** →**Visualization** → **Screen**) is applied to this scale.
Zoom	When this toggle is ON, Zoom mode is active, and you can zoom in

	any view by positioning the *Zoom Cursor* (a magnifying glass) and dragging a rectangle while pressing MB1. To cancel Zoom mode, choose Zoom again or click MB2.
Zoom In/Out	Position the magnifying glass on the current display (if there are multiple displays, the view the magnifying glass is positioned over will be affected). Hold down MB1, and drag the cursor towards the top of the screen to reduce the view (Zoom Out) or, drag the cursor towards the bottom of the screen to magnify (Zoom In) the view.
Rotate	When this toggle is ON, the **Mouse-Driven XY Axes** option from the **View → Operation → Rotate** dialog becomes active. In this mode the cursor in the graphics window changes to the *Mouse-Driven Rotation Cursor*. Simply position this cursor in a view and press and hold MB1 while dragging. The view will rotate around the XY axes. How to cancel Rotate mode works in the same as canceling Zoom.
Pan	Turn this option toggle ON to activate the *Mouse-Driven Pan Cursor*. Once the cursor is visible and you are in Pan mode, position it over a desired starting location for a pan in a view. Next, while pressing MB1, drag the cursor to dynamically pan the view.
Update Display	Performs a display cleanup. This includes updating curves and edges displayed by line segment approximations, if the scale has increased such that the approximations are no longer smooth. Rotations cause Update Display to redisplay silhouette curves of faces and hidden edges of solids. Update Display also performs the tasks of the Refresh option, the erasure of temporary displays and the redrawing of the entire screen.
Restore	Restores the original view immediately after these operations: **Format → Layout → New**; **Format → Layout → Open**; **Drawing → New**; **Drawing → Open**; **View → Operation → Fit**; **View → Fit All**; **View → Operation → Regenerate Work**; **Format → Layout → Regenerate**; **Format → Layout → Fit All Views**, or **Fit** from the View Popup menu.

Display Mode	Specifies the shading mode for the selected view. You can set the mode to one of five options: Wireframe, Shaded, Partially Shaded, Face Analysis and, Studio. The first three will be used in this book. NOTE: The setting for the curve tolerance (**Preferences** → **Visualization** → **Line** → **Curve Tolerance**) may affect both the image quality and the performances of the display modes. For the Partially Shaded option, you must have the Partially Shaded attribute ON, in the **Preferences** → **Visualization** → **Visual** → **Display Mode** list box, for selected geometry to function. To use any of the Display Mode options, your graphics display device must support hardware shading, and you must have a 3D graphics driver loaded.
Hidden Edges	Specifies how hidden edges display in the selected view. You can use one of four options: (a) Visible (makes all hidden edges appear as solid lines, (b) Gray Thin (shows all hidden edges in the color gray, with solid font and thin width), (c) Dashed, and (d) Invisible. If your Display Mode setting is Shaded and you change the Hidden Edges setting, the Display Mode changes to Wireframe, and the new Hidden Edges settings are applied.
Expand	This is available when multiple views are present. When the cursor is positioned over a specific view, the view under the cursor position is expanded to a full display area view and now becomes the work view.
Orient View	Lets you change the alignment (orientation) of the view in which the pointer currently resides to one of canned views such as Top, Right, Trimetric, etc. Only the alignment of the view changes, and not the view name.
Replace View	Lets you switch the view in which the pointer currently resides with a canned view.
Undo	Cancels the last operation performed.

Terminologies and Unigraphics Capabilities

The Unigraphics Modeling application provides the capabilities to help design engineers quickly perform conceptual and detailed designs. It is a feature and constraint based solid modeler that allows the user to create and edit complex solid models interactively. With this feature, the design engineer can create and edit more complex models with far less effort than traditional wireframe and solid based systems.

Early CAD systems built models using geometry construction and editing techniques. These techniques created models made up of wireframe and surfaces, which could be edited by geometry editing. However, the system had no understanding of relationships between the geometry.

Later parametric systems introduced conceptual modeling techniques, which could be used to build relationships between geometric entities. These techniques relied on constraints and parametric expressions defined by the user to build the model. This approach built a more intelligent model, but could become restrictive. The constraints would sometimes stop a user from carrying out a modification, which had not been originally foreseen. Parametric systems also relied heavily on bodies created from swept sketches, and did not have a wide variety of construction and editing techniques.

The Modeling application is a new generation of modeler, combining traditional and parametric approaches to modeling. This gives you the freedom to choose the design approach that best suits your needs. There are times when a simple wireframe model is adequate for the job, and there is no need for the complexity that a constrained solid model introduces. However, it also provides a rich set of parametric and traditional solid modeling capabilities, which enable realistic solid models to be developed and manipulated easily.

Once a model has been built, dimension driven editing techniques can be used, even if it was not built using parametric functions - constraints are automatically inferred from the model. These constraints are not imposed, however, if you decide to modify the model so that they are no longer valid. This means that the tendency to "model yourself into a corner", which can happen with old parametric systems, is avoided using Unigraphics Modeling.

There are many other Unigraphics Capabilities. We give brief descriptions below for some of them that are going to be covered in the later chapters in detail.

Start with a Sketch

You can use the Sketcher to freehand sketch and dimension an "outline" of curves. The sketch can then be swept (extruded or revolved) to create a solid or sheet body. The sketch can later be refined to precisely represent the object of interest by editing the dimensions and by creating relationships between geometric objects. Editing a dimension of the sketch not only modifies the geometry of the sketch, but also the body created from the sketch. This is discussed in detail in Chapter 10.

Creating and Editing Features

Feature based solid modeling lets you create features, such as holes, slots, and grooves, on a model. You can then directly edit the dimensions of the feature and locate this feature by dimensions. For example, a hole is defined by its diameter and length. You can directly edit all of these parameters by entering new values. This is addressed in detail in Chapters 5 and 6.

Associativity

Associativity is the term used to indicate geometric relationships between individual portions of a model. These relationships are established as the designer uses various functions for model creation. Constraints and relationships are captured automatically as the model is developed. For example, a through hole is associated with the faces in a model that the hole penetrates. If the model is later changed so that one or both of those faces moves, the hole updates automatically due to its association to the faces. This concept is addressed throughout this book.

Positioning a Feature

Within Modeling, you can position a feature relative to the geometry on your model using positioning dimensions. The feature is then associated with that geometry and will maintain those associations whenever you edit the model. You can also edit the position of the feature by changing the values of the positioning dimensions. This is discussed in Chapter 5

Reference Features

You can create reference features, such as a datum plane or datum axis, that can be used as reference geometry when needed. These datum features can be used as construction devices for other features. Any feature created using a reference feature is associated to that reference feature and retains that association during edits to the model. Datum planes can be used as a reference plane in constructing sketches, creating features, and positioning features. Datum axes can be used to create datum planes, for placing items concentrically, or for creating radial patterns. Chapter 8 is devoted to this subject.

Expressions

You can also incorporate your requirements and design restrictions by defining mathematical relationships between different parts of the design. For example, you can define the height of a boss as three times its diameter, so that when the diameter changes, the height changes also. This is addressed in Chapter 6.

Boolean Operations

Modeling provides the following Boolean operations: *unite*, *subtract*, and *intersect*. A unite operation combines bodies; for example, uniting two rectangular blocks to form a T-shaped solid body. A subtract operation removes one body from another. An intersect operation creates a solid body from material shared by two solid bodies. These operations can also be used with free form features called sheets. This is studied in Chapter 9.

Undo

A design can be returned to its previous state any number of times using the **Undo** function. You do not have to take a great deal of time making sure each operation is absolutely correct, because a mistake can be easily undone. This freedom to change the model liberates you from worrying about getting it wrong and lets you explore many more iterations in order to get it right.

Other Capabilities

Other Unigraphics applications can operate directly on solid objects created within Modeling without any translation of the solid body. For example, you can perform drafting, engineering analysis, and NC machining functions by accessing the appropriate application. Using Modeling, you can design a complete, unambiguous, three dimensional model to describe an object. You can extract a wide range of physical properties from the solid bodies, including mass properties. Shading and hidden line capabilities help you visualize complex assemblies. You can identify interferences automatically, eliminating the need to attempt to do so manually. Hidden edge views can later be generated and placed on drawings. Fully associative dimensioned drawings can be created from solid models using the appropriate options of the Drafting application. If the solid model is edited later, the drawing and dimensions are updated automatically. This concept is called the Master Model and is discussed in Chapter 13.

Exercise Problems

1.1 What is the paradigm of the twenty-first century manufacturing companies?

1.2 What are the four phases of the product-life cycle?

1.3 Give typical steps taken in the product design process.

1.4 CAD significantly changes the design process steps listed in the above question. (True/False)

1.5 Which design process step uses geometric modeling most?

1.6 What are thee common geometric modeling approaches?

1.7 Name two common methods for solid modeling discussed in this chapter.

1.8 Between the two methods for solid modeling, which one will be used in this book to model objects?

1.9 What are the limitations of wireframe modeling?

1.10 Describe CAE briefly.

1.11 Describe CAM briefly.

1.12 What is the relation between the paradigm of the twenty-first century manufacturing companies and CAD/CAM/CAE?

1.13 What is Unigraphics?

References

Dransfield, J. (1994), Design for manufacturability at northern telecom., In Successful Implementation of Concurrent Engineering Products and Processes (S.G. Shina, ed.), Van Nostrand Reinhold, New York.

Earle, J.H. (1992), Graphics for Engineers: AutoCAD Release 11, Addison – Wesley, Reading, Massachusetts.

Singh, N. (1996), Systems Approach to Computer-Integrated Design and Manufacturing, John Wiley & Sons, Inc., New York.

Chapter 2. A Case Study for CAD/CAM/CAE

The objective of this chapter is to give a quick overview on how UG can support CAD/CAM/CAE. A simple part is used to take you through step-by-step from design, analysis, then to manufacturing of the part. The figure of the part appears in Figure 2.1. The part is made of stainless steel. One functional performance requirement of the part is that the maximum displacement of the part (i.e., deformation) is less than a threshold value, .01 inch, under the following two conditions. The first condition is that 10,000 lb of force is applied to the hole downward. The second condition is that the fixed constraint is applied to the back long rectangular face such that this face is not allowed to move.

Figure 2.1 A case study part

2.1 CAD for 3-D solid modeling

You will first create a 3-D solid model for this part.

Step 1. Create a block.

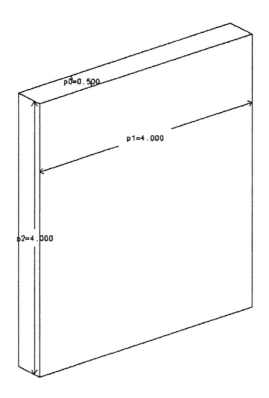

Figure 2.2 Creating a block

1.1 Create a new part with filename ***_casestudy.prt, where *** is your three letter name initials. (File → New).

1.2 Enter Modeling under Application (Application → Modeling).

1.3 Replace the current view with TFR-TRI view (Move your cursor into the part display screen, click the right mouse button → Replace view → TFR-TRI).

1.4 Click the block icon ⬚ from the tool bar (alternatively, Insert → Form Feature → Block). A block dialog appears.

1.5 Click the left icon "Origin, Edge Lengths"

1.6 Enter

Length (XC) = .5 (Use the Tab key to move to the next field)

Width (YC) = 4

Height (ZC) = 4

1.7 Click "OK" or the middle mouse button. You will see the block created and located at the origin of Work Coordinate System (WCS).

1.8. Click "Cancel" to stop creating any more blocks.

Step 2. Create a thru hole in the block.

2.1 Insert → Form Feature → Hole or choose the Hole icon . A small dialog "Hole" opens.

The simple hole is defaulted and default hole values are already in place.

2.3 The Cue Line is prompting to select the planar placement face, so select the large square face of the block to place a hole on the face. As you click the face, you may see a small dialog pop out to show that there are two faces that can be selectable. Click "1".

2.4 The Cue Line is prompting to select the thru face so select the other large square face to specify the thru face of the hole.

2.5 The hole parameters change to only requiring the diameter so enter Diameter = 1 and click "OK". A hole with diameter =1 is created.

2.6 Position the hole on the face. Dialog "Positioning" appears to guide where to place the hole on the face.

The hole center will be located 2 inch from the top edge and 1 inch from the left edge as shown below.

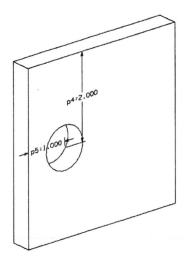

Figure 2.3 Positioning a hole on the block

You will use two perpendicular positions to locate the hole. Use the first perpendicular position by picking the fourth icon from the 1st row. Pick the upper edge of the face and enter 2 as shown in figure and click "Apply". Use the second perpendicular position by picking the same icon. This time pick the left edge of the face and enter 1 and click "OK".

2.7 Click "Cancel" to stop creating any more holes.

Step 3. Apply a chamfer operation to two edges.

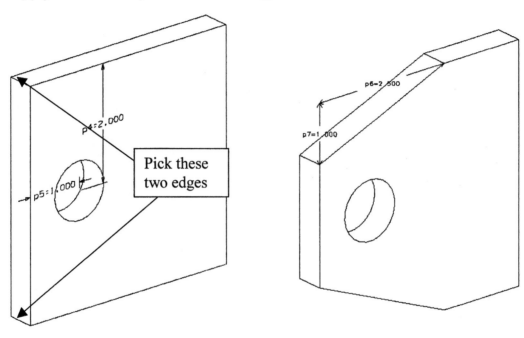

Figure 2.4 Before and after chamfering two left corner edges

3.1 Insert → Feature Operation → Chamfer or choose the chamfer icon, .

3.2 Chamfer dialog appears. Click "Double Offset".

3.3 Pick two small edges that you want to chamfer, one upper left and the other bottom left as shown in Figure 2.4, and then click "OK". As you click the edge, you may see another small dialog pop out to show that there is more than one object that can be selectable with your last click. Click among the selectable numbers one number that indicates the edge.

3.4 Enter the following chamfer offset distances and click "OK".

First Offset = 2.5

Second Offset = 1

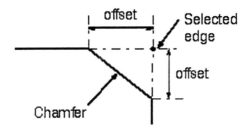

3.5 Click "Cancel" to stop creating chamfers.

Step 4. Apply two edge blend operations to four small edges created from the chamfer operation.

4.1 Insert → Feature Operation → Edge Blend or choose the edge blend icon . The Edge Blend dialog appears.

4.2 Pick two small edges to blend, one leftmost upper and the other leftmost bottom as shown in Figure 2.5.

4.3 Enter Default Radius = 1.25 and click "Apply" on the bottom of the dialog. These two edges are blended and the Edge Blend dialog is still open.

4.4 Do the edge blend operation one more time. Pick another two small edges resulting from the chamfer operation: one small edge on the top face and the other on the bottom face.

4.5 Enter Default Radius= 1 and click "OK". Now the 3-D CAD model for this part is created.

Figure 2.5 Before and after blending two left corner edges

Step 5. Assign material type, stainless steel, to this part.

5.1 Tools → Material Properties

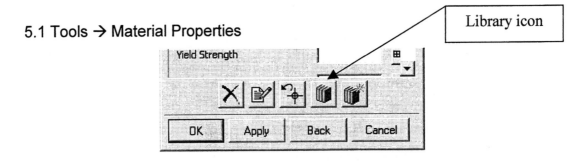

5.2 Materials dialog appears. Click "Library" on the near bottom of the dialog.

5.3 Another dialog "Search Criteria" appears. Accept the default setting by just clicking "OK".

5.4 Pick Ref 15 "Stainless_Steel" among the list of metals found in the library and click "OK".

5.5 Pick the part in the display window and click "OK". The selected material, stainless steel, has been assigned to the part.

2.2 CAE for Design Analysis

You will find the part weight and conduct the structure analysis of the part.

Step 1. Save your model by pointing your cursor to File→Save.

Step 2. Find the Volume/Area/Weight of the block.

    2.1. Choose Analysis → Mass using Solids

    2.2. Choose OK on the dialog for Tolerances and Accuracy.

    2.3. Choose OK to the menu that follows for Area = 1 and Volume = 1 as another measure of accuracy.

    2.4. Next the system asks you to select the solid to analyze, so select the part in the graphic window.

    2.5. Choose OK to confirm and tell the system you are finished selecting.

    2.6. The next dialog is the menu to choose the analysis you wish to see.

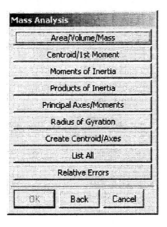

Also appearing in the graphics area are the orthographic vectors that identify the centroid and principle axes. You may choose from the list on the dialog or you may choose List All to see all of the results in a tabular form. We are interested the Area/Volume/Mass.

    2.7. Choose the Area/Volume/Mass button.

The result is this dialog. The units are in lbs and inches.

Step 3. Select Application→Structures to enter the analysis application. When prompted with a message "...Do you want to save changes?", select Yes.

Step 4. A Scenario Navigator window comes up with our part name inside. Select the name of the part with MB1 and right click the name with MB3.

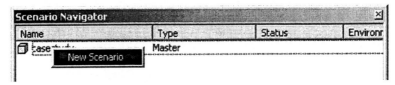

The Cue Line is prompting to create a new scenario or select an existing one so select window New Scenario as shown above.

Note the icons that are dedicated to analysis are added to the toolbars above and we are ready to do the analysis.

Step 5. Apply a vertical load.

5.1. Select the Loads Icon from the tool bar to bring up the following dialog.

5.2 Make the following adjustments to the dialog if necessary (as reflected in the dialog shown).

    5.2.1 Variation→Constant

    5.2.2 Type→Force

    5.2.3 Apply to→Face

5.3 Enter in a load of –10000 pounds in the FZ field (note that this is in direct relation to the coordinate system shown on the graphics screen).

5.4 Select the face as shown below followed by OK.

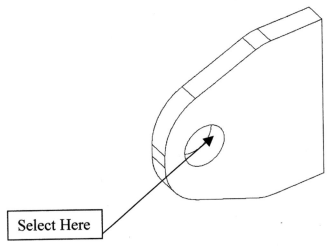

Select Here

Step 6. Apply the Boundary Condition.

6.1. Select the Boundary Conditions Icon to bring up the following dialog.

6.2. Select the Fixed radio button from the dialog.

6.3. Select the back face as shown below followed by OK.

Select Here

At this point, your graphics screen should look as shown below. Next, we will apply the solid mesh that will carry the load.

Step 7. Create the Mesh

7.1. Select the 3D Tetrahedral Mesh Icon to bring up the following dialog.

7.2. Select the solid body followed by OK to create the mesh. When complete, your model looks similar to one as shown below:

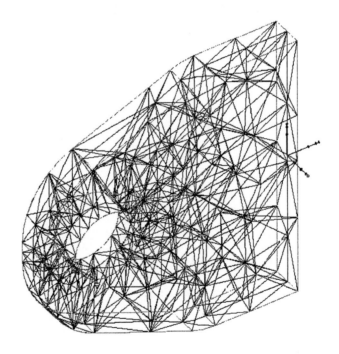

At this point, we are ready to run the analysis.

Step 8. Run the Analysis

9.1. Select the Solve Icon ▦ followed by OK to submit the analysis. A monitor window will come up so wait for it to notify complete.

Step 9. View the Results

9.1. Select the Results icon 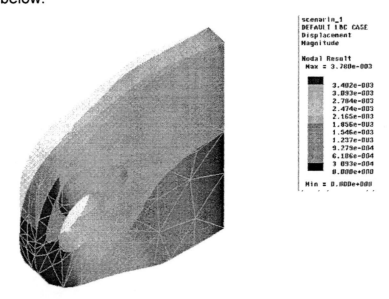 to see the deflected shape as shown below.

scenario_1
DEFAULT IBC CASE
Displacement
Magnitude

Nodal Result
Max = 3.780e-003

3.402e-003
3.093e-003
2.784e-003
2.474e-003
2.165e-003
1.856e-003
1.546e-003
1.237e-003
9.279e-004
6.186e-004
3.093e-004
0.000e+000

Min = 0.000e+000

As you can see the graphical results above from the analysis, you can observe a couple of points. Relatively large displacement, colored in red, occurs around the hole where the force of 10,000 pound is applied as specified in Step 4. The maximum displacement estimated by this analysis is 3.78 x 10^{-3} inch (your number may slightly be different). This is less than the threshold value, .01 inch, thus meeting the functional performance requirements. Very little displacement, colored in blue, occurs in the back rectangular face, where the fixed boundary condition is applied in Step 5.

9.2. Animate the deflections by selecting the animation icon followed by OK. When you are through viewing the animation, select Cancel.

9.3. Quit the Results processing by selecting the Quit Icon and confirming the message shown below.

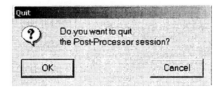

2.3 CAM for Cutting Tool Path Generation

Step 1. Applications → Modeling. Create a new part file and name it as ***_casestudy_block.prt, where *** is your three letter name initials. Create a block and assign the same material type (i.e., stainless steel) to it by following Steps 1 and 5 of Section 2.1. This part serves as a blank part. Save and close this file. You will be guided to create a cutting tool path to cut this blank part into the final part shown in Figure 2.1.

Step 2. Create another new part and name it as ***_casestudy_mfg.prt. This part will contain the information required to generate the tool path.

Step 3. Add the two parts, the blank part (***_casestudy_block.prt) and the final part (***_casestudy.prt), into the manufacturing part (***_casestudy_mfg.prt).

3.1 Application → Assemblies

3.2 Assemblies → Components

3.3 Slide out and click "Add Existing" button.

3.4 "Select Part" dialog appears. If you see ***_casestudy_block in the list of loaded parts, pick it and then click "OK". If not, click "Choose Part File" button and find the part file by navigating the file directories in the same manner as you do in "File → Open".

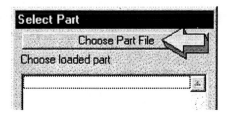

3.5 Accept the default setting on "Add Existing Part" dialog by clicking "OK".

3.6 "Point Constructor" dialog appears. Click "Reset" button and then click "OK".

Now the blank part has been added.

Replace the current view with TFR-TRI if necessary by clicking Right Mouse Button → Replace View.

3.7 Click "Back" which takes you to the dialog "Select Part". Repeat 3.4 to 3.6 above except adding ***_casestudy.prt in place of ***_casestudy_block.prt.

3.8 Click "Cancel" to stop adding any more parts and save this file.

Figure 2.6   ***_casestudy_mfg.prt after adding the two parts in Step 3

Step 4. Application → Manufacturing to enter the Manufacturing Application. "Machining Environment" dialog appears.

Step 5. Initialize the machining environment.

   5.1 Pick "mill_contour" from a list of options available in "CAM Setup". Click "Initialize" from the bottom of the dialog.

   The system displays "Operation Navigator" window.

   5.2 Select Insert → Operation and the Create Operation dialog comes up.

   5.3 In the Create Operation dialog, there are 20 icons displayed, corresponding to the available operation options. Use the default, which is the first operation.

Step 6. Specify the correct machine tool coordinate system (MCS). The part display window shows that the current ZM direction, which is a cutting tool

access direction to the part, points upward. It needs to rotate by 90 degrees such that it points right.

6.1 Select Tools → Operation Navigator → View → Geometry View or click the Geometry View icon located on the toolbar, which changes window "Operation Navigator" into Geometry view.

6.2 In window "Operation Navigator –> Geometry", double click "MCS_MILL" to edit MCS.

6.3 "Mill_Orient" dialog appears. Click "MCS rotate" icon, which is the third one on the top as shown below.

6.4 "Rotate MCS about" dialog appears. Click "+YM axis; ZM -> XM" and click "Apply" (accepting default angle 90°). Now the ZM direction points right. Click "Cancel", and then "OK" to close the "Mill_Orient" dialog.

Step 7. Specify a 0.5-inch end mill tool for the cutting tool.

7.1 Select Insert → Tool or select Create Tool icon from the toolbar.

7.2 Dialog "Create Tool" appears. Click the Mill icon on the left and click OK. Dialog Milling Tool-5 Parameters appears.

7.3 Enter (D) Diameter = .5 to cut the 1" diameter hole, and click "OK" by accepting the default values for other parameters.

7.4 Select Insert → Operation, or click "Create Operation" icon on the toolbar,

. Dialog "Create Operation" appears.

Step 8. Setup the Cavity Mill dialog.

8.1 Click "Cavity_Mill" on the top, left of the operation Subtype icons of the "Create Operation" dialog. Select OK.

8.2 Cavity_Mill dialog appears. The Tool has to be selected. Select the Tool :
NONE radio button if not already selected. Click the Select button under
the radio buttons.

8.3 The Select Tool dialog comes up, click the window down-arrow and click
MILL. Click OK.

8.4 Assign which part among the two in the display window is the Blank and
the final Part, respectively.

8.5 Click "Part" icon under the word Geometry. Click "Select" button on
the next line.

8.6 "Part Geometry" dialog appears. Select the final part in the display
window. If more than one is selectable, you will see the selection
dialogue looking like appear on the display window. Click the right
number between the two to pick the final part, but not the blank part.
Click "OK" to close the Part Geometry dialog.

8.7 Click "Blank" icon right next to "Part" icon. Click "Select" button.

8.8 Select the blank part in the display window. Click "OK" to close the Part
Geometry dialog.

Step 9. Generate the tool path.

9.1 On the Cavity_Mill dialog, click the "Generate" icon near the bottom of the dialog.

9.2 Dialog "Display Parameters", click "OK". The tool path is shown on the part. Continue to click "OK" until it finishes generating the tool path.

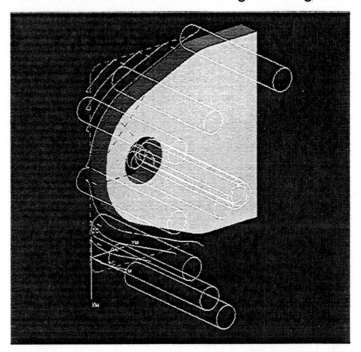

9.6 Animate the tool path for verification. Click "Verify" icon right to "Generate" icon. Dialog "Toolpath Visualization" appears. Click "Play" button and observe animation of the cutting process. Click "OK" to take it back to the Cavity_Mill dialog.

9.7 Click "List" icon right next to "Verify" icon. This lists the generic NC program list called the cutter location source file (CLSF). This can be post-processed to a specific NC machine tool. Close the list window.

A top portion of CLSF

```
TOOL PATH/CAVITY_MILL,TOOL,MILL
TLDATA/MILL,0.5000,0.0000,3.0000,0.0000,0.0000
MSYS/0.0000,0.0000,0.0000,0.0000000,0.0000000,1.0000000,0.0000000,1.000
0000,0.0000000
PAINT/PATH
PAINT/SPEED,10
PAINT/COLOR,4
RAPID
GOTO/0.3400,0.6552,0.6000,0.0000000,0.0000000,1.0000000
PAINT/COLOR,1
RAPID
GOTO/0.3400,0.6552,0.3500
PAINT/COLOR,6
FEDRAT/IPM,10.0000
GOTO/0.3400,0.6552,0.2500
GOTO/0.2400,0.4075,0.2500
PAINT/COLOR,3
CIRCLE/-
1.8465,1.2500,0.2500,0.0000000,0.0000000,1.0000000,2.2501,0.0020,0.5000,0.
5000,0.0000
GOTO/-0.1603,-0.2399,0.2500
PAINT/COLOR,7
RAPID
GOTO/-0.1603,-0.2399,0.6000
PAINT/COLOR,1
RAPID
GOTO/0.3400,1.3307,0.6000
RAPID
```

9.8 In dialog "Cavity Mill", click "OK" to accept this tool path. Save and close all the files.

Exercise Problems

2.1 Suppose the block size of Section 2.1 changes from .5 x 4 x 4 to .5 x 4 x 5. Redo all the steps of Sections 2.1, 2.2, and 2.3 for CAD/CAE/CAM.

2.2 In Problem 2.1, you are asked to redo all the steps from scratch in order to address the design change in the block size. Is there an easier way?

Chapter 3. Unigraphics Essentials

In this chapter, we will present some of the fundamental UG essentials that will be frequently used during a session with Unigraphics. These include using and manipulating coordinate systems as references, defining virtual points, layering standards, a selection method to select a desired object among many, and other user interfaces of Unigraphics. We will also discuss default files that determine how Unigraphics is set up as well as how to obtain help when you need it.

3.1 Different Approaches to Modeling Objects in Space

It is important to be familiar with the fundamental aspects of Unigraphics in order to take full advantage of the functionality that lies within the software. First we discuss different ways objects are modeled in industries and their implications. Although companies use the same software, they can differ in the way they manage design information and models. These different aspects and edicts are generally referred to as company standards. These standards include layering conventions, part file storage, views in a model, colors of objects, and how objects are modeled in space. We will discuss the last subject more in detail in this section.

There are three ways that companies model their parts in space: in the exact location they are assembled in, without regard to the location where they are assembled in, or a mix of the two approaches. In aerospace industries, parts are typically modeled in their final assembled location. For detail drawings of parts, the parts themselves are generally defined by using datums as references for dimensions. As you begin to put the details together in an assembly fashion, the assembly drawings will also have datums. In fact, in most aircraft programs today, these same datums are also used for purposes of generating tooling to support the synthesis of the assembly. This concept is referred to as **coordinated datums** whereby the tooling uses the same references as the assembly it is designed to build.

This approach generally insures that items used in defining the aircraft are in their correct place (and are actually referenced by their location) and that all tooling usages for the synthesis of the design are in their correct place as well. So does this mean that when parts are modeled without regard to their correct assembled location, they do not end up in their correct location at the assembly level? No, it does not. The result of modeling parts of an assembly without regard to location is generally easier than modeling to true, assembled space but the final result is the same. This approach is typically employed on simpler assemblies, but is still scalable and viable to be used on larger assemblies as well. For example, take the assembly of a door slab and three hinges. In this situation, you would have to provide a detail model of the door itself (the slab), a model of the hinge plate, and a final model of the hinge pin. While we do need three hinges, they are all the exact same hinge. Therefore, we will model them only once and then add three complete hinge assemblies to our door at the assembly level. Below is a sample drawing tree of this approach to further explain this concept.

In this case, we would model everything without regard to its final location in space and locate the items (Hinge Pin Subassembly) upon assembly. While the Hinge Sub Assembly shows up three times, all three are the exact same indicating that the Sub Assembly itself is only modeled once and simply added three times to the Door Assembly.

The final approach that we will discuss is that of a mixed approach that models some items, particularly, unique items in their exact location in model space, and more common items (of which there are usually many) without regard to location. These common items would then simply be added to the assembly and positioned as needed for the design. This approach is also used in the aircraft and automotive industries where common items include standard brackets, fasteners, and clamps just to name a few.

3.2 Coordinate Systems and Right-Hand Rules

In the previous section, we discussed different approaches that objects are modeled and assembled in space. All these approaches deal with locating objects in space, thus, a coordinate system. We discuss three coordinate systems in this section. These are the absolute coordinate system, the work coordinate system, and the feature coordinate system. All these coordinate systems use right-hand rules to determine the principal axes of coordinate systems and the positive directions of revolution.

The conventional right-hand rule is, that if the origin of the coordinate system is in the palm of the right fist, with the back of the hand lying on a table. The outward extension of the thumb corresponds to the positive X-axis; the outward extension of the index finger corresponds to the positive Y-axis, and the upward extension of the middle finger corresponds to the positive Z-axis.

The Conventional Right-Hand Rule

The right-hand rule for rotation is used to associate vectors with directions of rotation. When the thumb is extended and aligned with a given vector, the curled fingers determine the associated direction of rotation. Conversely, when the curled fingers are held so as to indicate a given direction of rotation, the extended thumb determines the associated vector. For example, to determine the counterclockwise direction of rotation for a given coordinate system, the thumb is aligned with the ZC axis, pointing in the positive Z direction. Counterclockwise is defined as the direction the fingers would move from the positive X to the positive Y-axis.

The Right-Hand Rule for Rotation

3.3 The Absolute Coordinate System (ABS)

The Absolute Coordinate System defines 0,0,0 (in X, Y, and Z) in model space and is fixed. This is not a mobile coordinate system and therefore provides a 100% consistent reference point for everything from part to part as well as within an assembly. It is commonly used as the general reference for modeling and large complex assemblies when employing the "in correct space" approach to modeling a product assembly. You cannot physically see the Absolute Coordinate System unless you superimpose (in origin and orientation) a mobile coordinate system over top of it.

With all of this in mind, you may be thinking that having a coordinate system that is fixed is very limiting and that it will be difficult to do anything away from it.

Well, that aspect is covered by a mobile, construction coordinate system called the Work Coordinate System or the WCS. The WCS is the system that may be placed on top of the Absolute Coordinate System to provide visualization of the ABS.

3.4 The Work Coordinate System (WCS)

As mentioned above, the WCS is a mobile coordinate system that may be moved around the model space to facilitate the construction of objects. It may also be used for determining specific points in a model and even for establishing direction vectors (for extrusions and revolutions for example). The WCS is also useful for helping to model parts in their correct origin and orientation relative to the ABS.

Generally speaking, most of the operations you will perform in Unigraphics will not require you to manipulate the WCS as features are generally built and referenced from existing geometry. However, you will often need to manipulate the WCS in order to create that initial geometry, as some items in Unigraphics are heavily dependent on the WCS. One Example of this is the creation of primitive features that depend on the various axes of the WCS for direction. The WCS is readily identifiable by a "C" next to each of the axes (XC, YC, and ZC) and will always be shown in the system color (red is the default) as shown below.

It may be helpful for you to remember the "C" as standing for Construction as this is the primary purpose of the WCS.

3.5 Manipulating the WCS

Generally speaking, there are three ways to manipulate the WCS. You can change its location or its **Origin**, you can **Rotate** the system (which does not alter its location but its orientation only), or you can **Orient** the WCS, which results in not only a rotational change to the WCS but a location change as well. All of these options may be found under the WCS pulldown from the Main Menu as shown below.

WCS → Origin...

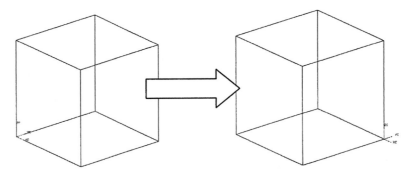

In the above illustration, the WCS was simply moved from one corner to the other. Notice that the general orientation of the WCS remained the same and that only the location was changed.

WCS→Rotate ...

Again, using the **Rotate** option simply changes the orientation of the WCS and not the location. The dialog shown below is the result of following the menu selection. The basic way to read this dialog as shown would be, "Rotate the WCS about the positive ZC axis from XC to YC by 90 degrees".

Performing this operation on the last image shown would yield:

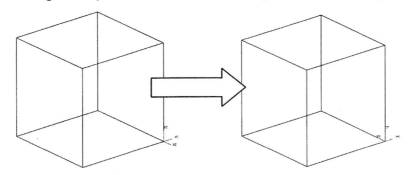

WCS→Orient …

This will allow you to change the location and the orientation of the WCS simultaneously. There are many options to choose from as shown below.

Origin, X-Point, Y-Point

X Axis, Y Axis

CSYS of Object

The icons represent various methods to select objects to locate the WCS aligned with or coincident with those objects. The options most used are the icons labeled above. Notice also the option for Absolute CSYS. This is the one way that you will be able to visualize the Absolute Coordinate System by moving the WCS to its location. Activity 3-1 shows how to use some of these options.

3.6 The Feature Coordinate System

Often times during the creation of various features within Unigraphics, you will notice that the system temporarily moves the WCS for you. After the feature has been created, you will then notice that the WCS goes back to its previous location. What you are actually witnessing when this happens is the system created Feature Coordinate System. This coordinate system is stored with the feature and is called upon by the software mainly during editing purposes and is transparent to you, the user.

3.7 Defining Points for Reference and Location in Unigraphics

Many times you will be asked by the system to provide point information so that you may locate certain items of interest. For example, when changing the origin of the WCS, you will have to tell the system where you would like to move the WCS on the model or in the model space. In another example, if you are constructing a block, you will need to tell the system where in the model space the block is. The way this is accomplished in Unigraphics is with the Point Constructor dialog. We will go over only a few brief items but the help documentation has everything that you need to explore the various options further.

The Point Constructor Dialog

The dialog shown above is the Point Constructor Dialog and in this case was the result of a desire to change the location of the WCS. From this dialog, you are able to specify points relative to model space or even relative to existing objects for many varied purposes. In this instance, the Inferred button has been selected (which it is by default). The Inferred selection button has been put in place to facilitate selection by having the system attempt to interpret the user's selection.

With the exception of the Cursor Location, the other types require the selection of existing modeling objects from the graphics screen. Below is a sample of some of the points that are selectable from the screen.

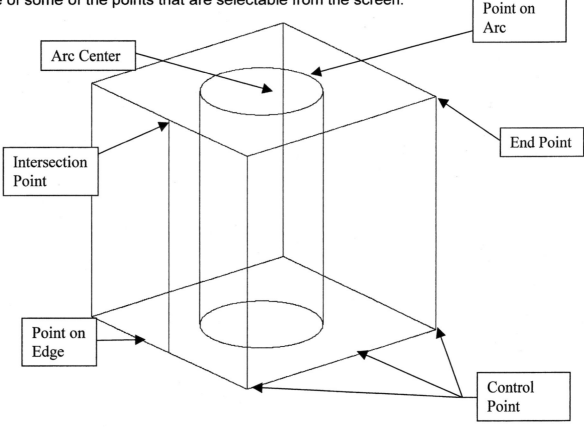

In addition to those shown, the inferred selection icon is also available by default. The inferred selection icon will basically attempt to understand your selection (infer what it is that you are attempting to select) and is very useful once you get used to it. You may also specify a point that is relative to the WCS or ABS depending on which toggle you select (the WCS is selected by default).

In the activity that follows, you will attempt to manipulate the WCS on your own. Try exploring different options and ways of doing things. You will not break the system!

Activity 3-1. Working with the WCS

Step 1. Open part file activity3-1.prt by selecting File → Open (or Ctrl + O).

Step 2. Select WCS → Origin and notice the Point Constructor dialog has been opened with Inferred point selection as the default.

Step 3. Select the points shown below. Notice the movement of the WCS. Does it change orientation? Should it be?

Step 4. Select Cancel.

Step 5. Select WCS → Orient and the icon for X-Axis, Y-Axis and select the lines as shown below to re-orient the WCS. Be careful to select the lines where shown!

Step 6. Now, do the same thing again for the locations shown below.

Step 7. Rotate the WCS by selecting WCS → Rotate …

Step 8. Select Apply.

Step 9. Select Cancel. Your Screen should look as shown below.

3.8 Controlling the Visibility of Objects

As you will see, there can be many reference data created throughout your use of Unigraphics when you build a model. Like many CAD systems, Unigraphics allows the user to organize your modeling file by using what are known as layers. You can think of a layer as a single piece of transparent film that has information on it. If you view only a single piece of film, then you will only see what is on that piece. In order to view other pieces of film at the same time, you would then simply lay the others overtop of your original. Also, you may desire to create new objects and as a matter of convention, they must reside on some piece of film (maybe call it your Work Film). Some of the pieces of film you will want to only see (not write on, visible only) and some of the pieces you will actually want to work with (make selectable).

Unigraphics' Layers work in much the same way. There are a total of 256 layers (layers of film) at your disposal in every single part file. At any one given time, you can only create objects on a single layer, the Work Layer. You also have the flexibility to make any or all of them Selectable (so that you can pick and work with the objects on a layer) or Visible (so that you can see, but not pick nor modify the items on that layer). Now that you have the background information, let us look at some of the mechanics of Layers from a User Interface standpoint.

To get to the Layer Settings Dialog, go to Format → Layer Settings to bring up the following dialog. The following bulleted items are intended to be a straightforward reference to help you in using the dialog.

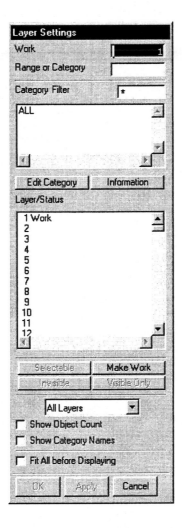

- At the very top of the dialog, you may directly change the Work Layer by entering in a layer number (between 1 and 256) followed by the enter key on your keyboard. Note that you must press enter for this to work correctly.

- To make a layer Selectable, you can
  - pick the layer number from the listing window in the middle of the dialog and click the Selectable button or
  - double-click the layer number directly on the list.

- To make multiple layers Selectable, you can drag over the layers and then click the Selectable Button.

- For any of your changes to take effect, you must select OK or Apply.

Many companies have rigid standards in place when it comes to layering. These standards are typically referred to as layering standards. These standards basically tell the modeler what objects should be placed on what layer. Implementation of layering standards is a key way that companies achieve consistency in the models they produce. Adherence to these standards helps companies realize gains in productivity throughout the definition of products. We give some of the layering standards commonly used by companies like Boeing that will be also adopted in this book as follows:

Layers 1 to 20 for Solid objects
Layers 21 to 40 for Sketch objects
Layers 41 to 60 for Curve objects
Layers 61 to 80 for Reference Datum objects

One way that companies implement these standards is through the use of a seedpart (sometimes referred to as a null file). These empty seedparts have the layers and corporate standards prearranged to make the adherence to the standard easier. The basic process is that when a user begins a new model, he or she opens the appropriate seed part and performs a Save As operation to save it with the correct file name for the model. With this in mind, the new part file has the standards built in. While this does not guarantee compliance with the standards, it does facilitate the process.

3.9 Selecting Items from the Graphics Window Using Quick Pick Selection

Beginning in V16, the software has employed a quick pick method for selection. The basic concept of this is to make the selection of items an easier task that may be automated using either the mouse buttons or the cursor. In addition to this, there is a large amount of graphical feedback to help you determine the current selection.

When first selecting an item, your cursor will begin looking like normal crosshairs. However, if the cursor dwells over multiple potential items for selection, the cursor will quickly change to look like ┼ . Notice the three periods after the cursor. At this point, the system is attempting to convey to you that there are multiple items "behind" the cursor that are available for selection if you select MB1.

Upon selecting at that point, you will be presented with another dialog box (generally to the right of where you selected) filled with numbers, one for each potentially selected item. Also providing graphical feedback is the Cue Line and Status Line. The system will automatically give you hints on how to accelerate the process as well as tell you what type of object the current selection represents. A sample of both the dialog and the Cue/Status Line are shown below.

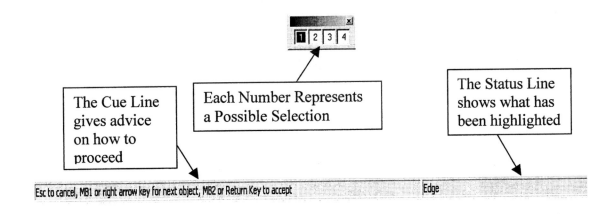

The Cue Line gives advice on how to proceed

Each Number Represents a Possible Selection

The Status Line shows what has been highlighted

Esc to cancel, MB1 or right arrow key for next object, MB2 or Return Key to accept   Edge

At this point, you have many options available to you as bulleted below:

- Move your cursor along the numbers while watching the screen and Status Line until the system has found your desired selection and pick the number with MB1 (or press enter on your keyboard) to select the object.

- Use the right arrow key to run along the numbered selections and pick the resulting number with MB1 (again, you may also simply press enter on the keyboard) to select the object.

- Finally, you may advance through the numeric choices by using MB1 (just picking in the graphics screen without regard to location, which is almost like picking the object again.) and confirm your selection with MB2 (the middle mouse button).

Again, the third method is the preferred way for productivity sake. While it may seem somewhat unnatural to approach it in this fashion, try to use some discipline in selecting until it becomes second nature.

3.10 Utilizing the Class Selection Dialog

There are many situations where you will encounter the **Class Selection** dialog. This dialog is little more than a global filter that allows you to decide what is available for selection and what is not. The dialog is shown below and is a result of following the selection, **Information → Object**.

This dialog offers more flexible selection than a global selection filter. By default, all items are available for selection when first invoked. From this point, you are able to determine what can be selected. You may choose from the types of objects, the colors of objects, the layer the objects are on, or various other items (line font for example) by selecting the Type, Color, Layer or Other buttons respectively. For example, if you needed to select only the White, Solid Bodies on Layer 12, you would follow the selection process as depicted below. The selection process of this example may look somewhat involved. However, you will only employ such a selection process when you NEED that level of control (when there is a lot of clutter in the graphics screen perhaps). Remember that, by default, all these items are available for selection, and in most cases you will be able to pick them directly from the screen.

Step 1. Choose the Type button meaning to select by object type. The Select by Type dialog appears. Select the Solid Body selection and choose OK.

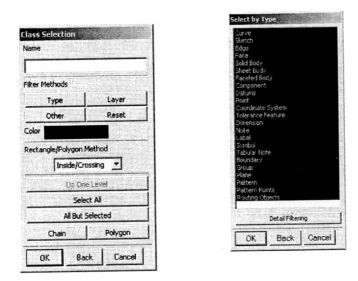

Step 2. Choose the color window and the Color map dialog comes up. Choose the color White as verified on the bottom of the dialog and choose OK.

Step 3. Choose the Layer button and the Select by Layer dialog comes up.
Select the layer number you want to use and choose OK.

Step 4. Now the filters have been set to select only a solid body, of white color
and on layer x, we are now ready to select.

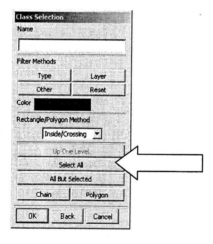

Step 5. Choose the Select All button and objects fitting the criteria of Step 4 will
be chosen. Choose OK to complete the selection process.

Drag Rectangle Selection

It is often necessary to select many objects at once. To select a group of objects using a rectangle, press and hold MB1 and drag the cursor. When the rectangle expands to enclose the desired objects, release the mouse button to complete the selection.

The rectangle (and polygon for that matter) has five selection methods:

- "Inside" only selects items within the rectangle.
- "Inside and Crossing" selects items within the rectangle or crossing its boundaries.
- "Outside" only selects items outside of the rectangle.
- "Outside and Crossing" selects items outside the rectangle or crossing its boundaries.
- "Crossing" selects only items crossing the rectangle boundary.

To set the default rectangle selection method, use **Preferences→Selection→Rectangle Method**. You can set the method on a case by case basis using the Class Selection Tool's Rectangle/Polygon Method option. Note that if you specify a method from the Class Selection dialog, that method will be retained by the system until you change it again in the Class Selection dialog, or reset it in **Preferences→Selection**.

Chaining

This utility is used to select *connected* curves or edges, Chain is available as a button on the Class Selection dialog. To chain curves that form a closed boundary or an open section of closed curves, select a starting curve followed by the ending curve. Take care in selecting the end of the starting curve that is pointing towards the ending curve as this dictates the chain direction. Next you can pick a curve that ends the chain. Alternatively, in either case of a closed boundary or an open boundary you can select only the starting curve of the chain and select End Chain on the dialog. This will chain all the curves that are connected from the starting curve toward the chain direction.

Polygon Method

The polygon method is used in situations where a rectangle is not feasible. To use this option, choose the Polygon button followed by screen picks that form a polygon. Once you have selected the screen picks and are satisfied, select OK to close the polygon off and have the system select the objects for you.

3.11 User Interface Shortcuts

In this section, we introduce some of the shortcuts that exist in the software to speed up your productivity. Moving a mouse around a computer screen can take time, causing loss of productivity for repetitive operations. To the right of most entries in the pulldown from the main menu, there are key combinations listed which are known as hot keys. When pressed in the correct combination on the keyboard, these hot keys simply activate the given menu item. For example, to create a new file, you may use either the method of moving your mouse to File, then find New and select it from the pulldown or you may simply press Ctrl+N to accomplish the same task. Below is an abbreviated table of some of the more commonly used hot keys for your reference.

Hot Key Combination	Action Performed
Ctrl + N	File→New
Ctrl + D	Edit→Delete
Ctrl + B	Edit→Blank→Blank
Ctrl + Shift + D	File→Change Displayed Part
Ctrl + S	File→Save
Ctrl + Shift + A	File→Save as
Ctrl + A	Toggle, Activates Assembly Navigator
Ctrl + T	Edit→Transform
F4	Hide/Retrieve Information Window

Ctrl + J	Edit→Object Display

While the above is not a complete list, it does represent some of the more common items.

3.12 Default Files in Unigraphics

Unigraphics offers various options and features, and has many defaults set up for users. You may have had the question, "Can I set these up so that the interface looks like X?" The answer to the question is yes. In Unigraphics, there are three main default files that may be modified to customize things from default values to user interface all the way to where certain files are located. These files are located in the installation directory of the software and should typically be modified by someone with Administrator (Root on Unix) privileges. A typical path to find these files might be C:\UGS160\ugii\. Typically, companies assign a group of people to the task of configuring these files for the rest of the company. In the next few paragraphs, we will discuss what these files are and what the purposes are.

The ug_english.def and the ug_metric.def files are default files that determine the preset values or approaches that are used in the software. Only one of these two files is used at a given time. Which one to be used depends on the main units that are used for modeling objects. For example, if you always model in millimeters, then you would use the ug_metric.def (conversely if you modeled in inches then you would use ug_english.def). Modifying either of these files will cause changes in the initial drafting or modeling standards that they employ and by modifying the default files, many of these may be easily accomplished and minimize the chance that the standard will not be conformed to.

The ugii_env.dat (.ugii_env on Unix) file mainly tells the system values that are seen when you start a session of the software. Many companies differ in where certain files or directories are on the system. This file also tells the system which default file to use out of the two.

3.13 Obtaining Help

You may have questions on Unigraphics that this book does not address. A very good source for assistance with your questions is contained within the online help that should be installed with your software. To activate the online help, simply use your mouse and point to Help→Documentation (HTML) or Help→Documentation (Other). For most users, the HTML should suffice. Once in the help, you have the ability to search on topics or simply browse through several aspects of the software.

Exercise Problems

3.1 Outline and discuss the two main approaches to modeling (spatially) in Unigraphics and the implications these two methods have on using the software.

3.2 Discuss the three coordinate systems presented in this chapter. Be sure to include their purposes.

3.3 What situations might cause the manipulation of the WCS?

3.4 Who sets up the default files in Unigraphics? Why are they available for modification?

3.5 What is the purpose of Hot Keys?

3.6 What does CAX stand for?

3.7 What is the Point Constructor used for?

3.8 What is the purpose of the Class Selection Dialog?

3.9 Explain how you would select green lines on layer 11 using the Class Selection Dialog.

3.10 Explain the preferred method for confirming a selection.

3.11 How many layers does Unigraphics have?

3.12 Name two options on Layer Settings that can make layers easier to manage.

3.13 What is the difference between a layer being Selectable and Visible?

3.14 Name two of the default files used by Unigraphics.

Chapter 4. Primitives

Primitive features are base features to which other features are added. UG uses five primitives, which take on the following basic analytic shapes: **Blocks, Cylinders, Cones, Spheres, and Tubes.** Primitives are non-associative, meaning they are not associated to geometry used to create them. However, you can edit certain parameters.

Section 4.1 discusses a common procedure to create a primitive. Sections 4.2 to 4.4 describe the first three primitives, Blocks, Cylinders, and Cones respectively that will be used in this book.

4.1 Common Procedure to Create a Primitive

There is a general procedure that can be followed when creating a primitive:

1. Select the type of primitive (block, cylinder, etc.) you want to create.
2. Choose the creation method.
3. Enter the creation parameter values.

After performing step 3 above, if a solid body already exists, you need to specify how the new primitive will be used with the existing solid body. In this case, the following Boolean options are displayed:

Create	To create a new solid body.
Add	To add the primitive to the current target solid.
Subtract	To subtract the primitive from the current target solid.
Intersect	To intersect the primitive with the current target solid.

For the primitives with curved edges (all except Block), if you do not have silhouette edges displayed, it can be hard to see them. Therefore, it is recommended that you have silhouette edges displayed when creating these features, which is the default. If silhouette edges are not displayed for some reason, you can do so by using **Preferences → Visualization → Visual**. Also, after you have finished performing the Boolean operation, you can use **Edit →**

Object Display and select the newly formed solid body to add U-V grid lines to make the shape of the resulting body more obvious.

You cannot position solid primitives using positioning dimensions as you can most other features. Positioning methods will be discussed in Chapter 5. During the creation of the primitive, you supply its location either using the *Point Constructor* that was discussed in Section 3.7, or by selecting geometry. We will give the examples in the subsequent sections.

4.2 Block

There are three ways that you can create block primitives by selecting proper options as shown in the table below.

Origin, Edge Lengths	Define the length of each edge and a corner point.
Two Points, Height	Define the block height and two diagonal points of the block base.
Two Diagonal Points	Define two 3D diagonal points representing opposite corners of the block.

All of these options create the block such that its faces align with the axes of the WCS. Below we discuss each option in detail.

Origin, Edge Lengths

This option creates a block by defining a corner point and the length of each edge.

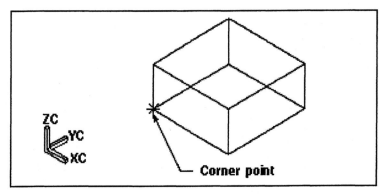

After choosing this method from the left most icon you must:

1. Define the corner point of the block, which is the origin of the block.
2. Enter the XC, YC, ZC edge length values which must be positive. Use the Tab key to move from window to window.
3. Choose OK to accept the choices and create the block.

The system creates the block using the input values, starting from the specified point. The edges of the block are parallel to the axes of the WCS.

A special case for the block exists such that if you want the origin to be at 0, 0, 0 you do not need to select it—just enter the edge lengths and choose OK.

Two Points, Height

This option creates a block by defining the block height and two diagonal points of the block base.

Select the middle icon to choose this method and you must:

1. Enter the positive block height.

2. Define the diagonal points of the block base.

The value entered causes the system to create the block of that height in the direction of the +ZC axis. Define the opposite corners of the block base by specifying two diagonal points. To define the points you may have change the setting of the Point Method menu or utilize the Point Constructor dialog. The first corner point also determines the plane of the block base. This plane is parallel to the XC-YC plane of the WCS. The second point defines the opposite corner of the block base. If you specify the second point on a different plane (different Z values) than the first, the system projects the point normal to the plane of the first point, to define the opposite corner. The edges of the block are parallel to the axes of the WCS.

Two Diagonal Points

This option creates a block by defining two 3D diagonal points representing opposite corners of the block. And you may need to change the Point Method menu and utilize the Point Constructor dialog.

4.3 Cylinder

You can create cylinder primitives by specifying an orientation, size and location, using the following options:

Diameter, Height	Define diameter and height values.
Height, Arc	Creates a cylinder by selecting an arc and entering a height value.

Diameter, Height

This option creates a solid body cylinder by defining diameter and height values.

To create a cylinder using this method you must:

1. Define the cylinder direction vector.
2. Enter the diameter and height values.
3. Define the cylinder origin.

Define the cylinder direction using the *Vector Constructor*. The direction you specify also determines the cylinder orientation. The cylinder is created along the axis with one circular face passing through the axis origin and the other circular face at a distance of the input height value.

Height, Arc

This option creates a cylinder by selecting an arc and entering a height value.

To create a cylinder using this method you must:

1. Enter the height value.
2. Select an arc.
3. Confirm the cylinder axis direction. You can reverse the direction.

The system derives the orientation of the cylinder from the arc you select. The axis of the cylinder is normal to the plane of the arc and passes through the arc center. A vector indicates this orientation. The arc you select does not have to be a complete circle. The system creates a complete cylinder based on any arc objects. Note that the cylinder is not associative with the arc. You may create the cylinder along the displayed axis, or reverse the creation direction. The system creates a complete cylinder of the specified height and direction initiating from the selected arc. The figure below illustrates the results of the height value and direction reversals.

4.4 Cone

You can create cone primitives by specifying an orientation, size and location, using the following options:

Diameters, Height	Define the base diameter, top diameter, and height values.
Diameters, Half Angle	Define the base diameter, top diameter, and half angle values.
Base Diameter, Height, Half Angle	Define the base diameter, height, and half vertex angle values.
Top Diameter, Height, Half Angle	Define the top diameter, height, and half vertex angle values.
Two Coaxial Arcs	Select two arcs, which do not need to be parallel.

For these options, the cone direction (its central axis) is defined using the *Vector Constructor*. The origin of the base of the cone is defined using the *Point Constructor*. We will discuss below only the most commonly used option, which is, the first option in detail.

Diameters, Height

To create a solid body cone using this method, you must

1. Define the cone direction.
2. Enter the base and top diameters and the cone height.
3. Define the origin.

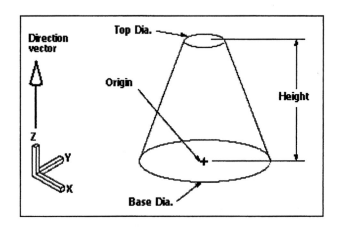

The base diameter is defined as the starting plane and origin for the cone. The top diameter is merely the diameter the height distance away. One diameter may be larger than the other—there is no rule here. To obtain a cone with a point on it the top diameter must be defined as 0. The base diameter must be a positive integer.

Activity 4-1. Creating a Model with Two Blocks

Step 1. Create a new part file by choosing **File → New** and name the part file *****_activity4-1.prt**. Start the Modeling Application.

Step 2. The first block is created with the first option, edge lengths (2.25, 2., 0.5) and a corner (refer to Section 2.1 Steps 1 for detail).

Step 3. Move the **WCS**

You will place the second block at the end of the first block, and angled from it 30 degrees. One way to do this is to change the position of the **WCS**, and then use that orientation to create the second block. First, you will move the WCS to a different location.

    3.1. Choose **WCS → Origin**.

You can indicate a new origin. The **Point Constructor** dialog displays to assist you, or you can simply select a point in the view.

    3.2. Select this corner (end point of an edge).

The **WCS** immediately moves to the corner.

Step 4. Rotate the **WCS**

In order to create the second block angled from the first, you must rotate the **WCS** to make its **XC** axis point in the correct direction.

   4.1. Choose **WCS → Rotate**.

The **Rotate WCS about...** dialog lets you specify how you want to rotate the WCS.

   4.2. Click on the button by **+YC Axis: ZC → XC**.

The **X length** of this second block needs to slope downward at a 30 degree angle from the first block.

   4.3. Double-click in the **Angle** field of the dialog and key in an angle value of 30 (degrees). Choose **OK**. The **WCS** should be oriented like this.

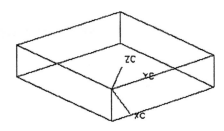

Step 5. Create the second **Block**

You can create the second block using the **Two Diagonal Points** method, which requires you to define the two diagonal points that will represent the opposite corners of the block. The dialog of three block methods should still be displayed.

    5.1. If not, **Insert → Form Feature → Block**.

    5.2. Choose **Two Diagonal Points** icon.

Step 6. Specifying the Parameters.

Choose the Point Method menu, then the Point Constructor icon, and the **Point Constructor** dialog displays to help you to define the origin of the first diagonal point. This block needs to angle off the first, but have the same height and width. One easy way to do this is to place the first diagonal corner point a half inch below the **WCS** along the **ZC** axis.

    6.1. Toggle on the **WCS** button, if it is not.

    6.2. Choose the **Reset** option to change the base point values to zero.

    6.3. Key in the following values for the first diagonal point:

        XC field= 0, **YC** field 0, **ZC** field= -0.5 and choose **OK**.

In the graphics area, an asterisk displays the location for the first diagonal point.

This block needs to be 3.25 inches long (along the **XC** axis), 2 inches wide (along the **YC** axis), and a half inch high. Change Point Method again.

    6.4. Key in the following values for the second diagonal point:

        XC field = 3.25, **YC** field = 2.0, **ZC** field = 0 and choose **OK**.

An asterisk displays the second point. These two asterisks define where the block will be created.

The block is not created yet, because the system knows that two solids will occupy some of the same model space, so you must tell the system you want to use a Boolean operation. Select the Boolean Operation menu and a dialog of Boolean operations displays.

You can **Create** the block as a separate solid body, **Unite** the two solid bodies, **Subtract** the new solid body from the old, or find a solid body from the **Intersection** of the two solid bodies. You will **Unite** the two blocks into one solid body.

    6.5. Choose **Unite** to join the two blocks and choose **OK**.

    6.6. Choose **Cancel** on the Point Constructor dialog.

    6.7. Use **MB3** → **Fit** to fit the view.

If your part does not look correct you can use **Edit** → **Undo List** and choose 1 Block, use **Ctrl+Z,** or **MB3** → **Undo** to restore the part to the prior state.

Activity 4-2. Creating a cylinder

You will add a cylinder to the end of the angled block.

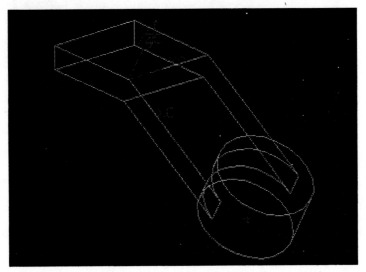

Step 1. Choose **Insert→Form Feature→Cylinder** or choose **Cylinder** icon. The **Cylinder** dialog lists two creation options. The **Cylinder** option lets you create a primitive cylinder by specifying its orientation, size, and location.

    1.1. Choose the Diameter, Height option.

Step 2. Specify the Direction.

The **Vector Constructor** dialog displays methods to define the direction of the cylinder (vector direction). The positive **ZC** axis of your **WCS** is already oriented in the correct direction for the cylinder. That is, the **ZC** axis is pointing normal to the top face of the angled block, which is the direction in which you will want to create the cylinder.

    2.1. Choose **ZC Axis** on the dialog.

A direction vector displays the direction in which the new primitive cylinder will be created.

2.2. Choose **OK**.

Step 3. Specify the Parameters.

In the next dialog that displays, you must specify positive diameter and height values for the cylinder.

    3.1. Key in the parameters: Diameter = 2.0, Height = 1.25 and choose **OK**.

The **Point Constructor** dialog redisplays. To position the cylinder correctly, you need to place its origin (base point) directly below the midpoint of the end of the angled block. There are several ways to define the origin point for the cylinder. When you began the cylinder procedure, you could have moved the WCS to a location where its origin could be used to define the center of the base of the cylinder. Another way to define this point is to calculate the **XC**, **YC**, **ZC** distance of the origin of the cylinder from the origin of the **WCS**. You will use the **XC** and **YC** values to center the cylinder at the end of the angled block, and use the **ZC** value to place its origin low enough to center its height on the end of the block.

    3.2. Check that the **WCS** option is toggled on.

    3.3. In the **Point Constructor** dialog, key in the parameters for the **Base Point**:

    3.4. **XC** = 3.25, **YC** = 1.0, **ZC** = -0.875 and choose **OK**.

In the view, an asterisk displays where the base point of the cylinder will be located. If you did not like this location, you could choose **Back** on the Boolean operation dialog and respecify the cylinder location. (If it's hard to visualize to location of the asterisk in 3D space, you may use the Rotate utility to move the part around to see where it is located relative to the block.)

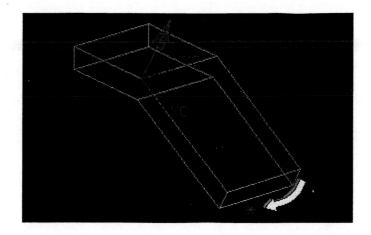

Step 4. **Unite** the Cylinder with the Block. In the four Boolean options,

    4.1. Choose **Unite**.

    4.2. **Cancel** the **Vector Constructor** dialog.

    4.3. **Save and close** all files.

Activity 4-3. Creating a cone

You will create this truncated cone.

Step 1. Create a new part file named *****_activity4-3.prt**.

Step 2. Specify the **Cone** creation method.

    2.1. Choose **Insert → Form Feature → Cone** or choose the **Cone** icon .

The cone creation methods are available on the **Cone** dialog.

    2.2. Choose the **Diameters, Height** option.

Step 3. Specify a direction for the cone.

    3.1. Choose **ZC Axis** option.

The direction vector displays at the location of the **WCS**.

    3.2. Choose **OK** on the **Vector Constructor** dialog.

Step 4. Specify the Parameters.

The **Base Diameter** must be greater than zero. The **Top Diameter** can be zero, which will create a pointed cone, or greater than zero for a truncated cone. (This value can be larger than the base diameter value.) For this cone, you can use these values:

      Base Diameter = 3

      Top Diameter = 1

      Height = 4

      Choose **OK**.

Step 5. Specify the **Origin**.

The **Point Constructor** dialog displays to help you to specify the origin (arc center) of the base of the cone. For this cone, you can use the following origin in the **WCS**:

    5.1. Enter **XC** = 2, **YC** = 3, **ZC** = 0 and choose **OK**.

The truncated cone is created slightly to the right of the WCS.

    5.2. If necessary, fit the view with MB3 → Fit.

As with cylinders and blocks, you can unite, subtract, or intersect multiple bodies in the part file.

Step 6. Save and close this file.

Project 4-1. Primitives

Using the primitives that you learned in this chapter, create a solid model that is depicted in the drawing below. Note that the cone and the cylinder are concentric and are centered in the block. Save it with filename ***_project4-1.prt, where *** is your three-letter name initials. You will use it again in Chapter 5.

It is important to note that generally it is not a recommended design practice to use more than one primitive to model a part. In Chapter 5, you will model this same part using only one primitive, adding form features to it. You will compare these two modeling approaches and learn why using more than one primitive to model a part is not a recommended design practice.

Exercise Problems

4.1 What are primitives?

4.2 State five primitives used by Unigraphics.

4.3 Write a common procedure to create a primitive.

4.4 Name three ways to create a block.

4.5 Name two ways to create a cylinder.

4.6 There are several ways to create a cone. Name one frequently used.

Chapter 5. Basic Form Features

Form features are features that are added to or subtracted from a base feature, either started with a primitive discussed in Chapter 4 or a swept feature discussed in Chapter 9. Thus, form features supply detail to your model. In this chapter, we introduce five form features that are most commonly used. These are hole, boss, pocket, pad, and slot. Section 5.1 discusses a common procedure to create a form feature and Section 5.2 discusses positioning methods to locate form features on the existing base feature. Sections 5.3 to 5.7 describe the five form features in order.

5.1 Common Procedure to Create a Feature

The basic procedure to add a form feature to your part is:

1. Select the **Planar Placement** face.
2. Select a **Horizontal Reference** if required.
3. Select one or more **Thru Faces** if required.
4. Enter values for the feature parameters.
5. **Position** the feature.

Planar Placement Face

Most form features require a *planar placement face*, which the form feature is created on and is associative with. The planar placement face can be a datum plane or a planar face on the target solid. The feature is created normal to the face and near the location where the face was selected. At a later time it can be more precisely located using positioning methods of Step 5. The feature is automatically linked to the selected face, so that when the face is translated or rotated, the feature remains perpendicular to the face, and the height of the feature remains constant with respect to the face.

If you select a datum plane as the planar placement face, a direction vector is displayed, showing the side of the datum plane on which the feature will be created. You are given the option to accept this default side or to flip the vector to the opposite side.   We will discuss the datum plane in Chapter 8.

Horizontal Reference

Some form features require a horizontal reference, which defines the XC direction of the feature coordinate system. You can select an edge, face, datum axis, or datum plane as the horizontal reference. The horizontal reference defines the length direction of those form features that require a length, including Slot, Pocket and Pad. For these options, you are not required to select a Horizontal or Vertical Reference during the positioning of the feature since it is already defined during feature creation.

Thru Faces

Holes and slots can be created to always go completely through selected faces, regardless of modifications to the solid body, using the Thru option. When a thru face is selected, the hole or slot feature is considered to extend completely through the solid limited only by the placement face and the thru face(s).

Parameter Values

Each feature type requires you to enter values, which define the dimensions necessary for that particular feature. These are sometimes referred to as the feature's *parameters*. These, for example, include length, diameter, or depth.

5.2 Positioning Form Features

You can position a feature or a sketch relative to existing solid body geometry or datum planes. Sketch will be discussed in Chapter 10, and in this chapter we will focus on feature positioning. Creating positioning dimensions called dimensional constraints does this. These constraints control the location of a feature relative to some existing solid body geometry or datum planes. For example, suppose that we want to create a hole feature in a block with the location of the hole shown in the below figure. Two positioning dimensions are used to locate the hole.

Horizontal and Vertical Positioning Dimensions

You can complete a feature without constraining its location by choosing OK before choosing a dimension type. The feature can later be positioned or moved using options found under Edit→ Feature→Edit Positioning Dimension. Depending on the number and type of positioning dimensions specified, the UG Status line indicates that the feature is fully specified, underspecified, or overspecified. The feature is fully specified when it is uniquely located by the positioning dimensions specified. It is underspecified when it is not yet uniquely located. It is overspecified when it has more positioning dimensions applied to it than are necessary.

To position a feature or a sketch, you must:

1. Choose the positioning dimension type.
2. Select the objects to dimension.
3. Enter the new value for positioning.
4. Choose OK to reposition the feature or sketch.

There are up to nine dimension types that can be used to constrain the location of a feature. These are Horizontal, Vertical, Parallel, Perpendicular, Parallel at a Distance, Angular, Point onto Point, Point onto Line, and Line onto Line, and their icons are shown in the figure below. Some features do not require all nine and only those will be shown that are needed.

When selecting the objects to dimension, you must select one of the objects from the target solid, curve, or datum and the other from the feature or sketch. When you position a boss or hole, the system automatically selects the object on the feature (the arc center) for you. Selection of objects varies with the type of dimension you wish to create. For example, if you want to use edges for a horizontal dimension, you must select their endpoints. For those positioning dimensions that require the selection of points, the points must be part of the solid body (i.e., midpoints, endpoints, arc centers, tangency points).

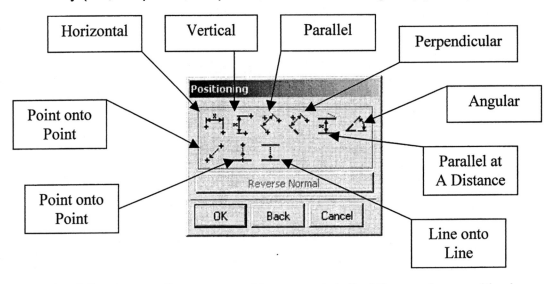

In the following section, we provide more detail of these nine positioning methods.

9 Positioning Methods

(a) **Horizontal**: This creates a positioning dimension between two points. A horizontal dimension is aligned with the Horizontal Reference, or is 90 degrees from the Vertical Reference

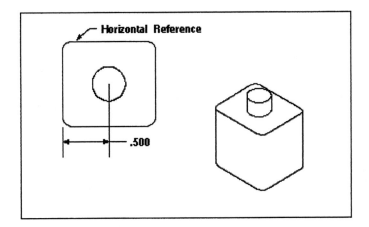

(b) **Vertical**: This creates a positioning dimension between two points. A vertical dimension is aligned with the Vertical Reference, or is 90 degrees from the Horizontal Reference.

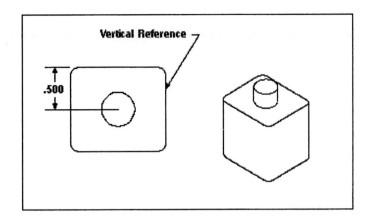

When creating horizontal and vertical dimensions, you may be required to define a Horizontal or Vertical Reference by selecting a linear edge, a solid face, or a datum axis or datum plane. A Horizontal (Vertical) Reference defines the horizontal (vertical) direction for dimensioning the feature's location. When using a face or datum plane for a Horizontal or Vertical Reference, the reference is formed by the intersection (a curve) of the selected face or datum plane and the selected planar placement face.

Positioning dimensions are associated to the geometry used to create them. If you move or delete geometry, the associated positioning dimension is also moved or deleted. Whenever a feature whose edge/face was used as a horizontal or vertical reference is deleted, any Horizontal or Vertical positioning constraints associated with the reference are also deleted.

(c) **Parallel**: This option creates a positioning dimension which constrains the distance between two points (e.g., existing points, entity endpoints, arc center points, or arc tangent points) and is measured parallel to a straight line between the two points. In the figure below, a pad is dimensionally constrained on a block. You can imagine a parallel dimension as a rope joining two points at a specified distance. It takes 3 "ropes" to locate this feature.

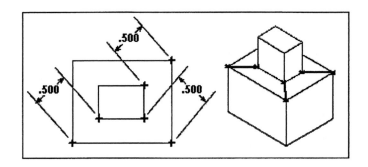

When you create a parallel or any other linear type dimension to a tangent point on an arc, there are two possible tangency points. You must select the arc near the desired point of tangency.

(d) **Perpendicular**: This creates a positioning dimension, which constrains the perpendicular distance between an *edge* of the target solid and a *point* on the feature. You can also position to a datum by selecting a datum plane or datum axis as the target edge, or any existing curve (which need not be on the target solid). This constraint is used to dimension linear distances that are not parallel to the XC or YC axis. It only locks the point on the feature to the edge on the target solid, or to the curve, at the specified distance.

(e) **Parallel at a Distance**: This option creates a positioning dimension, which constrains a linear edge of the feature and a linear edge of the target solid (or any existing curve, on or off the target solid) to be parallel and at a fixed distance apart. This constraint only locks the edge on the feature to the edge on the target solid or the curve at the specified distance.

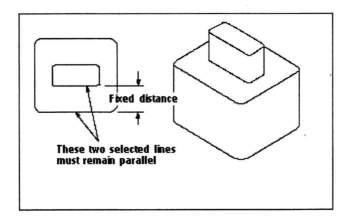

(f) **Angular**: This option creates a positioning constraint dimension between a linear edge of the feature and a linear reference edge/curve at a given angle. Be sure to select the lines to dimension at the proper location. Each line has three control points, one at each end and one at the exact center. The angle created depends on which side of the center control point you select.

The figure below shows two lines with their center control points highlighted by

asterisks (*). The 33°25' angle was created by selecting the lines at the positions indicated by A. The 146°36' angle was created by selecting the lines at the positions marked B. As you can see, selecting the smaller line at a position left of the center control point creates the complementary angle.

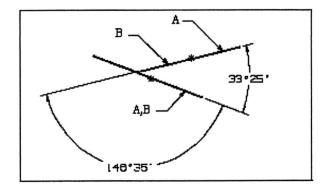

(g) **Point onto Point**: This option creates a positioning dimension the same as the Parallel option, but with the fixed distance between the two points set to zero. This positioning dimension causes the feature to move so that its selected point is on top of the point selected on the target solid.

(h) **Point onto Line**: This option creates a positioning constraint dimension the same as the Perpendicular option, but with the distance between the edge or curve and point set to zero. This positioning dimension causes the feature to move from its selected point, normal to the edge or curve selected on the target solid, until the point is on the edge. This constraint only locks the point on the feature to the edge on the target solid.

Selected endpoint

Selected edge on target solid

RESULT:

(i) **Line onto Line**: This option creates a positioning constraint dimension the same as the Parallel at a Distance option, but with the distance between the linear edge of the feature and the linear edge or curve on the target solid set to zero. This positioning dimension causes the feature to move from its selected edge perpendicularly to the edge or curve selected on the target solid. This constraint only locks the edge on the feature to the edge/curve on the target solid.

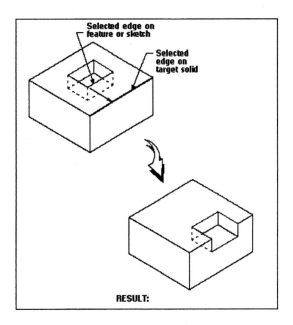

Selected edge on feature or sketch

Selected edge on target solid

RESULT:

5.3 Hole

This feature lets you create a simple hole, a counterbore hole or a countersunk hole in a solid body. For all hole creation options, the depth values must be positive. Choosing Insert → Form Feature → Hole or choose the Hole Icon presents the Hole dialog for the hole creation options.

Thru Hole

If you want any of the hole types to go through the target solid, you merely select the Thru face when prompted for it on the Cue Line. Thru holes do not stop at the first contact with the thru face, but continue completely through the thru face. If the hole intersects the thru face more than once, the hole will continue to the last intersection. If a Thru hole is not required, then set the parameters in the dialog and choose OK.

Simple Hole

To create a simple hole, you must specify a placement planar face/plane, diameter, depth and tip angle. Tip Angle lets you create either a flat or pointed end hole. A zero tip angle value results in a flat end (blind) hole. A positive tip angle value creates an angled tip, which is added to the depth of the hole. The tip angle must be greater than or equal to 0 and less than 180. If you choose to create a Thru Hole, the Tip Angle window and the Depth window are grayed out.

Counterbore Hole

To create a counterbore hole, you must specify two more parameter values than a simple hole, which are C-Bore Diameter and C-Bore Depth.

Countersink Hole

A countersink also requires two more parameter values than a simple hole, which are C-Sink Diameter and C-Sink Angle.

5.4 Boss

Feature Boss can be viewed as opposite to a hole, that is, adding a cylinder on an existing solid instead of subtracting it from. To create a boss you must specify three parameters, Diameter, Height, and Taper Angle and a planar placement face/plane. Taper Angle is the angle at which the cylinder wall of the boss inclines inward. This value can be negative or positive. A zero value results in a vertical cylinder wall with no taper.

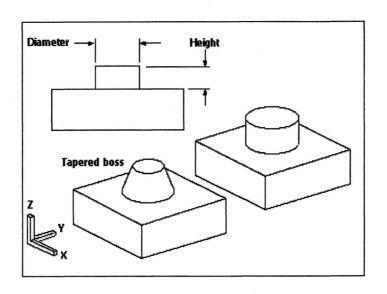

Activity 5-1. Creating holes

In this activity, you will create a simple thru hole and a countersink hole as shown below.

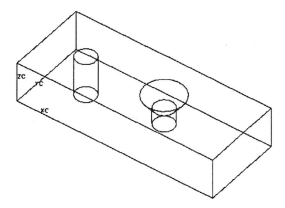

Step 1. **Open** part file **activity5-1.prt,** and save it as **xxx_activity5-1.prt** where xxx is your three letter name initials. Start the **Modeling** application.

    1.1. Choose **Insert →Form Feature → Hole** or choose the **Hole** icon. The **Hole** dialog is displayed.

    1.2. Specify the **Planar Placement Face** for the hole.

Step 2. We want a Thru hole, the **Cue Line** is prompting for a thru face so specify the thru face.

2.1. Select the top face of the block as near where you want the hole to be created.

2.2. Specify the **Through Face**.

All form features, except grooves, are created normal to the selected planar face. If you select where the top and bottom faces overlap in the view, the system will automatically select the bottom face. Select the bottom face like this.

Step 3. The Hole dialog is still up. In the Parameters windows, key in the diameter of 1.0 and choose **OK**.

The hole tool solid temporarily displays as a long green cylinder that extends beyond the thru face. The **WCS** temporarily moves to represent the feature coordinate system at the top center of the hole where the feature is first displayed.

The feature coordinate system shows the XC-axis and YC-axis that represent the horizontal and vertical references that will be used by the system to establish the relationship for positioning the hole.

The **Positioning** dialog displays positioning methods. Note for a hole only 6 positioning methods are available and the Perpendicular method is the default.

Step 4. Position the hole. One way to position it is to provide **Horizontal** and **Vertical** positioning dimensions to constrain the hole to the solid.

4.1. Choose the **Horizontal** icon . A **Horizontal** positioning dimension is the shortest distance along the X-axis between a target edge and in this case, a cylindrical feature like this hole, the dimension will be measured by default to the center of the hole (tool solid).

4.2. Specify a **Horizontal Reference**. The Horizontal Reference defines the direction of the positioning dimension. A horizontal positioning dimension will run horizontally with this reference. A vertical positioning dimension will run 90 degrees to it. Select the front face of the block.

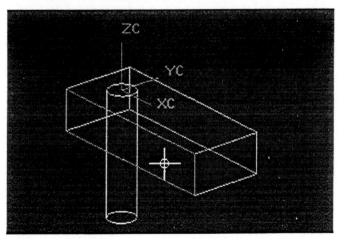

A temporary direction vector shows the horizontal reference.

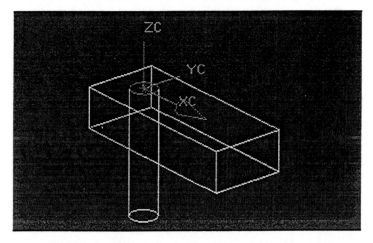

4.3. Specify a Target. Select the left edge of the top face as the target edge for the horizontal dimension, which aligns in the XC direction.

Select here

4.4. The temporary horizontal dimension displays from the target edge to the center of the hole. The Position dialog displays with the temporary value, so key in the distance of 2 and choose **Apply** (because we are not finished with the Positioning dialog). This places the hole two inches from the left edge. This horizontal positioning dimension constrains the simple thru hole in one direction. It is a parameter (an expression) that you could edit later.

4.5. With the **Positioning** dialog still displayed so that you can define the second constraint, so that the hole is fully specified (constrained).

Choose the **Vertical** icon .

4.6. Select the front edge of the top face as the target edge for the vertical dimension.

Select here

4.7. A temporary dimension displays to the center of the hole to the edge. The **Position** dialog displays the current distance value in the **Current Expression** window. Key in 2 and choose **OK** (because we are finished with the Position dialog). The hole is now positioned.

The dimensions are no longer displayed, but you can redisplay the feature dimensions by choosing **Information → Feature**, toggle on **Display Dimensions**, and choose SIMPLE_HOLE(1). Any feature created using the thru option will be associated to the thru faces. If you were to change the size of this block, the hole would remain a through hole positioned two inches from each of the two target edges. Activity 5-2 will address this associativity issue more in detail.

Step 5. Create a countersink hole on the top face of the block with the following parameters:

> **C-Sink Diameter** = 2.
> **C-Sink Angle** = 75
> **Hole Diameter** = 1.
> **Hole Depth** = 1.5
> **Tip Angle** = 0

Step 6. Create the hole without positioning it. The WCS is temporarily displayed at the top center of the countersink hole. Choose **OK** in the **Positioning** dialog to accept the present location. The countersink hole is complete even though the location is unconstrained, i.e., the hole is underspecified.

Step 7. **Undo** Step 5 by **MB3→ Undo.** Position the countersink hole such that its center is located with 2 inch away from the front face of the block and with 4 inch away from the right edge of the top face of the block as shown below. If you have difficulty in positioning, redo **Step 4**.

5.5 Pocket

You can use the Pocket option to create a cavity in an existing body, using one of the following three methods:

Cylindrical	Lets you define a circular pocket, to a specific depth, with or without a blended floor, having straight or tapered sides.
Rectangular	Lets you define a rectangular pocket, to a specific length, width, and depth, with specific radii in the corners and on the floor, having straight or tapered sides.
General	Lets you define a pocket with much greater flexibility than the cylindrical and rectangular pocket options.

Below we will give more detail description on the Rectangular Pocket. Specific parameters are described below:

X Length	The length of the pocket parallel to Horizontal.
Y Length	The width of the pocket.

Z Length	The depth of the pocket.
Corner Radius	The rounded radius (zero or greater) for the vertical edges of the pocket.
Floor Radius	The rounded radius (zero or greater) for the bottom edges of the pocket. The Corner Radius must be greater than or equal to the Floor Radius.
Taper Angle	The angle at which the four walls of the pocket incline inward. This value cannot be negative. A value of zero results in vertical walls.

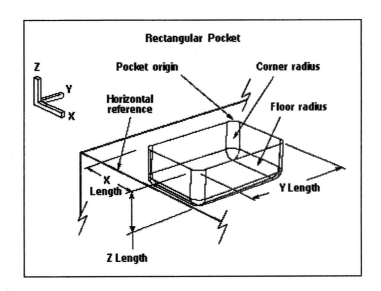

5.6 Pad

This feature creates a pad on an existing solid body. This is somewhat opposite to the Pocket feature as Boss is to Hole. There are two methods of creating a pad:

Rectangular	Lets you define a pad to a specific length, width, and depth, with specific radii in the corners, having straight or tapered sides.
General	Lets you define a pad with greater flexibility than the rectangular pad option.

Below we will give more detail description on the Rectangular Pad. Specific parameters are described below:

Length	The length of the pad in the direction of Horizontal.
Width	The width of the pad.
Height	The height of the pad.
Corner Radius	The rounded radius for the vertical edges of the pad. The radius specified must be a positive or zero. (A zero radius results in a sharp edged pad.)
Taper Angle	The angle at which the four walls of the pad incline inward. This value cannot be negative. (A zero value results in vertical walls.)

5.7 Slot

This feature create a passage through or into a solid body in the shape of a straight slot as if cut by a milling machine tool. The slot feature will be created so that the axis of the imaginary cutter tool is normal to the planar placement face or datum plane selected. The path of the slot is parallel to the horizontal reference selected. There are five types of slots to choose from and the parameters for each type of slot are described below. The depth value for all slot types is measured normal to the planar placement face.

Rectangular Lets you create a slot with sharp edges along the bottom.

Ball-End   Lets you create a slot with a full radius bottom and corners.

U-Slot   Lets you create a slot with a "U" shape (rounded corners and floor radii).

T-Slot   Lets you create a slot whose cross section is an inverted T.

Dove-Tail   Lets you create a slot with a "dove-tail" shape (sharp corners and angled walls).

For all types, the **Thru Slot** option extends the slot length along the placement face in the direction of the horizontal reference thru 2 other faces that you select. These faces are the **Starting Thru Face** and the **Ending Thru Face**, as shown in the figure below.

When positioning a thru slot, a single constraint that locates the slot perpendicular to its length is all you need. Do not dimension to the end arcs of the slot. Thru slots intersecting a thru face more than once may result in multiple solutions as shown below.

Rectangular Slot

This option creates a slot using a tool that has cylindrical end faces and leaves sharp edges along the bottom. Its parameters are

Width   The width (diameter) of the tool that forms the slot.

Depth   The depth of the slot is the distance from the origin point of the slot to the bottom of the slot.

Length   The length of the slot, measured in a direction parallel to the horizontal reference.

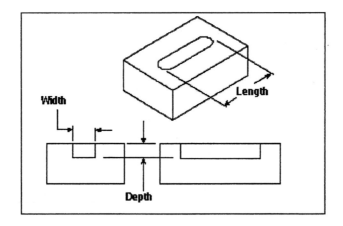

Ball-End Slot

A ball-end slot leaves a full radius bottom and corner. Its parameters are Ball Diameter (i.e., the width of the slot resulting from the tool diameter), Depth, and Length.

U-Slot

This option creates a slot with a "U" shape. This type of slot leaves rounded corner and floor radii. You must specify the following parameters: Width, Depth, Corner Radius (i.e., the cutting tool edge radius), Length. The Depth value must

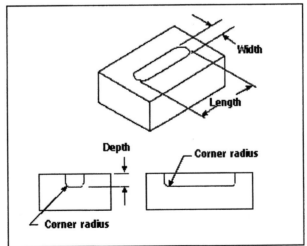

be greater than the Corner Radius value).

T-Slot

This option creates a slot whose cross section is an inverted T. You must specify the following parameters: Top Width, Bottom Width, Top Depth, and Bottom Depth, and Length.

Dove-Tail

This option creates a slot with a "dove-tail" shape. This type of slot leaves sharp corners and angled walls. You must specify the following parameters: Width, Depth, Angle, and Length.

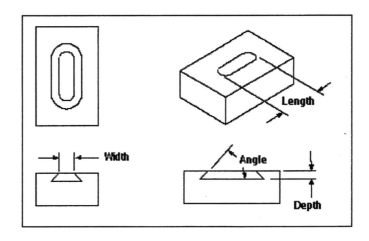

Activity 5-2. Creating a thru T-slot

The design intent here is that a T-slot be created and located so that it aligns with a pad near the back of the block as shown in the following figure.

Step 1. **Open activity5-2.prt** and **Save** it as *****_activity5-2.prt** and start the **Modeling** application.

Step 2. Choose **Insert → Form Feature → Slot** or choose the **Slot** icon. The **Slot** dialog displays.

    2.1. Toggle **Thru Slot** to on.

    2.2. Choose the **T-Slot** type.

Step 3. Select the top face as the planar placement face.

Step 4. Specify a horizontal reference to define the direction of the slot.

    4.1. For the horizontal reference, choose **Solid Face** on the dialog.

    4.2. Select the closest face of the pad. You may need to zoom in on the pad for careful selection.

Horizontal
Reference

A vector displays the X direction (length/path) of the slot.

Step 5. Specify the thru faces. Select these two thru faces.

Thru face

Thru face

Step 6. Enter the following parameters for the thru **T-slot**:

     Top Width = 9/32

     Top Depth = 1/4

     Bottom Width = 0.5

     Bottom Depth = 7/32 and choose **OK**.

A temporary tool solid displays on the part.

Step 7. Position the slot using the **Parallel at a Distance** option. This option constrains the linear edge of the feature to the linear edge of the target solid to be parallel at a specified distance.

    7.1. Choose the **Parallel at a Distance** icon ⊞.

    7.2. Select the target edge of the pad. You may need to zoom in to make selection easier.

Select target edge of pad

7.3. For a tool edge, select the top edge of the T-Slot closest to the pad feature.

Select edge

7.4. The **Create Expression** dialog displays the current distance. Key **6.0** into the value field, and choose **OK** twice to complete the positioning of the slot.

7.5. Cancel the dialog.

7.6. Fit the view by **MB3 → Fit**, if needed.

Do not close the file since you will continue to use it in the following activity.

Activity 5-3. Editing an existing slot and creating a pad

In this step, you will change the position of the thru T-slot that was just created, in the previous activity and then add a pad such that the resulting part looks as follows:

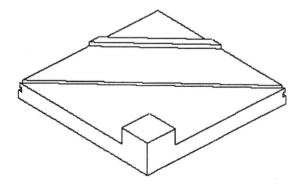

Step 1. Choose **Edit → Feature → Positioning** or choose the **Edit Positioning**

icon . The **Edit Positioning** dialog displays all features.

Step 2. Select **T_Slot** on the dialog, and choose **OK**. Three choices are available to modify the positioning.

Step 3. Choose **Edit Dimension Value**.

The current positioning dimensions are displayed on the part and the Cue Line prompts to select the dimension to be edited. Select the Parallel at a Distance dimension of 6.0. The Edit Expression dialog displays the current distance 6.0, so change **6** into **3.5.**

Choose **OK**. Choose **OK** until the slot changes (that's 3 times to choose OK). The model updates. Notice that the slot now pierces four walls.

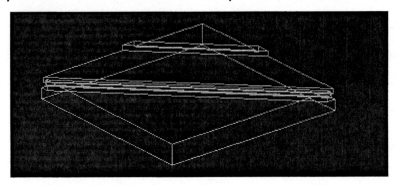

Step 4. Add a form feature **Pad** on the top face of the block with the following parameters: Length=2, Width=2, and Height=1. Position it using two **Line onto Line** 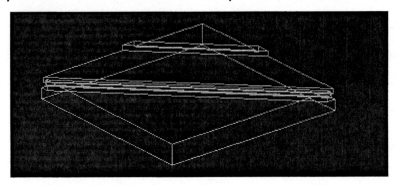 option such that the resulting figure appears at the beginning of the activity.

Step 5. **Save and close** all part files.

Activity 5-4. Comparison of Modeling Approaches: Primitives vs. Form Features

Form features are associative - if you change the geometry used to create a form feature, it is updated. Note that primitives such as Block and Cylinder are not associative. You will investigate this concept using this project. Use the same drawing of Project 4-1 and create a solid model using only one primitive. Note that in Project 4-1 you used four primitives to model the part. Save the new part file as ***activity5-4.prt, where *** is your three-letter name initials.

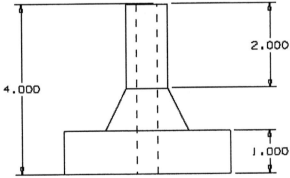

Step 1. Create a model starting with a block primitive.

Step 2. Add a tapered boss using the top face of a block as the placement face.

    2.1. Enter the taper angle as the following trigonometry function: **Taper Angle** = atan(0.5/1) * 180 / pi(). The arc tan function = 26.565 (degrees).

    2.2. Use two **Perpendicular** positioning dimensions to locate the boss.

Step 3. Add the second boss using the top face of the first boss as the placement face. Its taper angle is zero. Use the **Point onto Point** positioning dimension to align the circle center points of these two bosses.

Step 4. Add a thru hole using the top face of the second boss as the placement face. The thru face is the bottom face of the block. Use the **Point onto Point** positioning dimension to align the circle center of the hole to the circle center of the second boss.

In Steps 5 and 6 below, you are going to change the height of the block for this model and that of the block that you created in Project 4-1, and then to observe the difference of the two models.

Step 5. Choose **Edit → Feature → Parameters**. "Edit Parameters" dialog appears.

    5.1. Select **Block(0)** and **OK**.

    5.2. Click "**Feature Dialog**" and Change **Z length** from 1 to 2 and then click **OK** three times.

You will see the block height increase from 1 to 2 and all the form features move upward as the block top face rises due to the increased block height.

Step 6. Now open ***project4-1.prt. Repeat **Step 5**. As the block height increase from 1 to 2, you will see the cone primitive disappear (in fact, it is buried inside the block).

Why do the resulting models of the above two steps differ? This is because form features are associative but primitives are not. Consider how form features are constructed. The first tapered boss is associated with the block in that the block top face was used as the placement face of the boss. As this face rises, the boss on the face also rises. The second boss is associated with the first boss through the placement face (top face of the first boss), and the hole associated with the second boss through the placement face (top face of the second boss). As a result, these two features move upward as the first boss moves upward. On the other hand, the cone or cylinder primitives are placed in space of WCS with no association (relation) with the existing solid body, which is a block. The next question you may ask is which approach is right between the two. This is determined by the design intent of a designer. Therefore, modelers need carefully interpret the design intent when they model parts.

Design Intent

An important aspect of the design process is the conditions under which the designer must operate as defined by marketing, manufacturing and sales considerations that will affect the final design. All of these considerations are contained in the term design intent. More formally stated, design intent is the ability to capture geometric conditions, dimensional relationships, and relative positions between features on solid models. A CAD software application that can capture design intent is called a parametric modeler. Unigraphics has powerful parametric modeling functions. The program gives you a choice to add, change, or later remove, design intent. At the start of the design, you may not know what sort of design intent is necessary. Using expressions, positional dimensions, instances and feature editing, you can change the model easily as design conditions and intent change. In the following chapter, we will discuss editing models.

Project 5-1. Shaft Support

Create a model of the part using the drawings and dimensions (in inches) given below. Name your part as ***_project5-1.prt where *** is three-letter initials of your name.

Hint: One approach to model this part is to start with a block and add the following form features: two bosses and 6 simple thru holes.

Project 5-2. Bracket

Create a model of the part using the drawings and dimensions (in inches) given below. Name your part as ***_project5-2.prt where *** is three-letter initials of your name.

Hint: One approach to model this part is to start with a block and add the following form features: four simple thru holes, two bosses, two pads, three rectangular slots, and another two simple thru holes.

Project 5-3. Mounting Plate

Create a model of the part using the drawings and dimensions (in inches) given below. Name your part as ***_project5-3.prt where *** is three-letter initials of your name.

Hint: One approach to create a model is to start with a block and add the following form features: 4 pads, 1 rectangular pocket, 1 boss, 3 simple thru holes, 1 counter bore thru hole, and 1 rectangular slot. You need to apply various positioning methods to locate the form features.

Exercise Problems

5.1 Write a common procedure to create a form feature.

5.2 What is the planar placement face? Give me three form features that require the planar placement face.

5.3 What is the horizontal reference? Give me three form features that require it.

5.4 Name the nine positioning methods.

5.5 What is the advantage of using the Perpendicular positioning method over the Horizontal or Vertical positioning methods?

5.6 Is the Point onto Point positioning method a special case of the Parallel one?

5.7 What happens to the positioning dimensions when their reference objects or geometry used for positioning are deleted?

5.8 Suppose that you need add a cylinder shape of a solid to an existing solid body. You can do so by adding either a primitive Cylinder or a form feature Boss. Compare these two approaches.

5.9 What is the difference between two form features, the Rectangular Pocket and the Rectangular Slot?

5.10 The Thru Hole and the Thru Slot differ in picking "thru" faces. Discuss the difference.

5.11 What is the design intent?

Chapter 6. Querying and Editing Models

When you work on part models, particularly, ones designed by other engineers, you often need to query or interrogate a model for various pieces of information. Sometimes, this information is geometrically related such as the distance between two objects like edges or points. Other times, you need to understand how a model was constructed for editing purposes. Investigation of construction methods helps you to understand the design intent of the model. This design intent includes not only the dimension and function of the model itself, but also the intent of design change, that is, how the model is supposed to react to changes of parameter value(s).

This chapter consists of six sections. Section 6.1 discusses how to use layers to find objects. Section 6.2 addresses the Model Navigator, which helps to navigate your model easily for querying or editing. Section 6.3 discusses expressions and their relation to parametric modeling. Sections 6.4 through 6.6 discuss three other querying functions in order: (1) playing back to reconstruct a model from the beginning, (2) retrieving information on features, and (3) finding distance between objects.

6.1 Using Layers to Find Objects

In Chapter 3, you were introduced the concept of layers as well as the tool within Unigraphics to control them. In this section, the Layer Settings dialog is used to determine what layer an object is on, which is very helpful in determining the overall organization of the part file.

Most companies employ layering standards, which are company standards to dictate what layer or layers objects should be on. For example, a company may dictate that solids be placed on layer 1, and sketches on layer 21 in all part files. Obviously there are benefits of following the standards. For example, If these standards are well followed, it helps one to understand a part model developed by another by quickly identifying how many objects and what kinds of objects are on which layers.

To find the layer that an object is on, simply go to **Format → Layer Settings** to bring up the **Layer Settings** dialog shown below. Once the dialog has been opened, pick the category, **ALL** (this will select all 256 layers) followed by **Selectable** (so that you can see and select all of the objects in the model) followed by **Apply**.

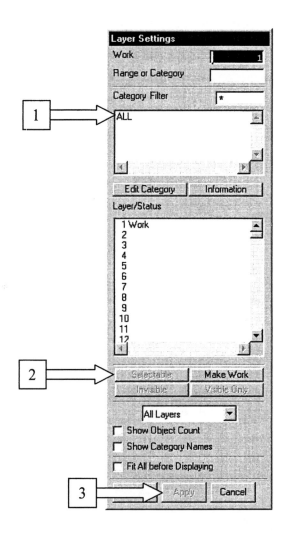

Now, with all objects being displayed on your screen, simply select them in the graphics area and look at the **Layer Settings** dialog. In the list of layers, the layer that the object you selected is on will highlight. You can then continue to do this for the objects that you are interested in. This procedure works whether you are displaying "**All Layers**" or "**Layers with Objects**" from the **Layer Settings** dialog.

6.2 The Model Navigator (MN)

The Model Navigator (MN) is one of the most useful tools in modeling. It gives you direct access to the various features that have been constructed in your model. From gathering information to changing parametric values, MN gives you single point access capabilities for a variety of tasks.

Open part file Mounting_Plate.prt. To turn on MN, select the Model Navigator icon ⬚ from the standard menu bar. A sample MN window is shown below.

Notice the correlation between the types of features that make up the model and the list of features in the MN window. For each hole, there is a feature "HOLE" that shows up in the Model Navigator along. The Model Navigator window shows that this model consists of 19 features. Right next to a feature name in the

MN window, there is a number in the parentheses, which is referred to as the timestamp. The timestamp simply indicates the order in which features are constructed. BLOCK(0) means that the block is the first feature created and COUNTER_BORE_HOLE(18) is the last feature created among the features in the list.

Notice also that the tool is on top of the graphics screen making it difficult to work on and see the entire part. Beginning in version 16, UG allows to "dock" the tool. To dock the tool, simply pick and hold down on the top bar of the Model Navigator and drag it to the left, right, or bottom (similar to that of the toolbars). The illustration on the following page shows the Model Navigator window after docking it to the bottom of the graphics screen.

Notice that the graphics screen has automatically moved to accommodate the docking of the tool. If you want to dock it to another place, undock the MN window by clicking the in the two vertical lines on the left edge of the window and repeat the process. You will find this same type of functionality when it comes to working with toolbars.

Next we explain commonly used functions of MN. With the MN window open, simply pick the feature from the graphics screen and the feature will highlight in the MN window. Once the feature of interest is highlighted, place your cursor over the highlighted listing in the Model Navigator and press the **right mouse button**. A quick menu pops out in the graphic window with various options to choose from. We explain these options below. In the illustration shown below, the feature of Rectangular Pocket (1) is highlighted.

Display Dimensions will show you the parametric expressions and their associated values that control the feature you are working with. This is very helpful for investigating a model.

Suppress will hide the feature from view. Note that this does not delete the feature but simply does not display it.

Edit Parameters will allow you to modify the controlling expressions for that feature (this would be a parametric modification). Selecting this option will result in the dialog shown below as for the Rectangular Pocket feature. Note that this dialog is similar to the one used when the feature was created, and thus the dialog format is feature-dependent.

At this point, you may either select one of the temporary dimensions that are shown on the graphics screen or simply select the Feature Dialog button. Selecting this button will bring up the following dialog.

Here, simply modify the values that you would like to change and select **OK** when done.

Edit Positioning (only available when dealing with form features) will allow you to modify a located feature's position relative to the model.

Replace Feature allows certain types of features to be replaced by another feature. This option is limited and must be used carefully.

Reorder Before/After modifies the timestamp of the given feature to show up earlier or later.

Make Current Feature allows the insertion of new features after the current feature highlighted in the MN window.

Parent Curves allows the display of construction curves, for the feature selected, to be displayed or hidden. The choices are Hide or Show.

Delete will remove the feature (and any of its dependents) from the model.

Rename allows you to rename the feature with a user-defined name.

Object Dependency Browser will show you what the feature is dependent upon for its existence. This can be rather helpful for investigative purposes and will help to establish the design intent mentioned earlier.

Group Features is a tool to create a new feature name that is a group of features you select to be part of the group. The group then acts as one group for manipulation.

List Information will open a window with information on the feature. This option is helpful for querying and investigating models. The sample list information is given below for feature RECTANGULAR_POCKET(1).

```
===============================================================
Information listing created by lee

Feature Expressions for RECTANGULAR_POCKET(1)
==========================================================

p3=44.45*2                              88.9
Length X

p4=47.75                                47.75
Length Y

p5=18.80                                18.8
Length Z

p6=0                                    0
Corner Radius

p7=0                                    0
Floor Radius

p8=0                                    0
Taper Angle

p10=120.65                              120.7
Positioning Dimension Horizontal Distance

p9=0.0                                  0
Positioning Dimension Parallel To Edge Distance

Feature Parameters for:RECTANGULAR_POCKET(1)
=================================================================

FEATURE TYPE - RECTANGULAR_POCKET(1)
X Length       =     88.90
```

```
Y Length       =    47.750
Z Length       =    18.80
Corner Radius  =     0.0
Floor Radius   =     0.0
Taper Angle    =     0.0

Feature Associativity for:RECTANGULAR_POCKET(1)
======================================================================
 Parent(s):
   BLOCK(0)
```

Properties option allows you to add and edit non-graphic comments and attributes to the feature selected. It allows renaming of a feature also.

6.3 Expressions

Expressions are algebraic or arithmetic statements used to control the characteristics of a part such as dimensions and relationships of a model. Expressions are created anytime you enter information into the system to dimension a feature or its location. For example, creating a hole feature leads to creation of expression of its diameter. Expressions are also created when a sketch is dimensioned or positioned. Expressions are considered as driving force behind parametric modeling and can easily be edited for model modification.

Expressions have their own grammar, which generally mimics the C programming language. An expression consists of both a name and a value. The name of the expression always appears on the left side of the equal sign and may be comprised of alphabetic and numeric characters provided that you begin with an alpha character. No spaces are allowed in expression names and expression names are case sensitive. The value of the expression is contained on the right hand side of the equal sign and may be a simple numerical value, an equation, or even a logical/conditional statement. You can use constants, multipliers, and even trigonometry and other built-in functions in the expression as listed in the table on the next page. An expression example is shown below:

$$\text{Width} = 6.8 * \sin(30) + p6 + 9$$

Notice that this particular expression references another expression, p6. Therefore, the Width of this part (or solution of this expression) is directly related to the solution of p6. If you rename p6 to something else, it changes not only its original location name and also any other place where it is referenced.

To open the expression dialog, go to **Tools→Expression** (or simply press Control + E). Its dialog shows below. Three common operations done through the dialog are as follows. To create new expressions, type in the name and the associated value in the editing area, and hit "Enter" key. To edit an existing expression, select it from the expression list and modify it in the editing area, and hit "Enter" key. To rename an expression, select it from the expression list, click "Rename", and enter a new name and hit "Ok". For all of these three operations, you must click OK or Apply after editing or creating, in order to have your changes saved and reflected in the model.

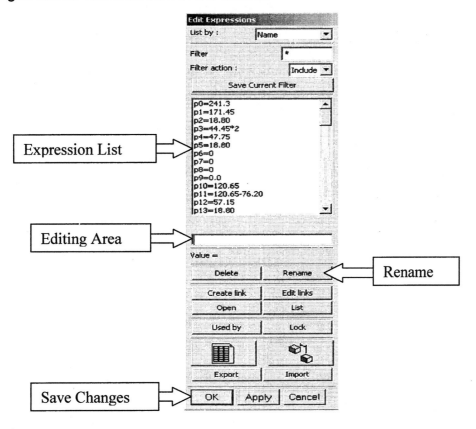

In order to find out where an expression is used, follow the simple graphical procedure shown below.

Where is it used?
1. Select the expression of interest.
2. Select Used By to see where it is used.

Table for Built-In Functions

Name	Description
abs	Absolute Value, abs(x) = |x|
acos	Arc Cosine, acos(x) = arc cos(x), (result in radians)
asin	Arc Sine, asin(x) = arc sin(x), (result in radians)
atan	Arc Tangent, atan(x) = arc tan(x), (result in radians)
atan2	Arc Tangent, atan2(x, y) = arc tan(x / y), (result in radians)
ceil	Ceiling, ceil(x) = x is a real number, function returns closest integer greater than or equal to x if a=ceil(.1), a evaluates to 1
cos	Cosine, cos(x) = cos(x), (x must be in degrees)
cosh	Hyperbolic Cosine, cosh(x) = cosh(x)
deg	Degree Conversion, deg(x) converts radians to degrees.
exp	Exponential, exp(x) = ex
fact	Factorial, fact(x) = x!
floor	Floor, floor(x) = x is a real number, function returns closest integer less than or equal to x if a=floor(.1), a evaluates to 0
log	Natural Logarithm, log(x) = ln (x) = loge (x)
log10	Common Logarithm, log10(x) = log10(x)
rad	Radian Conversion, rad(x) converts degrees to radians
sin	Sine, sin(x) = sin(x), (x must be in degrees)
sinh	Hyperbolic Sine, sinh(x) = sinh(x)
sqrt	Square Root, sqrt (x) = /x
tan	Tangent, tan(x) = tan(x), (x must be in degrees)
tanh	Hyperbolic Tangent, tanh(x) = tanh(x)
trnc	Truncate, trnc(x) removes any fractional portion (all digits to the right of the decimal point) from the number x
pi()	Takes no arguments and returns the value of pi

6.4 Playback a Model

Playback allows the replay of the construction of the model so you can better understand the way it was built. It is one of the Edit Feature menu choices. To run the playback tool, choose **Edit→Feature→Playback...** as shown below.

This brings up the playback dialog as shown below:

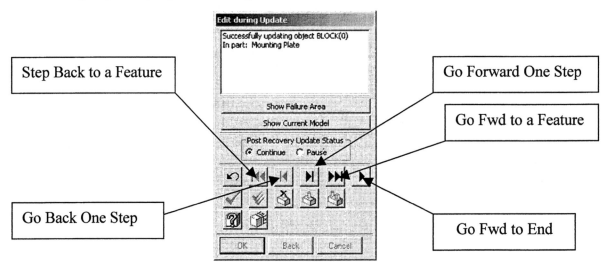

To use the dialog simply step forward or backwards through the model using the buttons. Note that some of other Edit Feature menu choices are directly accessible by the Model Navigator with the third mouse button click on the highlighted feature.

6.5 Information→Feature

Another way that you can get access to information about the features in a model is through the Information menu bar. Simply go to **Info → Feature** to bring up the dialog as shown below.

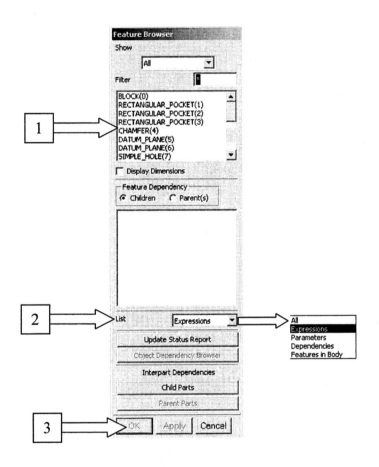

To get a listing window of information on a given feature,

1. Select the feature from the feature listing area
2. Change the **List** pulldown to reflect the information you seek
3. Select **OK**.

If you would like to have the information shown graphically as well, then you may turn on the **Display Dimensions** box in the dialog.

6.6 Distance Between Objects

In many instances, you need to know how far one object is from another. To find this distance information, go to **Analysis** → **Distance** to bring up the dialog shown below.

At this point, you must select two objects between which you would like the distance. The dialog shown above is little more than a selection filter to aid you in selecting objects from a crowded graphics screen. For example, if you would like the minimum distance between two edges and the graphics screen has too many objects, you would select the edge button, select the first edge and then select the edge button again followed by the second edge. At this point, a listing window will be displayed on the screen showing the distance between the two.

Activity 6-1. Query and Parametric Modification of a Part

In this activity, you will exercise two things: (1) how to interrogate the model to find desired information, and (2) how to modify a part using the information. You will use the shaft support part completed in Project 5-1 of Chapter 5. The figure below shows a part before and after modification.

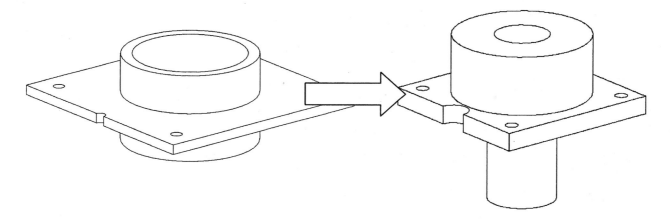

Step 1. Open your part *****_project5-1.prt** as it was completed, and save it as *****_activity6-1.prt**. Start the Modeling application.

Step 2. Turn on the **Model Navigator** and dock it to the bottom of your screen.

Step 3. Shade the model.

Step 4. Review the features in the model against those shown in the Model Navigator by selecting them from your graphics screen.

Step 5. Using **Analysis→Distance**, find the distance between the outer holes and record it.

5.1. Go to **Analysis → Distance**

5.2. Select the **Point Constructor** Button

5.3. Choose **Arc Center** icon and select the hole as shown below.

5.4. Choose the **Point Constructor** button again.

5.5. Choose **Arc Center** icon and select the second hole as shown below.

5.6. Record the **Distance** below

DISTANCE = _____

Step 6. Edit the top **Boss** from the **Model Navigator**.

    6.1. Find the top **Boss** in the **Model Navigator** by selecting it from the graphics screen.

    6.2. Place your cursor directly over the **Boss** in the **Model Navigator**.

    6.3. Click your right mouse button once, and choose **Edit Parameters**.

    6.4. Choose **Feature Dialog**.

    6.5. Change the **Diameter** to a value of **4**. (Note that this is also automatically modifying the expression that controls this value)

6.6. Change the **Height** to a value of **2**. (Note that this too automatically changes the expression that controls this value).

6.7. Select **OK** twice. **Boss** was updated.

Step 7. Edit the centerline hole diameter from the **Expression** dialog.

7.1. Find the simple hole feature for the centerline hole in the **Model Navigator** by selecting it from the graphics screen.

7.2. Place your cursor directly over the simple hole feature in the **Model Navigator**.

7.3. Click your right mouse button once and choose **List Information**.

7.4. Below, write down the expression name that controls the diameter (pXX).

Diameter is Controlled By: _____

Close the Information window.

7.5. Go to the **Expression** dialog by going to **Tools→Expression** or simply holding down Control + E. This will bring up the **Expression** dialog as shown below.

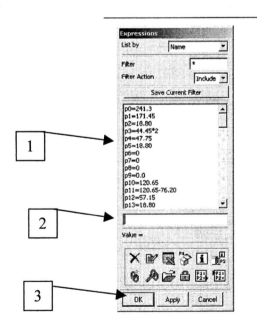

7.6. In the expression dialog, find the expression that controls the diameter (the one you wrote down above) and modify it to be 1.6. Your screen should look similar to one below.

Step 8. Make the following changes to your model using the two methods discussed above. Write down the controlling expressions for each feature next to each step or on a spare piece of paper.

    8.1. Change the lower boss to have a diameter of 2 and a height of 3.

    8.2. Change the corner mounting holes to have a diameter of .375.

    8.3. Change the plate thickness to be .6.

    8.4. Change the locating notch to have a diameter of .9.

Step 9. Find the distance between the two arc centers shown below.

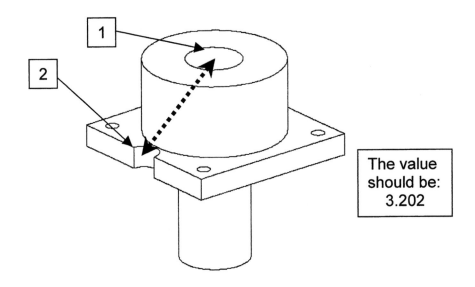

The value should be: 3.202

Step 10. Review the construction of your model by playing it back with the following menu picks, **Edit→Feature→Playback**.

Step 11. **Save and close** this part.

You will use this part on **Project 6-1**.

Project 6-1. Two Changes in Design Intent

Open ***_activity6-1.prt and save it as ***_project6-1.prt where *** are your three-letter name initials. There are two changes in design intent in this project and you will incorporate the changes into the model using expressions.

The first change. Until now, you have allowed the upper and lower bosses to be of a different size (diameter and height). In this project, both bosses will always have the same diameter and height. For ease of modification, use the expression names "dia" and "height" for them.

Hint:

1. Find the expressions for each boss.
2. Rename the expressions that control one of the bosses to be dia and height.
3. Edit the expressions that control the second boss to have a value of dia and height.

Verification:

Change dia and height to be of a different value and verify that both bosses update together.

The second change. There are four small holes on the plate. The diameters of all these holes are identical and are 1/8 of that of the bosses, "dia". After making proper changes in the expressions, verify if they are correct.

Exercise Problems

6.1   Describe how to find a layer on which a certain object is located.

6.2   Describe the functions of the Model Navigator.

6.3   When are expressions created?

6.4   What is Playback? Why is it useful?

6.5   Describe a procedure to find a distance between two edges.

Chapter 7. Feature Operations on Edge and Face

In this chapter, you will learn some of features that apply to edges or faces of a solid body. These include edge blend, chamfer, and hollow features. Edge blend and chamfer features apply to edges of a solid while a hollow feature apply to faces of a solid. Sections 7.1 to 7.3 discuss these three features and their options in order.

7.1 Edge Blend

An Edge Blend is a radius blend that is tangent to the blended (adjoining) face(s). This feature modifies a solid body by rounding selected edges. Blending works by rolling a spherical ball along the edge being blended (the blend radius), keeping it in contact with the two faces that meet at the edge. The ball will roll on the inside or outside of the two faces, depending on whether you are creating a fillet or a round.

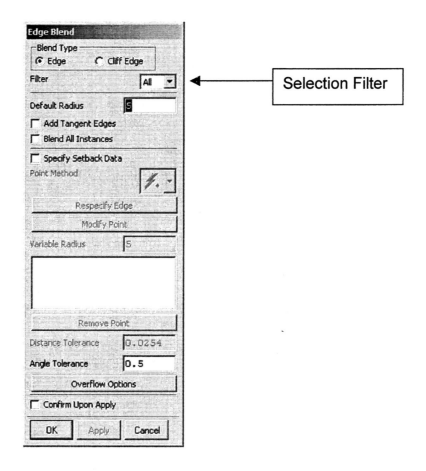

Selection Filter

The selection Filter on the dialog lets you mask your selections.

- All lets you select any of these objects.
- Edge lets you select only edges.
- Face lets you select all edges of a face.
- Body lets you select all edges of a body.

When possible, you should blend sets of edges rather than one edge at a time. When many edges are blended at one time, the result is a single blend feature that has many blended edges. However, if you blend several edges together, and later want to change the blend radius at only one edge, it will be more difficult than if you had blended them separately.

Different blending sequences of the same set of edges can result in different outcomes as shown below.

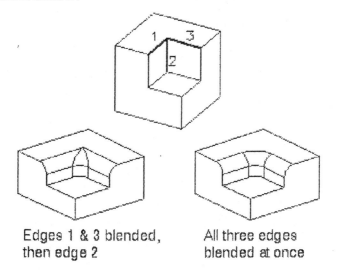

Edges 1 & 3 blended, then edge 2

All three edges blended at once

Using the Add Tangent Edges Option: Add Tangent Edges lets you select any one edge of a tangent string of edges, then the system selects the rest of the edges in the tangent string. The transition between adjacent faces of selected edges must be smooth.

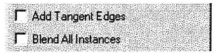

Selected edge

The system selects all edges tangent to the selected edge.

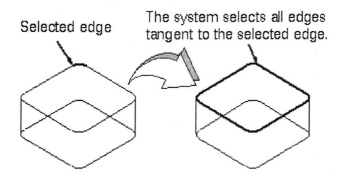

Activity 7-1. Creating Edge Blends

You will practice various edge blends in this activity.

Step 1. Open the provided part file **activity7-1.prt** and save it as *****_activity7-1.prt** where *** are your name initials.

Step 2. Start the **Modeling** application.

Step 3. Choose **Insert → Feature Operation → Edge Blend** or choose the

Edge Blend icon .

The **Edge Blend** dialog is displayed.

Create a radius .25-inch (default value) edge blend that removes material on edges of the tall post in the model by blending the four edges of the top face of the post and three sides of the post.

Step 4. First, change the **Filter** to **Face**. Select the top face of the post.

Step 5. Now, change the **Filter** to **Edge** and select the three vertical edges of the post as shown.

You can deselect any selected edge by pressing Shift and **MB1** on the edge you want to deselect.

Step 6. Choose **Apply** to complete the blend. Notice that blending three edges at a vertex requires the system to create an extra blended face.

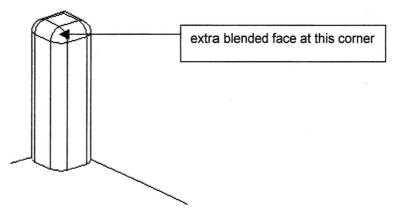

extra blended face at this corner

Step 7. Create edge blends with convex and concave faces.

    7.1. Key in 0.3125 in the **Default Radius** field.

    7.2. Pick the three edges of an inside corner.

    7.3. Choose **Apply** to create the blends that looks as follows:

Step 8. Key in .375 in the **Default Radius** field and select the two edges as shown below and choose **Apply**.

The message **Unable to apply Blend** is displayed, and the edge error is highlighted on the part file. This is because the hole feature in this model has a radius of 0.25 and the blend radius is larger than the hole radius. Choose **OK** in the **Message** dialog to dismiss it.

Step 9. Create the smaller blends on the lower edges of the rectangular pocket, using **Add Tangent Edges**.

    9.1. Toggle **Add Tangent Edges** to on.

    9.2. Key in 0.25 in the **Default Radius** field.

The two edges you selected before are still selected. You need to select the one edge of the tangent set of edges as shown below.

The system will select all the tangent edges. The entire string of edges highlights.

9.3. Choose **OK** to complete the blend and the resulting model looks as below.

9.4. **Save and close** the part file.

Project 7-1. Pivot Arm

Model the pivot arm part using the drawings below and save it as ***_project7-1.prt** in your directory.

Hint: Start out with a block and add an edge blend feature.

7.2 Chamfer

This option lets you bevel edges of a solid body by defining the desired chamfer dimensions. The chamfer function operates very similarly to the blend function by adding or subtracting material relative to whether the edge is an outside chamfer or an inside chamfer. Thus, the rules and restrictions for chamfers are basically the same as those for blends.

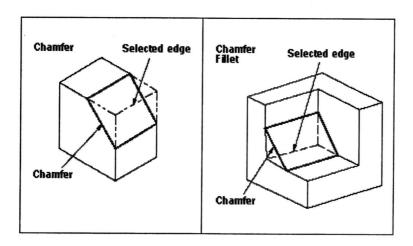

Below is given a general procedure to create a chamfer, which will be followed by more detail descriptions.

Chamfer Procedure

To create a chamfer, following these steps:

1. Choose a chamfer method.
2. Select the edges you wish to chamfer.
3. Enter the chamfer dimensions.
4. If the selected edges are part of an instance set, choose Chamfer all instances or Do not chamfer all instances.
5. (Optional) Choose Flip Last Chamfer to flip the direction of the chamfer. This step applies to Double Offset and Offset Angle.

You can create a chamfer using different methods. In this section, you will learn three of them. They are Single Offset, Double Offset, and Offset Angle. For these methods, the offset values are measured along the faces from the edge being chamfered.

Single Offset

This option lets you create a simple chamfer whose offset is the same along both faces. You must enter a single *positive* offset value.

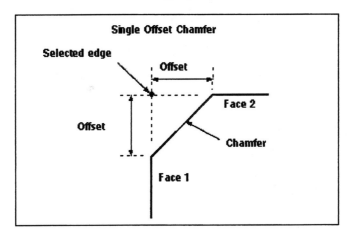

Double Offset

For this option, you must enter values for **First Offset** and **Second Offset**. These offsets are measured along the faces from the selected edge. Both of these values must be positive, and are applied as illustrated in the figure below. However, there is no way to assign which direction the First and Second Offsets will be applied.   Therefore, after creating the chamfer, you can choose **Flip Last Chamfer** if the chamfer's offsets were applied opposite to what you want.

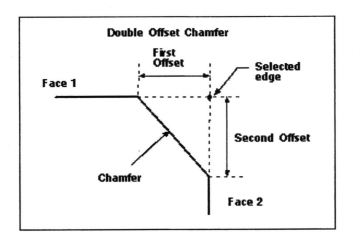

Offset Angle

Sometimes an angle is used to define a simple chamfer. For this option, you must enter values for the **First Offset** and **Angle**. The angle is measured from Face 2, as shown in the figure below. After creating the chamfer, you can choose **Flip Last Chamfer**.

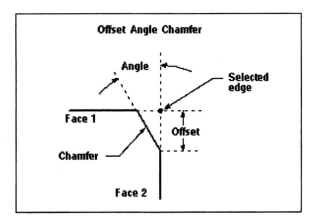

Edge Selection

All selected edges must belong to the same body, and can be of any curve type (see the figure below). The system tracks the total number of edges you have selected. Choosing Back during edge selection causes the system to deselect the last edge selected. Choosing Back repeatedly causes the system to deselect one edge at a time in the reverse order of selection. After you have selected all of the desired edges, choose OK to proceed with chamfering the edges you have selected.

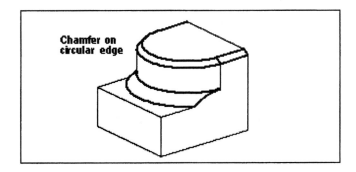

Instances

If you chamfer an edge of a feature that is a member of an instance set, a menu will be displayed at the end of the interaction, before the chamfer is created. You can choose either chamfering all instances of a feature or not. However, you cannot instance a chamfer. If you instance a feature that has a chamfered edge, the instance set will not contain the chamfer. There will be more discussion on instancing a feature in Chapter 11.

Activity 7-2. Creating Chamfers

In this activity, you will partially complete modeling the part below. You will practice chamfering edges that you learned in the above section. You will complete modeling the part in Project 7-5.

Step 1. Create a new part file named *****_activity7-2.prt**.

Step 2. Start the **Modeling Application**.

Step 3. Replace the view to the **TFR-TRI**, Trimetric.

Step 4. Create a **Block** using the outside dimensions of the solid above and locate it at **WCS 0,0,0**.

Step 5. Create a chamfer on the front face.

    5.1. Choose **Insert → Feature Operation → Chamfer...** or choose the **Chamfer** icon ⬦ .

    5.2. You are creating a 45° chamfer so you may choose the **Single Offset**.

    5.3. Select the top edge of the front face of the block.

5.4. The distance of the offset is next. Make the offset to end .5 from the back face of the block.

Enter the **Offset** distance as 2.24-.5

5.5. Choose **OK** and the chamfer is created.

Step 6. Create the chamfer on the right face of the block.

6.1. The Chamfer selection dialog should still be up so select the **Single Offset** again.

6.2. Select the top edge of the right face of the block.

6.3. This time the **Offset** distance is measured from the left face. It is a distance of 3.78-1.92-1.12 from the left edge. Enter this equation in the **Offset** distance window.

6.4. Choose **OK** and the chamfer is created. The block looks as below. Save and close the file.

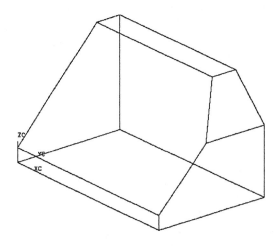

Project 7-2. Mounting Block

Open your part file ***_project5-3.prt that you created from Project 3 of Chapter 5, and save it as ***_project7-2.prt. Redesign the model by adding edge blend and chamfer features as shown in the bottom figure. All fillet and round R = .125.

7.3 Hollow

This feature lets you hollow out or create a shell around a single solid body based on specified thickness values. You can assign individual thicknesses for faces, and select regions of faces for piercing during hollowing.

Face to be Pierced

Before   After

There are three types of Hollow operation: **Face**, **Region** or **Body**. Each type leads you to choose different **selection steps**. In order to open the hollow dialogue, choose **Insert → Feature Operation → Hollow**, or choose the Hollow icon ⬚. The following Hollow dialog displays.

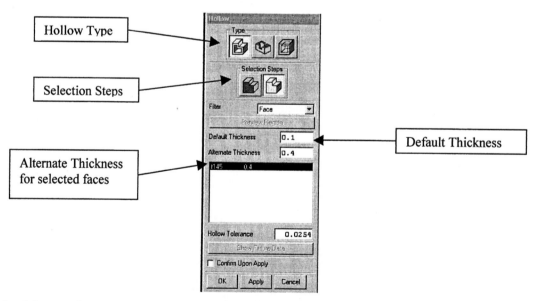

In this section, we will describe the first two types, Face and Body. For both types, you need to specify wall thickness. A positive thickness value hollows the existing solid so that the wall thickness is measured inward from the original faces of the solid. A negative value results in a hollow that forms a shell of the specified value around the original solid. The Variable Thickness is optional. Each selected offset face is created based on its variable thickness. Non-selected faces are created based on the default thickness (except for the face(s) selected to be pierced). The hollow operation will fail if any face that is to be pierced has a tangent face adjacent to it, such as a blend, and you use a thickness value that is less than the blend radius.

7.3.1 Face

This lets you create a hollow by collecting pierced and offset faces. You can select any faces to pierce, and you can offset the rest of the faces at different thickness values. To create a hollow using the Face Type, follow these basic steps:

1. Choose one or more faces to pierce for the hollow.
2. Choose one or more offset faces (optional). For each offset face you specify, an entry will appear in the Offset Face changeable window with an identifier and the default thickness value. You can change the thickness of individual offset faces by selecting its entry in the changeable window and specifying a new value in the Alternate Thickness field (see the figure above). Offset faces you select in the changeable window are highlighted in the graphics window in a cyan color.
3. Choose Apply or OK.

The figure below shows a hollow being created on a simple block using the Face type, with a single pierced face (the right face highlighted in magenta). The top face gets a variable offset of 0.4. The remaining faces automatically get the default offset of 0.1 (except the pierced face).

Face Type

Selection Step: Pierced Faces

Select single pierced
face (magenta)

Selection Step: Offset Faces

Assign 0.4 Variable Thickness
to top face (cyan). All other
faces get the default 0.1 offset

Result

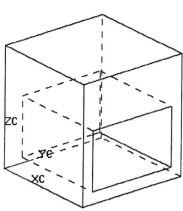

You can select any faces (more than one face) you wish to pierce before the hollowing takes place. In the figure shown below, three faces are pierced. You can use **Edit—>Feature—>Edit Parameters** or **the Model Navigator —> Edit Parameters** in order to select additional faces to be pierced, or to deselect previously selected faces.

7-18

Faces selected to be pierced during hollowing

Result

7.3.2 Body

This option lets you create a shell around a single solid body based on a specified thickness value. You can select any faces and distance values to offset during hollowing. You may not create an open face. To create a hollow using the Body Type, follow these basic steps:

1. Choose the body to be hollowed.
2. Choose one or more offset faces (optional).
3. Choose Apply or OK.

The figure below shows a hollow being created on a simple block using the Body Type, with two faces selected for variable offsets (0.3 and -0.2). The remaining faces get the default 0.1 offset: The -0.2 offset has the effect of adding to the solid body, since the negative thickness value causes the wall to move outward.

Body Type

Selection Step: Solid Body

Selection Step: Offset Faces

Select two faces for offset (shown in red). Assign 0.3 to one and –0.2 to the other.

Result

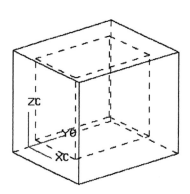

Activity 7-3. Creating Hollow

You will hollow the solid to create a model like this.

Step 1. Open the part file **activity7-3.prt**.

    1.1. Start the **Modeling** application.

    1.2. Save the part as *****_activity7-3.prt**.

Step 2. Choose **Insert → Feature Operation → Hollow**, or choose the icon

. The **Hollow** dialog is displayed.

Since you will be removing faces and creating a thin walled feature using the entire body, you need to use the **Face** hollow type.

    2.1. Choose the **Face** type icon, if it is not already active.

The **Confirm Upon Apply** option at the bottom of the dialogue lets you view the model before accepting it, when toggled on.

    2.2. Toggle off the option.

You can change the default thickness value. You can also specify a different (alternate) thickness for each wall that will be created. (You will change the alternate thickness value later.)

Step 3. Specify a wall **Default Thickness**, so key in the positive value of 0.120.

Step 4. Select faces to remove.

    4.1. Choose the **Pierced Face Selection Step** icon, if it is not active.

    4.2. Select the closest two faces first. Select the front face and the right face.

    4.3. Now, you can select the last two faces to be removed. Select the bottom face and back face.

The model should look like this.

Step 5. Change one face wall thickness because the design intent specifies one face needs a thicker wall than the other faces.

The **Default Thickness** will be set to .12″ and the **Hollow** operation will create all other faces (not selected to **Pierce**) to a .12 wall thickness without the need to select them. Therefore, to set a wall thickness to an alternative wall thickness we must select the face we want to be different.

You will make the left wall thicker than the other walls.

    5.1. Choose the **Offset Face Selection Step**.

    5.2. Select the left wall to receive the alternate thickness.

Now, the thickness parameter displays in the list box of the **Hollow** dialog. Whenever a wall thickness is highlighted in the dialog, you can specify its alternate thickness value.

> **5.3.** In the **Alternate Thickness** field, key in 0.25 as the value.

> **5.4.** Choose **Apply** to form the hollow.

The model is temporarily built. Notice that the left wall is twice as thick as the other walls.

Step 6. Inspect and close out the part.

> **6.1.** **Cancel** all dialogs.

> **6.2.** **Shade** the model.

> **6.3.** **Save and close** all part files.

Project 7-3. Hollow Project

Create a solid model of the part as shown below and save it as ***_project7-3.prt** where *** is your three letter name initials.

Hint: You may use features such as Block, Pad, Edge Blend and Hollow. Note that the part has two different wall thicknesses, .1 and .5.

Front and Top Views and Dimensions

Project 7-4. Swivel Bracket

Create a model of the part using the drawings and dimensions (in millimeters) given below. Name your part as ***_project7-4.prt where *** is three-letter initials of your name. When you create a new part file for this project, make it sure to set the unit in millimeters.

Hint: Use all of the features discussed in this chapter, edge blend, chamfer and hollow.

Project 7-5. Tool Holder

If you already completed Activity 7-2, open ***_activity7-2.prt and save it as ***_project7-5.prt where *** is three-letter initials of your name. Finish modeling the part using the drawings and dimensions (in inches) given below, and save it into this new file.

Hint: One approach to model this part is to start with a block and add the following form features: a simple hole, chamfers, and pockets.

Exercise Problems

7.1 Several edges need to be blended. Is it always better to use one Edge Blend feature to blend all of them at once?

7.2 When several edges need to be blended with more than one Edge Blend feature, does the order of edges being blended matter? Can you give such an example?

7.3 Is Single Offset Chamfer a special case of Offset Angle Chamfer?

7.4 Both Chamfer and Edge Blend can add material to or subtract material from the base solid body. How can the system know when to add and when to subtract?

7.5 Suppose that you want to create a void inside a solid body with a uniform surrounding wall thickness. What is a simple way to do so?

Chapter 8. Reference Features

Reference features are construction tools that assist you in creating other features and sketches in desired locations and orientations. You can create them either relative to an existing target solid, or fixed. Reference features are theoretically infinite in size but the display is limited to a size slightly larger than that of the solid model. There are two types of reference features: **Datum Planes** and **Datum Axes**. Section 8.1 discusses datum planes and Section 8.2 discusses datum axes.

8.1 Datum Planes

Datum Planes are reference features that can be used as construction tools in the building of a model. Such examples include (1) creating features on non-planar faces, (2) providing a planar location for a sketch (see Chapter 10), and (3) providing a planar trimming object. Suppose that you want to create a hole on a cylindrical face. A hole feature requires a planar placement face but a cylinder face is not planar. In this case, you need to create a datum plane and use it as the placement face for the hole feature. This is illustrated as follows:

There are two types of datum planes. You can create either relative or fixed datum planes. Relative datum planes are relative (constrained) to other objects in the model such as curves, faces, or other datums. Thus relative datum planes are associated to the objects. When the objects move, the relative datum planes move according to the relationships (constraints) used to create them.

On the other hand, fixed datum planes are only relative to the absolute WCS. Fixed datum planes do not reference, and are not constrained by, other geometric objects. Fixed datum planes are useful when a solid body started out from a sketch. We will focus on relative planes in this chapter.

Datum Plane Dialogue

The Datum Plane dialog displays by choosing **Insert → Form Feature → Datum Plane** or choose the Datum Plane icon 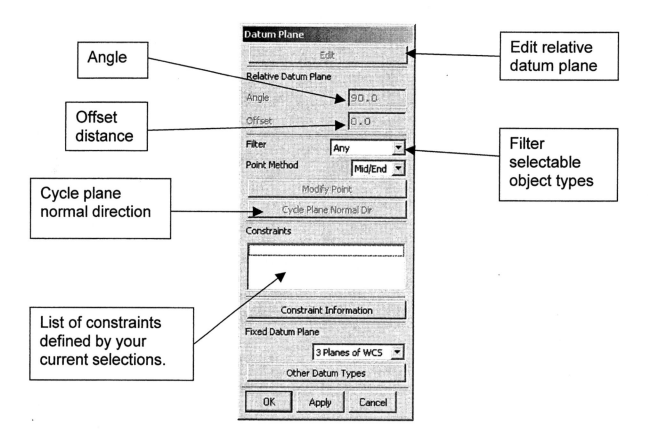. Using this dialog, you can create or edit datum planes. Grayed out options become available as you create different datum planes.

Constraints

You create a relative datum plane by selecting an existing object. With the selection of objects, a constraint (relationship) is established. A constraint is a restriction on a datum plane that positions it relative to some existing objects such as plane, face or feature. Datum planes are created with one of three constraint types: single, dual, or triple constraints. The objects you select and the sequence in which you select the objects determine a particular constraint type. The Constraints list box in the dialogue above displays the constraints defined by your current selections.

Single Constraints

Under this constraint type, the datum plane is constrained to the target solid by this single constraint. You can create single constraints using the following options:

- **Offset to Plane** creates a datum plane that offsets from (and is parallel to) a planar face or existing datum plane by selecting the face or plane. If the offset value is zero, the datum plane is coincident with the planar reference face/datum plane.

- **Through Face Axis** creates a datum plane that passes through the imaginary axis of a cylinder, cone, or revolved feature. Select the face of the feature.

- **Center plane** creates a datum plane at the center of two parallel planar faces or datum planes. When you select the first plane, the constraint listed in the Datum Planes dialog is **Offset to plane**. When you select the second plane, that constraint changes to the single constraint, **Center plane**.

- **Center of Face** creates a datum plane that passes through the imaginary axis of a sphere. Select the feature and choose **OK** or **Apply**.

Dual Constraints

Under this constraint type, constraints must be specified in pairs to create the datum plane. The options that can be used as the first constraint are described below.

First Constraint	Description
Through axis	Creates a datum plane that passes through a datum axis.
Through edge	Creates a datum plane that passes through an edge.
Through face axis	Creates a datum plane that passes through the imaginary axis of a cylinder, cone, or a revolved feature. **Through**

	face axis is the only constraint, which can create a datum plane both by itself (as a single constraint) and in combination with another constraint.
Through point	Creates a datum plane that passes through a solid body vertex (endpoint) or edge midpoint.
Parallel to plane	Creates a datum plane that is parallel to a datum plane or a planar face.
Angle to plane	Creates a datum plane that is oriented at an angle to a datum plane or a planar face.
Tangent to face	Creates a datum plane that is tangent to a cylindrical, spherical, or conical face.

With the first constraint options given above, the following table shows the allowable combinations of dual constraints.

First Constraint	Second Constraint
Through axis	Through axis Through edge Through face axis Through point Angle to plane
Through edge	Through axis Through edge Through face axis Through point Angle to plane
Through face axis	Through axis Through edge Through face axis

	Through point
	Angle to plane
Through point	Through axis
	Through edge
	Through face axis
	Angle to plane
	Parallel to plane
	Tangent to face
	Through curve
Angle to plane	Through axis
	Through edge
	Through face axis
	Through point
	Tangent to face
Tangent to face	Through point
	Angle to plane (0° or 90°)
	Tangent to face

We give below two examples of a datum plane created with dual constraints: (1) **Angle to plane** and **Through edge** and (2) **Through face axis** and **Angle to plane**.

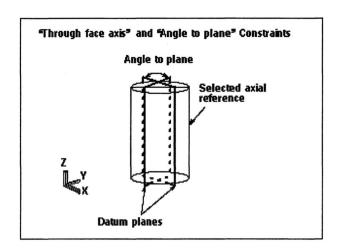

"Through face axis" and "Angle to plane" Constraints

Triple Constraints

There is one triple constraints method for creating datum planes: three **Through point** constraints. This creates a datum plane through three reference points, which can be endpoints or midpoints of an edge. The orientation of the datum plane is determined by how you select the points. The X direction of the datum plane is defined by a line drawn between the first and second selected point.

There are useful buttons in the Datum Plane dialogue. The Constraint Information button near the bottom of the dialogue, when clicked, opens an information window. This window displays all possible constraint combinations that can be used to create relative datum planes. You can also edit relative datum plane parameters. Choose the Edit button in the dialogue and select a relative datum plane (also enter Angle and Offset, if applicable). Dialog options that are not applicable to the selected plane are grayed out. You can also edit datum planes, both fixed and relative, by choosing **Edit → Feature → Parameters**.

Datum Planes should be placed on different layers and be named to help identify their construction role in the model.   According to the default layer standards, layers 61 to 80 are assigned for reference features. It is a good practice to properly change the work layer when you add a reference feature.

Activity 8-1. Creating Relative Datum Planes with a Single Constraint

In Activities 8-1 to 8-3, you will create relative datum planes and axis on the pin, and use them to create a hole that is associated, so that updates to the pin automatically result in updates to the hole.

Step 1. **Open** the provided part file **activity8-1.prt** and save it as *****_activity8-1.prt** where *** are your name initials.

Step 2. Start the **Modeling** application by choosing **Application→ Modeling**.

Step 3. Change the work layer into 61. Key in **61** in **Work Layer** field at the bottom of the graphic window and hit **Enter**. Alternatively, **Format → Layer Settings** and key in **61** in Work field at the top of the layer setting dialogue and click **OK**.

Step 4. Create a datum plane offset from the bottom face of the pin head.

    4.1. Choose **Insert → Form Feature → Datum Plane** or choose the icon

    4.2. Choose **Face** as the filter method.

    4.3. Select the head of the pin on its bottom face.

The edges of the bottom face of the head of the pin are highlighted. A direction vector displays pointing from the head of the pin and down the shaft of the pin.

    4.4. In the **Offset** field, double-click and key in **30.8** and choose **Apply**. The first datum plane is created.

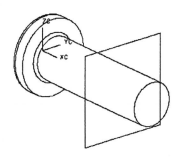

Step 5. Create a datum plane through the axis of the pin. The intersection of this plane with the first datum plane will define the axis for the angle of the hole.

    5.1. Select the cylindrical face of the shaft. Through face axis is listed in the Constraints box.

    5.2. Choose **OK**.

Step 6. If you did not create the datum planes of Steps 4 and 5 according to the reference feature layer standard (layers 61 to 80), you can move them to one of these layers by choosing **Format → Move to Layer** and picking the datum objects and specifying the destination layer. You can use this command and move any object to any layer.

Step 7. **Save and close** this part file.

Activity 8-2. Creating Relative Datum Planes with Dual Constraints

In this activity, you will create relative datum planes using dual constraints.

Step 1. Open ***_activity8-1.prt that you created in the previous activity, and save it as *****_activity8-2.prt** where *** are your name initials.

Step 2. Change the work layer into **62** (see Step 1 of Activity 8-1 if you are not sure how to do this step).

Step 3. Create a Datum Plane Through an Axis, at an Angle to a Datum Plane. You can create a datum plane at a specified angle from another datum plane, and through the axis of a conical, cylindrical, or revolved feature.

   3.1. Set the **Filter** to **Datum Plane**

   3.2. select the datum plane that passes through the axis of the pin. A direction vector displays and the datum plane highlights.

   3.3. Change the **Filter** to **Face** and select the cylindrical face. You will see five direction vectors (four solid font vectors and one dashed vector) appear as shown below.

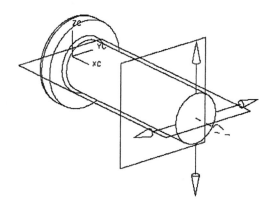

You must select the required vector for the placement of the datum plane. If you select one of the four solid font vectors, you create a datum plane tangent to the cylindrical face and offset in the direction of the selected vector. If you select the dashed vector, you can create the datum plane at an angle to the other datum plane and passing through the center axis of the cylinder.

   3.4. Select the dashed vector. An angle direction vector displays the positive direction of rotation.

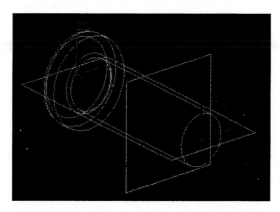

3.5. Enter 90 degrees in the **Angle** field of the **Datum Plane** dialog and choose **Apply**.

Step 4. Creating a Datum Plane Tangent to a Cylindrical Face.

Since the tangent datum plane could be located anywhere on the cylindrical body, you will specify that the tangent datum plane be parallel to an existing datum plane.

    4.1. Change the **Filter** to **Datum Plane**.

    4.2. Select the datum plane on the **XC-YC** plane.

The Constraints list box on the dialog displays **Offset to plane**. To create a tangent datum plane, you need to create another constraint.

    4.3. Change the **Filter** to **Face**.

    4.4. Select the cylindrical face.

The five direction vectors appear again. To make a tangent datum plane, you need to select one of the solid font vectors.

    4.5. Select the direction vector that points upward in the +ZC direction.

The **Constraints** box lists two constraints. One makes the new datum plane parallel to the first datum plane that you selected. The other constraint maintains tangency with the cylindrical face.

    4.6. Choose **OK** to complete the datum plane and the resulting model looks as below.

You can use a tangent datum plane to add features to the model.

Step 5. Save and close the part file..

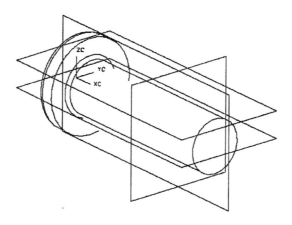

8.2 Datum Axis

Datum Axes are a reference feature, which is an imaginary axis. They can be used to create datum planes, revolved features, extruded bodies, etc. Datum axes can also be either relative or fixed. Relative datum axes are related to geometric objects (edges, faces, and planes). They are constrained not only by the objects you select, but also by the sequence in which you select the objects. On the other hand, fixed datum axes neither reference nor are constrained by, other geometric objects. This section focuses on relative datum axes.

The Datum Axis dialog displays by choosing **Insert** → **Form Feature** → **Datum Axis** or choose the Datum Axis icon 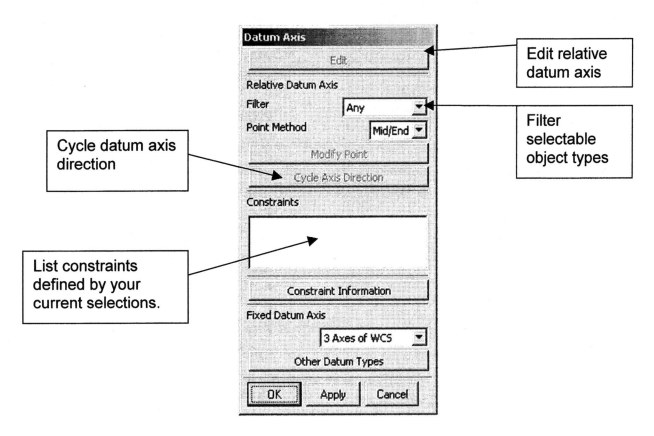. Using this dialog, you can create or edit datum axes.

The Constraints list box in the dialogue above works like the one for the relative datum plane and displays the constraints defined by your current selections of objects. Some of commonly used constraints are discussed below.

Through Edge: This constraint creates a datum axis through a straight edge or the two endpoints of a nonlinear edge. The positive direction of the datum axis is determined by the pick point of the edge. In the figure below, if the endpoints of the selected edge are V1 and V2, and the pick point is closer to V1, the direction of the axis is from V2 to V1.

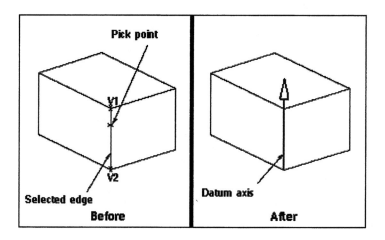

Through Point: Two through point constraints create a datum axis between two points. These points can be edge midpoints or edge vertices. The direction of the datum axis is from the first pick point to the second pick point. See the figure below.

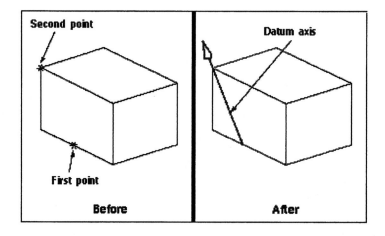

Intersection of Plane: The intersection of two plane constraints creates a datum axis through the straight edge formed by the intersection of two planes. These planes can be either faces or datum planes. The two planes must intersect at some point in space. The direction of the axis follows the righthand rule. That is, place your right hand fingers in the direction of the first face normal and curl your fingers towards the second face normal. The direction in which your thumb is pointing is the direction of the new datum axis (see the figure below).

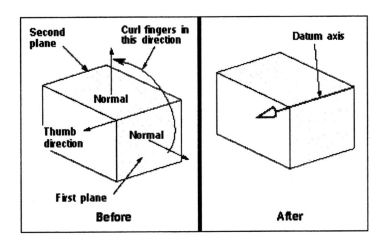

Through Axis of Face: This constraint creates a datum axis through the imaginary axis of any cylinder, cone, or revolved feature. The direction of the datum axis is the same direction as the original creation direction vector for the cylinder, cone, or revolved feature

Activity 8-3. Creating Relative Datum Axes

In this activity, you will create relative datum axes.

Step 1. Open activity8-1.prt and save it as *****_activity8-3.prt**.

Step 2. Create three datum planes in layer **61** as shown below. Review Activities 8-1 and 8-2 if you are not sure how to do this step.

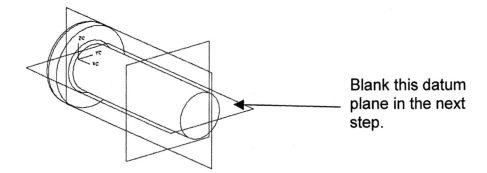

Blank this datum plane in the next step.

Step 3. **Blank** (temporarily hide from display) the datum plane indicated by the arrow above by choosing **Edit → Blank→ Blank** and picking the datum plane.

Step 4. Change the work layer to layer **62**.

Step 5. Create a datum axis through the intersection of two datum planes.

    5.1. Choose **Insert→Form Feature→Datum Axis** or choose Datum Axis icon 🔼.

    5.2. Click on the **Filter** options and choose **Datum Plane**.

    5.3. Select both of the remaining two datum planes at their edges.

The **Constraints** box of the dialog now lists the Intersection of Plane constraints. These constraints will create a datum axis through the straight edge formed by the intersection of the two planes. The datum axis direction is determined by the order of selection of the planes or faces.

    5.4. Choose **Apply** to create the datum axis.

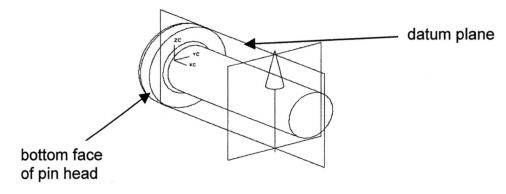

datum plane

bottom face
of pin head

Step 6. Create a Datum Axis at the Intersection of a Planar Face and Datum Plane that are indicated by two arrows in the above figure.

6.1. Select the vertical datum plane in the graphics area.

6.2. Change the **Filter** option to **Face**.

6.3. Select the bottom face of the pin head.

6.4. Choose **Apply** to create the datum axis.

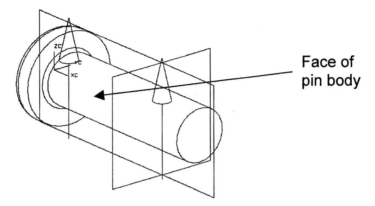

Face of
pin body

Step 7. Create a Datum Axis Through Axis of Face. In this step you create a datum axis that goes through the axis of the cylinder face of the pin body as indicated by the arrow above.

7.1. Change the Filter option to Face if necessary.

7.2. Select the cylinder face of the pin body.

7.3. Choose Apply to create the datum axis.

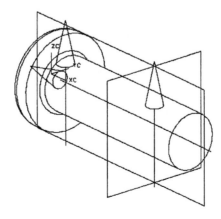

Step 8. Reverse the direction of the datum axis created in the previous step. With the datum axis dialogue still open,

8.1. Choose the **Edit** button on the top of the dialogue.

8.2. Select the datum axis created in Step 6.

8.3. Choose the **Cycle Axis Direction** button.

8.4. Choose **OK** to change the direction and close the dialogue.

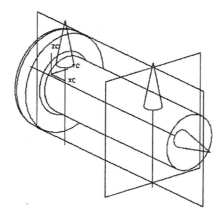

Step 9. **Save and close** this file, which will be used in the following activity

Activity 8-4. Creating an angled hole using reference features

In this activity, you will create two relative datum planes and an angled hole through the pin where the hole is associated to reference features.

Step 1. **Open ***_activity8-3.prt** that you created in Activity 8-3, and save it as *****_activity8-4.prt.**

Step 2. **Delete** the last two datum axes that were created in Steps 5 and 6 of Activity 8-3. You do not need them in this activity.

    2.1. Choose **Edit → Feature→ Delete** and select the last two datum axes in the feature list box and hit OK. Alternatively, you can use the Model Navigator tool that was discussed in Chapter 6.

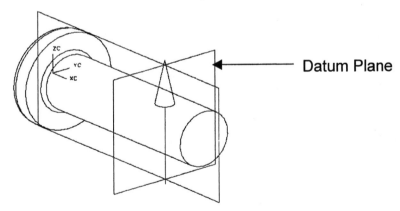

Datum Plane

Step 3. Change the work layer into layer **63**.

Step 4. Create a Datum Plane that is angled to the datum plane indicated above.

    4.1. Choose **Insert→ Form Feature→ Datum Plane**.

    4.2. Change the **Filter** to **Datum Axis** and select the datum axis in the graphics area.

    4.3. Change the **Filter** to **Datum Plane** and select the datum plane.

A direction of rotation vector displays the direction in which the angled plane will be created.

4.4. If the rotation vector appears like the one below, key in –45 (negative value) in the Angle field. Use a positive value (45) if your direction vector is pointing in the opposite direction.

4.5. Choose **OK**.

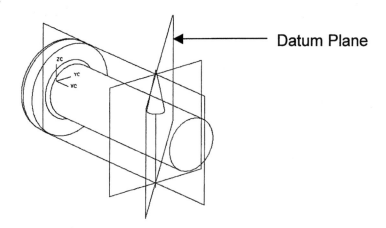

Datum Plane

Step 5. Create a Datum Plane offset to the angled datum plane indicated above.

5.1. Select the angled datum plane.

5.2. Key in an offset distance of **15** in the **Offset** field, and choose **OK**.

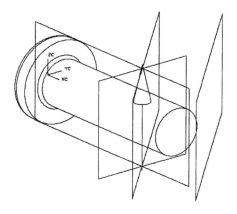

Step 6. Create a through hole on the pin.

    6.1   Choose **Insert→ Form Feature→ Hole** or the Hole icon.   The simple hole is the default.

    6.2   Select the offset datum plane created in Step 5 as the placement face. A direction vector displays the direction in which the hole feature will be created.

    6.3   Choose **Accept Default Side** if this is the case, otherwise choose **Flip Default Side**.

    6.4   Select the cylindrical face of the pin. This makes the hole go through the pin.

    6.5   Key in **3** for the diameter of the hole and choose **OK**.

The tool solid is initially placed at the center of the datum plane. The **Positioning** dialog is displayed.

Step 7. Position the hole.

You need to position the hole so that it goes through the center of the pin at the location of the datum axis.

    7.1. Choose the **Point onto Line** icon.

    7.2. Select the datum axis and choose **OK** on the **Positioning** dialog.

The hole moved downward to align with the center point of the datum axis. Your model is complete. Its top view must look like

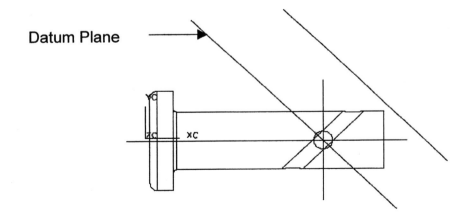

Datum Plane

Step 8. Change the angle of the angled datum plane indicated in the above figure. The hole location is controlled by several reference features and affected by their change(s).

    8.1. Choose **Edit → Feature → Parameters** and select the angled datum plane.

    8.2. Key in **–15** in the **Angle** field and choose **OK**.

The top view of the new model must look like the following figure. Observe that this edit changed not only the angle of the datum plane but also the angle of the hole that goes through the pin. This is because the placement plane of the hole is the datum plane offset from the angled datum plane.

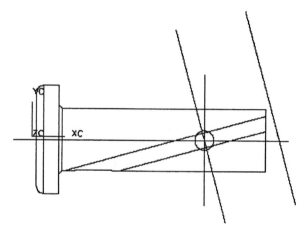

Step 9. **Cancel** the dialog of the hole creation.

Step 10. **Save and close** this file.

Project 8-1. Spindle

Model the spindle part using the drawings (in inches) below and save it as
***_project8-1.prt in your directory.

Hint: You may have to use trigonometric functions to compute the offset
dimension for Chamfer.

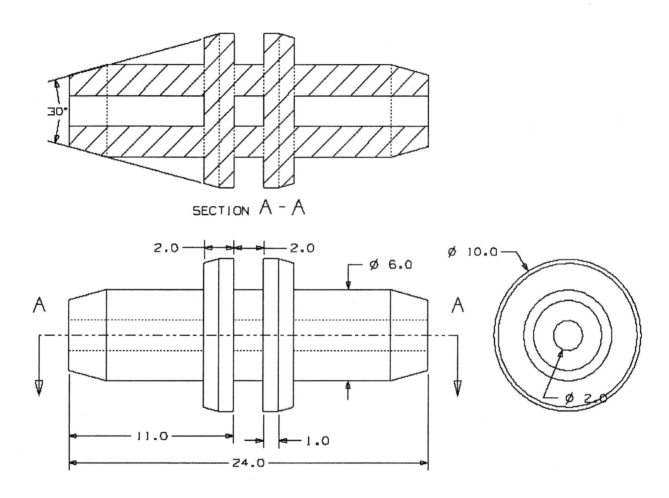

SECTION A - A

Project 8-2. Spin Block

Model the spin block using the drawings (in millimeters) below and save it as ***_project8-2.prt in your directory.

Project 8-3. Retainer

Model the retainer using the drawings (in inches) below and save it as
***_project8-3.prt in your directory.

Project 8-4. Block with an angled hole

A 1-inch diameter hole is to be created in a block. The origin of the hole is on the top face. The hole is centered in the block along both XC and YC axes. The angle of the hole shall be editable relative to a plane parallel to the bottom face. The block size can change. In the drawing below, the angle is 30° and the block size is (8, 6, 1). After the part is modeled, change the angle or the block size and confirm if the design intent is still met.

Save this project file as ***_project8-4.prt in your directory.

Hint: In this project, one datum axis and four datum planes need to be created to constrain the pivot location of the hole feature. In order to position the hole, use reference features (the datum axis and one datum plane) and the positioning method Point onto Line.

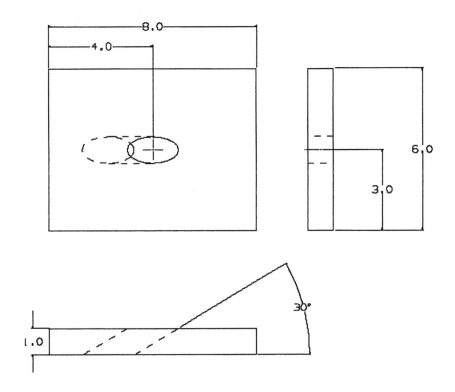

Exercise Problems

8.1 When do you need to use datum planes? Give two examples.

8.2 State two types of datum planes. What is the major difference between the two.

8.3 There are three categories of relative datum planes in term of the number of constraints. Give an example for each.

8.4 The number of constraints used to create relative datum planes is the same as the number of object selections. (True or False).

8.5 Datum Axes can be used to create datum planes. (True of False)

8.6 Datum Planes can be used to create datum axes. (True or False)

8.7 Relative datum planes and axes are associated to objects selected during their creations. What guides designers in identifying this association?

Chapter 9. Boolean Operations and Swept Features

This chapter introduces the Boolean Operations and Swept Features. The Boolean operations are **Unite**, **Subtract**, and **Intersect**. The Swept features are **Extrude**, **Revolve**, **Sweep along Guide**, and **Tube**. This text will cover Extrude and Revolve.

Boolean operations are used to create a single solid body out of two or more solid bodies. When a second solid body is created Unigraphics knows that one already exists and will prompt the user if it should create the solid and allow two solids to exist, or does the user want to Unite, Subtract, or Intersect the second solid with the first solid.

Swept features is the general name given to the family of four commands listed above that create a solid by sweeping a set of selected curves, edges, faces, and sheet bodies.

This chapter will include 3 sections. Section 9.1 will discuss the Boolean Operations. Section 9.2 will introduce the Extrude command. Section 9.3 will introduce the Revolve command.

9.1 Boolean Operations

George Boole, an English mathematician, approached logic in a new way by reducing it to a simple algebra, incorporating logic into mathematics. It began the algebra of logic called Boolean algebra published in 1854. Boolean algebra is used in expressing relationships between groups of objects or concepts. Boolean algebra can demonstrate the relationship between groups, indicating what is in each set alone, what is jointly contained in both, and what is contained in neither. We see it applied today in search engines on the Internet using operators AND, OR, and NOT. Therefore, if a search is done on "cats AND dogs", the result will contain information including both cats and dogs, and not each alone.

Likewise, our Boolean operations of Unite, Subtract, and Intersect follow the same Internet operators. However, we are working with solid bodies so the application is a little different, but conceptually the same.

Another English mathematician, John Venn, published an interpretation of Boole's work and introduced a method of diagramming Boolean algebra. We now call it the Venn diagram. The application of the Venn diagram to our Boolean operations looks like this.

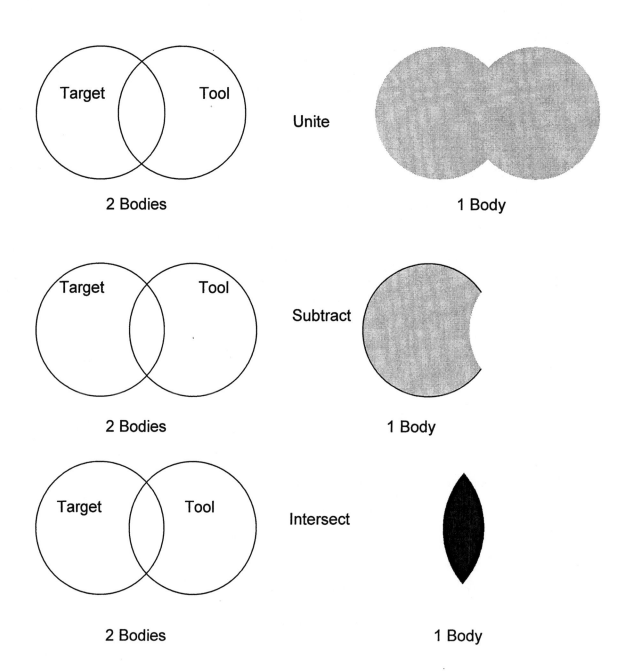

The above figures illustrate that when two solids are combined using a Boolean operator that different results are obtained with the Unite, Subtract, and Intersect. The Target solid and the Tool solid play integral roles. Notice in commonality that the 2 bodies must overlap somewhere, i.e., occupy the same space for at least a portion of their body for the operators to work.

Target Solid

The Target solid will be the first solid chosen, or in the case of a Form Feature will be the base solid on which the Form Feature is created. The target solid will control the color, material properties, layer, and any other attributes that may have been assigned, for the resulting common solid.

Tool Solid

The Tool solid is the secondary solid chosen. It is the solid that is united with, subtracted from, or intersected with, the target solid. Its properties will be lost to the target solid. There may be more than one tool solid as well. When using multiple tool solids care must be taken as to how the operations are carried out because operations might go in a different order and get different results.

Unite

This operator allows two or more solids to be combined into one. The volumes in common with each other unite to become one solid. The portions of the bodies not in the common area remain unchanged. In the Venn diagram above, notice in the Unite example that the overlapping portions of each cylinder were melded together and formed one body. You cannot unite a solid body with a sheet body.

Subtract

This operator allows material to be removed from the target solid by deleting the common volume (overlapping) of the tool solid. The tool solid is then removed completely leaving empty space where the tool solid used to be. In the Venn diagram above, notice in the Subtract example that the overlapping portions of each cylinder was removed from the target solid by the tool solid, thus taking a slice out of the target solid. You can subtract a solid from a solid, a solid from a sheet solid, and a sheet solid from a solid; however, you may not subtract a sheet from a sheet. Furthermore, the overlapping portions of the two solids must overlap some finite amount. Tangency conditions, such as a cylinder tangent to another cylinder, would not subtract. Same rule applies for a cylinder tangent to the planar face of a solid body. In other words, if only point or line contact is common between two solids, then the subtract will not work and an error message is received instead—Non-Manifold Condition exists.

Intersect

This operator unites (or melds) the common volumes of the target solid and tool solid(s) and removes (deletes) the rest of the solids that do not overlap each other. It combines the other two operators. In the Venn diagram above, notice the only portion of each solid remaining is the small wedge shape where the 2 bodies overlapped. The remaining solid body will retain the attributes of the target solid. This operator is particularly prone to unexpected results if more than one tool solid is chosen, so it is advisable to perform intersections one at a time. It is permissible to intersect a target sheet and a tool solid body.

Form Features

Form Features are special cases of combining solid bodies where the Boolean is built into the command and the operation done automatically. The Hole feature, Slot feature, Pocket feature, and Groove feature all do a Subtract with the original solid body the target and the form feature is the tool. The Boss feature and Pad feature both do a Unite with the original solid body the target and the Boss and Pad the tool. Have you noticed when creating form features that a solid body is displayed after creation and before you position it? That is the tool body that operates on the original solid body.

Creating a Second Solid Body

When a second solid body is created, the system will prompt asking you to make a choice of creating it as a standalone body, or to perform a Boolean on it as the tool body with the existing solid body as the target body. The menu that comes up looks like this.

As soon as a choice is made from the dialog the operation is performed.

9.2 Extrude

The Extrude option is found under the Insert menu bar with the commands of **Insert → Form Feature → Extrude…** This option allows a solid body to be created by sweeping planar, section string geometry in a linear direction over a specified distance.

There is a Preference setting, found in **Preferences → Modeling**, that specifies if a solid body or a sheet body is created when sweeping. The setting is defaulted to create a solid body and when set to solid some rules will apply.

- Extruding a set of closed planar connected curves creates a solid body.

- Extruding a set of closed planar connected curves with another closed set within the boundary of the first set creates a solid with an interior hole, e.g., circle within a circle creates a pipe.

- Extruding a curve or set of planar connected curves that are not closed creates a sheet body; unless, the offset option in Extrude is used.

When the Preference setting is set to create a sheet body, then a sheet body will be created whatever the curve configuration is as listed above. Note that if a closed set of curves is swept, a body will be created that looks like a solid body but will in fact be hollow inside, only a shell with sheets on the outside surface.

General Procedure to Extrude

The general procedure to Extrude a set of curves is as follows:

1. Choose the Extrude option.
2. Select the set of curves.
3. Choose the method of specifying the distance and direction.
4. Verify the direction of the sweep with the displayed arrow.
5. Enter the distance and offset parameters and choose OK.

Activity 9-1. Creating an Extrusion

An extrusion is a feature. It also results in a solid body. Therefore, the Work Layer should be set, color of the body and other attributes that your company wants set.

Step 1. **Open** part file **activity9-1.prt.**

We will extrude the set of curves that are available, but first some housekeeping and set ups.

Step 2. Open the **Modeling Application**.

Step 3. Change the **Work Layer** to be Layer 1.

Step 4. Choose **Insert → Form Features → Extrude…** or the Extrude icon

 and the dialog comes up to select the objects to sweep.

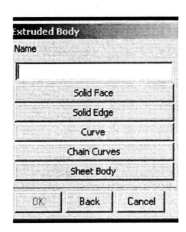

The generator for the sweep may be curves, a solid face, a solid edge, or a sheet body. The **Cue Line** prompts to select a section string, but you may select any of the types. The options in the menu are there to help in selection by limiting what may be selected. If a sketch is to be the generating curves, you just need to pick one curve in the sketch and the rest will be selected also. If you have a string of curves it might be helpful to use **Chain Curves**. Furthermore, the resulting solid body is associated to the curves and may be edited by editing the curves.

Step 5. When the objects to sweep are selected choose **OK** to complete the selection.

The next dialog allows five options for extruding that specify the limits and the direction to extrude.

Direction Distance—Allows you to specify the direction of the extrude and the length of the extrude by specifying a **Start Distance** and **End Distance**. The extrude does not have to start at the curves and it may start before the curves. For instance, think of creating the curves in the middle of a part and extruding in both directions, so a negative Start or End Distance would be entered.

Trim to Face/Plane—With this option the direction and distance are determined by the curves selected and the Face or Plane selected. The extrude will be normal to the plane of the curves selected and stop at the Face or Plane. The extruded solid will be associated to the Face or Plane.

Trim Between Two Faces/Planes—With this option the direction of the extrude is normal to the plane of the curves selected and be limited by selection of two Faces or Planes. The extruded solid body will be between the two Faces or Planes. And the solid body will be associated to both Faces or Planes.

Through Multiple Bodies—This option allows the extruding of the curves through multiple solid bodies and then a Boolean subtract is performed. The direction of the extrude is normal to the plane of the curves and the distance is completely through the farthest solid body selected. The extruded solid is the Tool body and the selected multiple bodies are the Target bodies.

Trim to Body—This option allows the extruding of curves to a solid body. It is used when the body topology may change and therefore a face would change so the Trim to Face is not an option.

Step 6. We will choose the first option **Direction Distance**.

A direction vector is displayed in the vicinity of the curves and normal to the plane of the curves. Another dialog comes up to accept or change the direction of the extrude.

The choices here are to accept the default direction (the direction displayed) by choosing **OK**, reverse the direction displayed by choosing **Cycle Vector Direction** or to re-define the direction using the other options.

    6.1. Choose the accept direction by choosing **OK**.

The dialog comes up to enter parameters for the sweep.

Here is where the parameters for **Start** and **End Distance** are entered, as well as **Offset** dimensions and **Taper Angle**.

    6.2. Enter the parameters shown in the figure and choose **OK** to accept the values.

The solid body is created immediately. The selection dialog remains active to select another set of objects to sweep again.

Activity 9-2. Another Extrude

Step 1. **Open** part file **activity9-2.**prt and save it as **xxx_activity9-2.prt**.

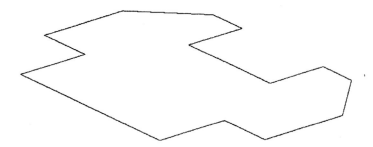

Step 2. Change the **Work Layer** to Layer 11.

Step 3. **Extrude** the curves.

    3.1. Choose the **Extrude** command or the icon.

    3.2. Select the curves and choose **OK** to accept.

    3.3. Ensure the direction vector is pointing up.

    3.4. Enter the extrude parameters of **Start** of 0 and **End** of 0.75. The **Offsets** and **Taper Angle** are 0.

    3.5. Choose **OK**.

Step 4. Create the **Holes** as shown on the drawing below.

Step 5. Save and close the file.

Activity 9-3. Extrude with Offset

This activity will demonstrate an extrusion of curves with an offset to create an extruded wall of the curves (the offset determines the wall thickness).

Step 1. Open part file **activity9-3.prt.**

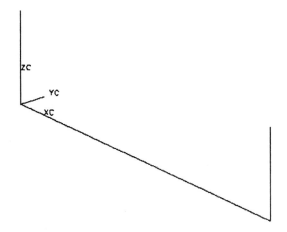

We will extrude these curves to create a length of channel and offset the curves to the outside to create a solid body channel.

Step 2. Choose **Modeling Application** to ensure it is active.

Step 3. Choose the **Extrude** command.

Step 4. Select the curves to extrude and choose **OK** to confirm.

Step 5. Choose the **Direction Distance** option from the dialog.

Step 6. Ensure the Direction arrow comes up pointing to the back of the screen (in the **+YC** direction).

6.1. Choose either **OK** or **Cycle Vector Direction** as appropriate.

Step 7. Enter values in the parameters dialog as shown below.

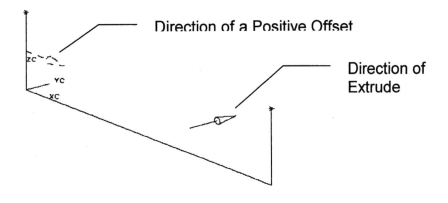

Direction of a Positive Offset

Direction of Extrude

The **Start Distance** is 1 and the **End Distance** is 13, indicating the extrusion will start 1 inch from the curves and end 13 inches from the curves.

The **First Offset** value is **-.25**, indicating that the offset will be .25 inches from the curves. The negative sign indicates the offset will be opposite the direction of the **Offset Vector Arrow**.

Step 8. Choose **OK** to confirm the values and extrude the curves.

The offset capability gives the flexibility to create a range of solids easily that would otherwise require more construction. Using Offset values has these characteristics:

- If a value is entered only for the First Offset, the value acts like an end value and the offset will extrude from the curves to the offset distance.
- If a value is entered for both the First Offset and the Second Offset, the offsets act like starting and ending distances. The offset extrude will start at the First Offset and end at the Second Offset.

9.3 Revolve

The second type of sweep we will cover is the **Revolve** option. It works conceptually the same as the extrude except it revolves the objects around a radius and through an angle instead of a direction and distance.

The Revolve option is found under the **Insert** menu bar with the commands of

Insert → Form Feature → Revolve… or from the Revolve icon .

This option allows a solid body to be created by revolving planar, section string geometry around an axis and through an angle. The section geometry may be curves, solid edges, solid faces, and sheet solids and combinations of these types.

Just like the Extrude option, there is a Preference setting, found in **Preferences → Modeling**, which specifies if a solid body or a sheet body is created when sweeping. The setting is defaulted to create a solid body and when set to solid some rules will apply. The results of revolving are the same as the extrude command, with the following exceptions:

- Revolving open strings of curves will cause the system to automatically cap the end faces to produce a solid body; however, the rotation must be a full 360° and the **Modeling Preferences Body Type** must be set to **Solid.**
- The direction of revolve is determined by the Right Hand Rule.

When the **Preference** setting is set to create a sheet body, then a sheet body will be created whatever the curve configuration is as listed above. Note that if a closed set of curves is swept, a body will be created that looks like a solid body but will in fact be hollow inside, only a shell with sheets on the outside surface.

General Procedure to Revolve

The general procedure to Revolve a set of curves is as follows:

1. Choose the **Revolve** option.
2. Select the set of curves.
3. Choose the method of specifying the rotation and angle.
4. Choose the axis of rotation.
5. Enter the rotation angle and offset parameters and choose **OK**.

Activity 9-4. Revolve to create Solid

Step 1. Open the part file **activity9-4.prt.**

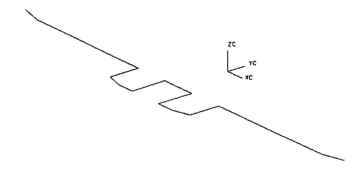

Step 2. Ensure the **Modeling Application** is active.

Step 3. Change the **Work Layer** to be Layer 1.

Step 4. Choose **Insert → Form Feature → Revolve...** or the icon .

Step 5. Select the string of curves to revolve. This string is a sketch. Notice that you may select any curve and they are all selected.
Confirm with **OK**.

Step 6. The method of revolution dialog comes up with three choices on it. The methods allow three options of specifying the axis of rotation and the limits to the rotation.

Axis_Angle—This method allows creation of a solid body or sheet solid by selecting a rotation axis and entering the angle of the rotation. The plane of the curves is defined as 0° and normal rotation occurs according to the right hand rule. Some caveats:

- Total rotation is determined by entering a **Start Angle** and **End Angle** with the total angle not exceeding 360°.
- If the value for the **Start Angle** is greater than the **End Angle**, then the rotation will occur in a negative direction.

Trim to Face—This method allows the creation of a single feature by rotating around an axis from the plane of the curves to a trimming face or datum plane on a target solid. You must have a target solid from which you select the trimming face or a datum plane associated with the target solid.

Trim Between Two Faces--This option lets you create a single feature by revolving section curves between two trimming faces or datum planes. To use this option, you must have a target solid from which you select the trimming face or datum plane.

Step 7. Choose the **Axis_Angle** method.

The **Cue Line** prompts to Enter direction and define the vector. The Vector Constructor dialog appears to assist in the selection and give options.

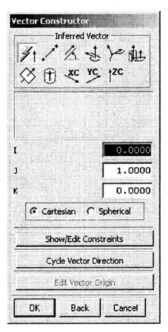

The axis of rotation may be an edge, a line, a datum axis, or one of the options at the top of the dialog, or I, J, K coordinates.

We will choose to use a datum axis.

Step 8. The datum axis is on layer 51 so make layer 51 Selectable.

Don't worry—the axis selection menu will return when you have completed the layer control procedure.

Step 9. Select the datum axis lying along the length of the curve geometry.

A direction vector appears along the length of the datum axis. The right hand rule applies to the direction of rotation. If rotating less than 360°, the direction must be planned and appropriate **Start** and **End Angles** input to rotate in the proper direction—a positive (normal) rotation or a negative rotation by entering a **Start Angle** larger than the **End Angle**.

In our case, we are rotating 360° so we don't need to be concerned about it this time.

Choose **OK** to accept the selection of the axis.

The **Parameters** dialog comes up.

Step 10. Enter **Start** and **End Angles** of **0°** and **360°**.

Ensure the **Offsets** are **0**.

Step 11. Choose **OK**.

The solid body is swept.

Step 12. Change Layer 51 to **Invisible**.

Step 13. Inspect the solid and notice the ends have been closed with a planar face.

Step 14. Choose **File → Close**.

Activity 9-5. Create the Revolve with Offset

Step 1. **Open** the **activity9-4.prt.**

Step 2. Ensure the **Modeling Application** is active.

Step 3. Change the **Work Layer** to be Layer 1.

Step 4. Make layer 51 **Selectable**.

Step 5. Choose **Insert → Form Feature → Revolve…**

Step 6. Select the string of curves to revolve. Confirm with **OK**.

Step 7. Choose **Axis Angle** from the revolution methods dialog.

Step 8. Choose the **Datum Axis** lying along the direction of the curves.

Notice the direction vectors that come up: the solid vector along the Datum Axis is for the direction of rotation and the dashed vector gives the direction for a positive offset.

This time we will change the sweep and do an **Offset** to demonstrate its capability.

We will do a 180° rotate and 0.25 Offset as shown above. Since the rotation is less than 360° we need to be concerned with the direction of rotation. We want the body of the solid to be under the curves and open to the top.

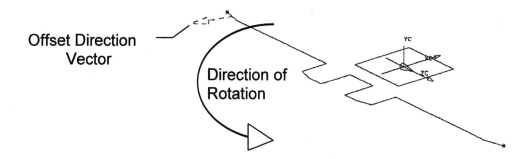

The right hand rule indicates the direction above is the one we want with the angles we want and the offset. The positive offset value will perform the offset in the direction of the dashed arrow; a negative offset value will perform the offset in the opposite direction to the dashed arrow. Therefore, the solid will grow outward from the curves with a .25 wall thickness.

Step 9. Choose **OK** to confirm the values above.

The resultant solid looks like this.

Offset was this direction

Original Curves

What a difference in the topology of the solid—right!

Step 10. File → Close. It doesn't need to be saved.

Project 9-1. Retainer 2

The project will practice some revolving techniques with other features such as datum planes and axis, a slot and chamfer. You constructed this part as a project in Chapter 8, but you probably used primitives as this was used to demonstrate Reference features. This time you are required to build the part using revolve and offset to learn a different way to build the part.

The finished part looks like the figure below. The dimensions for the part are the same as those found in Chapter 8, Project8-3.

The project steps are to rotate the curves provided into the multi-level cylinders, add the slot and chamfer the ends of the various cylinders. The revolve will require the use of an offset in each case.

Start this project by opening part file project9-1.prt.

Save the finished part as ***_project9-1.prt where *** is your three letter name initials.

Project 9-2. Angled Bracket

This project will require two extrudes and an intersect operation along with some simple holes. But it gives an idea of the possibilities. The finished part looks like below. You will need to sweep and intersect, and interrogate the curves to determine the distance for sweeping by using **Analysis → Distance**.

Open part file project9-2.prt and the starting geometry looks like this.

Investigate whether the order of sweeping affects the completed solid body. In general, intersecting three or more solid bodies will give different results depending on the order of intersecting.

Then add the holes as shown.

All dimensions above are in millimeters and note that the thickness of the part is
2 mm. Save this file as ***_project9-2.prt.

Exercise Problems

9.1   What kinds of objects may be selected to sweep?

9.2   What kinds of techniques are available to limit the extrude?

9.3   What techniques are available to set the direction of the extrude?

9.4   What techniques are available to limit revolving?

9.5   What techniques are available to determine the direction of revolving?

Chapter 10. Introduction to Sketching

This chapter introduces sketching. It covers how to create and edit sketches in Unigraphics, and how to use them as a design tool to capture the design intent. Up to this point in this book you have only been given one way to start in creating your solid model—the primitive. Other features were added to the primitive, including holes, pads, pockets, blends, and so forth. The last chapter introduced how to extrude and revolve curves to create solid models, but did not discuss how to create the curves. That chapter is a prelude to this chapter.

Sketching is a new way to create the initial solid. And sketching is also a way to add features to an existing solid whether created by a primitive or from a sketch. The sketch is not a solid. Extrude and Revolve operations use the sketch as the source of curves and sweep the shape of the sketch into a solid.

This chapter contains 4 sections to cover the topic of sketching. Section 10.1 discusses the concept of sketching of what it is and why we use it. Section 10.2 discusses creating sketches. Section 10.3 addresses constraints and how to use them. Section 10.4 shows how to use sketches for adding non-standard features to an existing solid.

10.1 Concepts of Sketching

A sketch is a collection of two-dimensional curves constituting a profile. A sketch varies from explicit two-dimensional curve geometry because of its ability to parametrically control the profile using a set of rules applied by the user. These rules are called constraints, and constitute the essence of constraint based modeling, which is a very powerful feature of Unigraphics solid modeling.

A sketch may be used anytime to create the solid. There are no specific criteria that suggest when not to use one. Some designers believe that nothing else but sketches should be used to create the solid. Other designers suggest starting with a primitive and building the solid from there, if the basic solid has a primitive topology. In this case, the sketch is reserved for those shapes that are not one of the primitives in basic shape. A third method is to create curves outside the sketcher and extrude the curves. When changes are made the curves are then added to the sketcher and the changes made inside the sketcher. Some designers believe that the only way to start a part is with a sweep from either curves or a sketch.

A sketch is a set of curves joined in a string that form the profile that when swept forms a solid body. The sketch represents the outline of that part. The sketch is created with the intention of sweeping that outline into a solid (Chapter 9). The curves are parametrically associated to each other, and they are parametrically associated to the solid that is created when the curves are swept. The curves can be created in the Sketcher and on a plane so they are 2D; and they are associated to the plane the sketch is created on. The curves may be created in a free-hand manner with no exact size, or they may be created exactly to size, or the free-hand creation may be changed to exact size at a later time. Adding dimensional or geometric constraints that define relationships among the curves or between curves and other objects can control the curves. The constraints may be edited to change sizes if desired.

Thus, the most obvious reason for sketching is when design intent is well known and constraints can be quickly applied to capture the intent. The design intent consists of two items:

- Design Considerations – The geometric requirements on the actual part, including engineering and design rules that determine the detail configuration of the part.
- Potential Areas for Change – Known design changes or iterations, and their effects on the part configuration.

As a general rule, the more design considerations and potential areas for change, the more likely there are benefits from sketching.

The sketch profile outline that is made up of a set of curves is very flexible for creating unusual shapes, but also flexible to allow changes to that profile in the future. The curves are parametric and associative and they are easily changed, or removed and new curves put in their place. A primitive block topology cannot be changed—only its dimensions.   Sketched profiles may be used to create extruded or revolved features or to define section or guide strings for sweep features. As the design intent changes, constraints applied to sketched profiles are updated to reflect the intent change and the resulting features and models are immediately and automatically updated.

In summary, the sketch is one the best tools from which to create solid bodies because of flexibility in shapes and the ability to edit and change that shape parametrically and associatively.

10.2 Creating Sketches

The sketch is a feature and is created like other features with a dialog and options of its own like holes, pads, pockets, and blocks. The sketcher is found off the main menu bar under **Insert**. Choose **Insert → Sketch...** from the menu bar or choose its icon ![icon]. Since the sketch is a standalone feature, it should be put on its own layer with all the objects that go with it. The sketcher dialog comes up named the Sketch Tools dialog. This dialog contains the groupings of commands to create the sketch, create the curves, constrain the sketch, position the sketch, perform operations on the sketch, and edit the sketch.

Create and edit curves

Create Sketch

Constraints and Curve Operations

Add and edit sketch objects

Change view orientation

Layer and Sketch Name List

Active Sketch shown here

Activate or Deactivate sketches on this line

The Sketch Tool dialog above is shown in the pre-sketch mode, before an action has been taken to create a sketch or select an existing one to edit. Therefore, many of the options are grayed out.

Create and Edit Curves—The icons shown may be used to create curves in the sketcher or without the sketcher. When one of the icons is chosen another dialog comes up with options for that type of curve.

Create Sketch—When this option is chosen, another dialog appears with options to name and orient the sketch. If this option is chosen before the curve options above, then curves will be created in the sketcher.

Change View Orientation—When this toggle switch is turned on, then the view orientation will be changed under Create Sketch and when the planar orientation is selected for the sketch.

Constraints and Curve Operations—These icons are useful after the sketch is created. The **Constraints** option is chosen to add constraints to the curves to define them exactly. The **Show/Remove Constraints** option is to list all the constraints applied to the curves and the opportunity to remove some or all of them if desired. The other options are out of the scope of this text.

Add and Edit Sketch Objects—The Positioning icon positions the sketch relative to space in the part file or relative to other objects in the space. It is the positioning tool, identical to the RPO of form features.

Layer/Sketch Name List—After sketches have been created in a part file, this window will list all sketches in this part file.

Active Sketch—The name of the active sketch is shown in this window. If no sketches are created, the window will be empty. To activate a sketch, choose the sketch from the **List** above, then choose **Activate**.

Activate/Deactivate—These buttons toggle to change the status of whatever sketch has been selected.

Retain Dimension Display—This toggle allows the display of an active sketch's dimensions to remain on after the sketch has been deactivated.

Update Model—This button is used to tell the model to be updated when the sketch has been changed. It allows all changes to be made before updating.

General Procedure to Create a Sketch

The following steps are the general procedure to create the sketch, add curves, constrain and be ready to extrude to a solid.

1. Choose **Insert → Sketch…**
2. Toggle the **Change View Orientation** button to **ON**.
3. Choose **Create Sketch** icon.
4. Choose plane to locate sketch on.
5. If a plane of the WCS is chosen you may proceed. However if a face or datum plane is chosen will have to choose **Horizontal** direction.
6. Enter name for sketch.
7. Choose a Curve Construction option and create the curves for the sketch.
8. If desired, constrain the curves.
9. If desired, position the curves in space.
10. Whenever comfortable with the sketch, **Replace** view to a Trimetric and sweep the sketch into a solid body.

General Curve and Sketch Creation Options

String Mode

When String Mode is toggled ON, the system prompts for the start point of the curve, and then it prompts for the end point of the curve. The system is ready for the next curve to be created by selecting only its end point, assuming the start point is the end point of the previous curve. This serves two purposes: it's quicker, and it ensures continuity of the curves one to another because it guarantees the end points are coincident on each other.

Point Method

The Point Method option allows the type of point to be specified to ensure that the specific point is selected and not another point. Most of the time the Inferred

Point option is the most useful because it allows Unigraphics to decide what type of point is being specified depending on what geometry is in the selection ball.

Snap Angle

The Snap Angle is a global preference setting in the Preferences → Sketch dialog that controls how the system automatically infers horizontal and vertical lines as they are created. The default Snap Angle is set to 3° meaning that any line created within ± 3° of true horizontal or vertical, the line will "snap" into true horizontal or vertical. The Snap Angle may be set from 0° to 20°. The 0° setting means that no snap angle will be applied and lines stay at the angle created.

Activity 10-1. Creating a Free-Hand Sketch

Step 1. Create a new part file and name it *****_activity10-1.prt.**

Step 2. Choose **Application → Modeling** to ensure it is active.

Step 3. Change the Layer Setting **Work Layer** to layer **21**.

Step 4. Choose **Insert → Sketch**.

Step 5. Ensure that **Change View Orientation** is toggled **ON**.

After the sketch plane is identified, this toggle will orient the view to show the sketch plane flat on the screen with horizontal pointing to the right.

Step 6. Choose **Create Sketch** icon.

This opens a new dialog, the **Create Sketch** dialog. It looks like this.

Step 7. Set Up Sketch Parameters.

    7.1. Type in a sketch name. Use **s21_profile** as the sketch name.

    7.2. Use the **Sketch Plane** pull-down and select the **YC-ZC** plane for the sketch.

    7.3. Choose **OK** to create the sketch.

Notice right away the view flitters, it places the **XC-YC** WCS flat on the screen and a datum plane and 2 datum axes are created to aid in construction.

Step 8. Move the Reference features to Layer **61**.

    8.1. Choose **Format → Move to Layer**

8.2. Choose **Select All** from the **Class Selection** menu, and then **OK**.

8.3. Type in layer number **61** and choose **OK**.

Step 9. We are ready to create curves, so choose the **Basic Curves** icon

Step 10. Ensure that the **String Mode** is toggled **ON** with a check mark.

Step 11. Ensure that the **Point Method** is selected to be **Inferred Point**.

Step 12. Ensure that the **Line** icon is selected.

The dialog will not change. It means that a line will be created. When an arc, a circle, or a fillet is needed, then select those icons.

Step 13. Construct the profile shown.

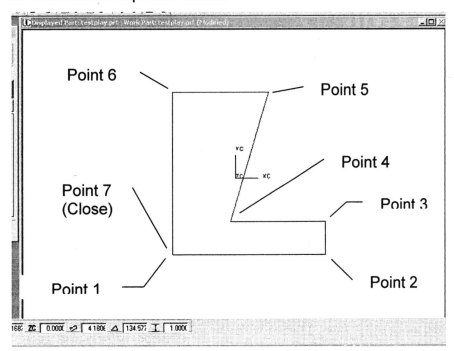

Do not worry about the exact size and location on the screen. Concentrate on approximating this shape. We will adjust the size later.

13.1. Select the points in the order shown above and place the points approximately where shown. Note that if lines are constructed within the Snap Angle (3°) they will snap to horizontal or vertical.

Notice the **Cue Line** prompts first to select the start point. Once the start point has been selected, the **Cue Line** prompts for the line end point each time for the next line, assuming the start point for each line is the end of the previous line.

13.2. With **String Mode** turned on, the line will rubber-band on the cursor and you may place the point just by punching **MB1**.

13.3. Select Point 7 to be the same as Point 1.

13.4. After all points are selected, choose **Break String** on the dialog.

Step 14. Add a fillet into the corner of the profile.

14.1. Choose the **Fillet** icon .

14.2. The **Fillet** dialog comes up.

The two icons on top are the fillet choices: **Simple Fillet** and **2 Curve Fillet**.

14.3. Ensure the **Simple Fillet** is selected.

14.4. The **Radius** is defaulted to .25 inches. That is ok. Otherwise, it would be necessary to change the radius before geometry is selected.

14.5. Locate the cursor over Point 4 such that the circle encompasses both lines at the intersection and select at point 4.

The fillet arc is immediately created. The profile now looks like the figure below.

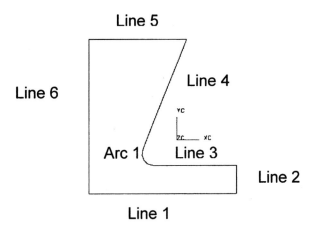

The goal of the construction is that lines L1, L3 and L5 are horizontal and lines L2 and L6 are vertical.

If your profile looks more like this, then that's ok too.

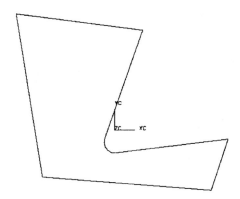

We will show you how to fix this also a little later in the lesson.

Step 15. Choose **File → Save**.

Activity 10-2. Sweep the Profile into a Solid Body

The purpose of this activity is to illustrate vividly how a solid is created from the sketch. It will use the **Extrude** command, covered in Chapter 9, and just the necessary steps will be shown assuming you know how to extrude.

Step 1. Open the previous file *****_activity10-1.prt** if not already open, and save it as *****_activity10-2.prt**.

Step 2. Replace the current view with the Trimetric, TFR-TRI.

Step 3. Change the **Work Layer** to layer 1.

Step 4. Choose **Insert → Form Feature → Extrude...** from main menu bar.

Step 5. Select one of the sketch curves. Notice they will all highlight. Choose **OK**.

Step 6. Choose **Direction Distance** option from the dialog that comes up.

Step 7. Choose **Accept Default Direction** from the new dialog that comes up.

Step 8. Another new dialog comes up. Enter **Start Distance** of 1 and **End Distance** of 5, and then choose **OK**.

Step 9. Use **MB3** and choose **Fit** (or use the **Fit** icon).

You see the solid has been created.

Step 10. Choose **File → Close → Save and Close**.

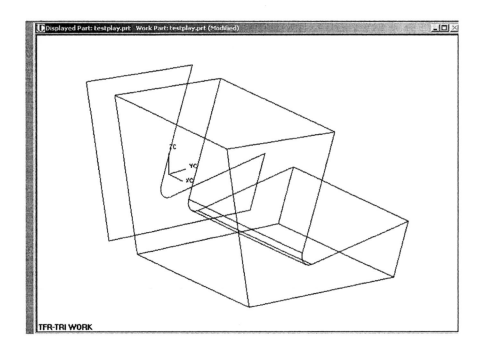

10.3 Sketch Constraining

The constraining of a sketch is the method that Unigraphics uses to enable a designer to capture the benefits of sketching that was mentioned earlier in the chapter. It was stated that the benefits of sketching were flexibility in the shape of the part, flexibility in the ability to make changes for design intent changes, or the flexibility to make changes to create families of similar parts, and finally, to capture the design intent of the rules and guidelines the designer has been given that the part must be designed within.

As was seen with Activities 10-1 and 10-2, sketches do not have to be constrained for Unigraphics to function and to build parts. And as stated earlier, the designer has the option to construct the curves exactly to size and shape, with no constraints, and to perform all their design functions with no constraints if desired. Furthermore, constraining is not an all or nothing methodology either. Sketches may contain any continuum from no constraints at all, through just a few constraints, to completely constrained.

However, the real power in designing with Unigraphics is the ability to sketch with constraints to capture the design intent and to be able to easily make design changes to the model, for whatever reasons the model may change. This text will view constraining a sketch as the optimal method and proceed accordingly.

Constraining Concepts

We discussed the purpose for constraining above and earlier. Constraining physically means to define exactly the physical size and orientation of curves and to define its relationship to other curves. There are two types of constraints that accomplish this: Dimensional constraints and Geometric constraints.

Dimensional constraints are very much like dimensions on a drawing done in drafting. They physically define the size of a curve by a dimension. The dimension may be edited to change the physical size of the curve it dimensions.

There are 8 types of Dimensional constraints.

Horizontal—The horizontal distance between two points parallel to defined horizontal on the sketch plane.

Vertical—The vertical distance between two points perpendicular to the defined horizontal on the sketch plane.

Parallel—The shortest, or parallel, distance between two points.

Perpendicular—The perpendicular distance from a selected line to a point.

Angular—The angle between two selected lines measured counter-clockwise from the ends of the lines on the end nearest where the lines were selected.

Radius—The radius for an arc or circle.

Diameter—The diameter for an arc or circle.

Inferred—This dimensional type uses the points or object selected and depending on where you drag the dimension to place it, infers what type of dimension to apply. There are some geometry configurations where it is difficult to get the dimension you want by inferring.

Geometric constraints define the geometric characteristic of a curve or define the relationship between 2 or more curves. They may be added or removed from curves to make changes.

There are 20 Geometric constraints. These are listed alphabetically, not in order of the most widely used.

Coincident—Defines two or more points as located on top of each other (occupying the same space).

Collinear—Defines that two or more lines all lie in the same straight line.

Concentric—Defines two or more arcs or circles as having the same center.

Constant Angle—Defines a line having a fixed angle.

Constant Length—Defines a line having a fixed length.

Equal Length—Defines two or more lines being the same length.

Equal Radius—Defines two or more arcs or circles having the same radius.

Fix—Defines the location in space relative to Absolute of points and objects. It applies differently to the different kinds of objects as to what is important in each object.

Horizontal—Defines a line to be fixed horizontal.

Midpoint of Curve—Defines the selected point on a curve to be coincident with the midpoint of a selected curve.

Mirror—Defines two objects as mirror images of each other.

Parallel—Defines two or more lines as parallel to each to each other.

Perpendicular—Defines two lines as being perpendicular to each other.

Point on Curve—Defines the location of a point on a curve as lying on another curve.

Point on String—Defines that a point on a curve is located lying on a selected string of curves.

Slope of Curve—Defines that a spline selected at one of its defining points is tangent to another curve at its selected point.

Scale, Non-Uniform—Defines that when a spline is changed, it will only scale in the horizontal direction and stay the same in the vertical direction.

Scale, Uniform—Defines that a spline will scale proportionately in both the horizontal and vertical directions when the horizontal length changes.

Tangent—Defines two curves are tangent to each other, i.e., arc and line, or two arcs.

Vertical—Defines a line as fixed vertical.

The Dimensional and Geometric constraints application will be demonstrated through an activity.

Activity 10-3. Application of Constraints to a Profile

Step 1. Open the previous profile *****_activity10-2.prt** and save it as

***_activity10-3.prt.

Step 2. Ensure that **Modeling Application** is still active.

Step 3. Change the **Work Layer** to that of the sketch, layer 21, and change the solid body layer to **Invisible**.

Step 4. Activate the sketch.

    4.1. Choose **Insert → Sketch**.

    4.2. Ensure the **Change View Orientation** toggle is **ON**.

    4.3. Select the sketch name **s21_profile** from the **Layer/Sketch Name** window.

    4.4. Choose the **Activate** button.

The view flips around to show the sketch full, flat on the screen.

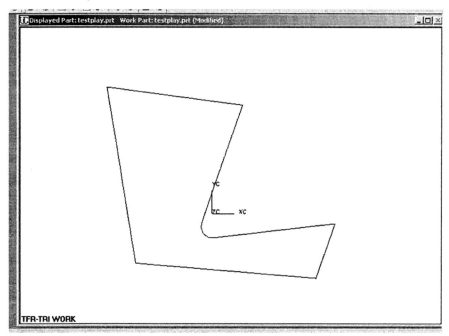

This model will be used as the profile to constrain because it's so extreme.

Step 5. Interrogate the model and determine if any constraints already exist that were applied by Unigraphics as a result of our geometry construction.

Show/Remove Constraints icon

5.1. Choose the **Show/Remove Constraints** icon shown above.

5.2. Toggle the **All in Active Sketch** button to **ON**.

The current status of all **Geometric** constraints is displayed in the window. In this case only two appear. These are the tangency of the fillet to the adjoining lines.

The constraints in the list may be selected, or the **UP** and **DOWN** arrow buttons may be used to select each constraint, and the affected geometry will be highlighted and named to graphically show which objects are affected.

5.3. Cancel this dialog.

Step 6. View the sketch for constraining.

6.1. Choose the **Constraint** icon on the **Sketch Tools** dialog.

Note that four significant actions occur: the **Constraints** dialog comes up, the graphic area of the sketch displays arrows, the **Status Line** declares that there are 13 constraints that need to be defined to be fully constrained, and the **Cue Line** is prompting to select objects to constrain.

Let's discuss the arrows in the graphic window first. These are Degree of Freedom arrows and represent the directions that each point is free to move because its location is not defined. Note the arrows are parallel to horizontal and vertical. Because this is 2D by definition, and defined to be on a plane, there is no freedom to move in a Z direction. When working in a sketch, remember that the conventional way of thinking about a curve of being locked in space is no longer valid; everything is free to move until defined by a constraint.

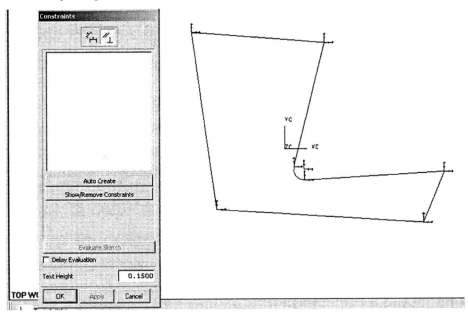

Also, a reminder there is no requirement that all 13 degrees of freedom be satisfied, or that any constraints at all need to be applied. But we choose to constraint the sketch completely in order to take advantage of the benefits discussed earlier in the chapter.

The degree of freedom arrows indicate the direction the point is free to move. Technically this means that Unigraphics is unable to define the exact location of the points. As the constraints are added, and Unigraphics is able to locate a point exactly, the arrows will disappear one by one. The arrows will appear wherever there is a defining point on a curve: end points, center points, and the defining points of a spline.

In the sketch above there are degree of freedom arrows at the end points of each line, at the center of the radius, and also the end points of the arc of the fillet.

We know that some lines should be horizontal and some lines should be vertical so we will start constraining with these curves.

Step 7. Use Geometric constraints on the horizontal and vertical lines.

7.1. On the **Constraints** dialog choose the **Geometric** icon .

7.2. Select the lines L1, L3, and L5 to be horizontal.

The **Cue Line** is prompting to select objects to constrain. Select the lines in the middle of the lines and do not select on the end points. You want to select the object and not the points. The window in the **Constraints** dialog fills with options. If end points are selected, different constraint options will be available.

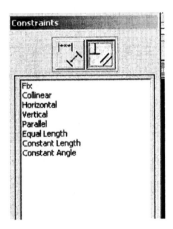

The list of Geometric constraints in the window represents the types of constraints that may be applied to the specific selection of curves we made. The list will vary depending on which and how many curves were selected. And the list will update each time a curve is selected, so it is dynamic and interactive.

7.3. In our case we want the lines to be horizontal, so choose **Horizontal**.

7.4. Choose **Apply** to make it happen.

Notice the lines snapped to horizontal and the selection window is empty.

7.5. Select the vertical lines L2 and L6 and remember to select in the middle of the lines. Watch the **Constraint** window list again.

7.6. Choose **Vertical** off the list and choose **Apply**.

Again, the lines snap to vertical.

Step 8. Interrogate the sketch again for constraints by repeating Step 5 and you will see that the **Horizontal** and **Vertical** constraints have been added.

The sketch will be positioned now relative to workspace by moving the whole sketch to be coincident with the WCS 0,0,0. Using the **Datum Axes** does this.

Step 9. Constrain the location of the sketch in space.

9.1. Change layer 61 to **Selectable** so the **Datum Plane** and **Axes** are visible.

9.2. Select the lower left corner of the sketch by selecting an end point.

9.3. Select the vertical datum axis. It may be selected anywhere.

9.4. The **Constraint** window shows only one option, the **Point on Curve** constraint. Choose it and choose **Apply**. The sketch jumps horizontally to make the end point coincident with the vertical datum axis.

9.5. Now let's do the other direction. Select the same lower corner end point and select the horizontal datum axis and choose **Apply**. The sketch jumps vertically to make the end point coincident with the horizontal datum axis.

Step 10. Change layer 61 to **Invisible** so the Datum's will be out of the way again.

Notice our profile is somewhat distorted now. Let's work on getting the correct shape. We will now use the **Dimensional** constraints.

Step 11. Add Dimensional constraints.

11.1. Choose the **Dimensional** icon at the top of the **Constraints** dialog. The **Constraints** dialog changes to include the dimension types.

11.2. Choose the **Infer** dimension type.

Notice the degree of freedom arrows disappear individually as the dimensions are placed.

11.3. Add horizontal or vertical dimensions for the bottom line, left side vertical line, and the right end line by selecting proper lines. If it is difficult to select or get the correct dimension, then switch from the Infer dimension type to the needed dimension type and try again.

11.4. Choose the **Radius** constraint dimension and select the arc.

11.5. Choose the **Angle** constraint and select the two lines forming the angle and select out toward the end of each line, but not the end points, and select counter-clockwise.

11.6. Choose the horizontal distance from the left corner to the center of the radius.

The dimensionally constrained profile looks like this now. Notice the sketch is fully constrained (says so in the **Status Line**).

Step 12. Edit the dimensions to get the desired shape.

Each of the dimensions may be edited by selecting them in the window, or in the graphics area, and typing in a new dimension in the **Current Expression** window.

```
p4=4
p5=3.5
p6=1
p7=.375
p8=1.75
p10=75
```

Current Expression

p10 = 75

Value: 75

The value is highlighted and a new value may be typed in. Hit a **Carriage Return**, or choose **OK**, when finished typing each new value and the new number will take affect and change the sketch. Observe the sketch to ensure it is changing in the manner you are expecting it to.

    12.1. On the **Constraints** dialog, select each of the dimensions and enter a new value to approximate the desired profile. You may experiment with values until you arrive at what is pleasing to you.

Please note that some dimension values will not work. The values that are entered must still have physical reality behind them and make sense physically. Unigraphics cannot make sense of physical configurations that don't make sense to you. Unigraphics must try and satisfy all the constraints and make sense of it.

Activity 10-4. Update the solid body

Step 1. **Cancel** out of the constraint dialog leaving the **Sketch Tools** dialog.

Step 2. **Replace** the current view with the Trimetric.

Step 3. Change the layers to make the body **Selectable**, layer 1.

Step 4. Choose the **Update Model** button on the bottom of the **Sketch Tools** dialog.

Watch quickly as the solid body updates to the new shape of the profile.

10.4 Using Sketches to Create Form Features

Sketches may be used in many ways to enhance the design and carry out the design intent of the designer. One of its more flexible uses is to put sketches on the planar face of a solid body or to create the sketch on a datum plane away from the solid body and extrude the sketch into the solid body to create a feature.

An example is a figure like the one below.

The following activity will be to create this part demonstrating this usage of sketching.

Activity 10-5. Creating the Rotator Arm

The dimensions and views for the part are shown here. The completed solid model for the part is shown above. Note that the part is in mm.

Step 1. Open a **New** part file and name it ***_activity10-5.prt**.

Boss

Rectangular Pad

Cylinder

Step 2. Construct the body of the part using Cylinder, Pad, and Boss with the dimensions given.

Hint: Create the cylinder first. Then you will need some datum planes to create the pad.

After creation of the cylinder, pad and boss, the model looks like this and we are ready to add the sketch feature.

The sketch must be placed on a planar object and we have a couple of choices on how to proceed.

- One option is to construct the sketch on the existing datum plane running through the middle of the part. Since the sketch is in the middle of the part, the **Extrude** is defined to be at a **Start** of –XX to **End** of +XX.
- The other option is to create a new datum plane parallel to the same existing datum plane but **Offset a** distance away. The **Extrude** would then happen from **Start** of 0 to **End** of XX.

Let's choose the first option and build the sketch on the datum plane in the middle of the part.

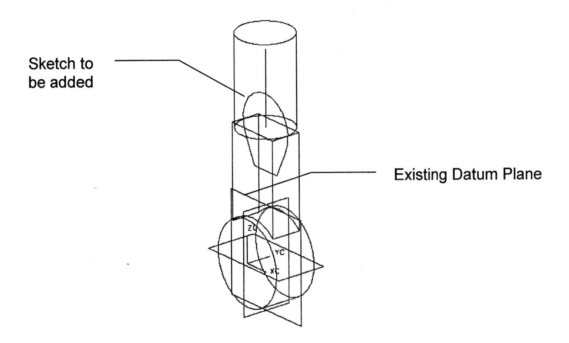

Sketch to be added

Existing Datum Plane

We now are ready to create the sketch on this datum plane. A brief note here about the feature we are adding. It does have a keyway in it so it is worth thinking ahead and determining how we are going to create that keyway. It is true that our sketch will contain the outside profile of the feature, but it could also contain the inside profile of the keyway and hole through the part. However, general recommendations are that sketches only profile one feature at a time. Therefore, that means create a sketch for the outside profile and create a separate sketch for the inside profile. But notice, using a Hole Feature and a Slot Feature or Pocket Feature could also create the inside profile in this case. This is really your choice about how to create the inside profile. Both options give great flexibility and are easily editable, however Form Features are easier to create the first time. For this reason, this activity will use the Hole and a feature option.

Step 4. Create the sketch for the outside profile.

- **4.1.** Choose **Insert → Sketch**
- **4.2.** Make the Work Layer 22.
- **4.3.** Ensure the **Change View Orientation** toggle in **ON**.
- **4.4.** Choose the **Create** sketch icon.
- **4.5.** On the **Create Sketch** dialog, type in the name for the sketch as **s22_feature**.
- **4.6.** On that same dialog, ensure the **Sketch Plane** is changed to **Face/Plane**.
- **4.7.** The **Cue Line** prompts to select the face or plane. Select the newly created datum plane. Choose **OK**.
- **4.8.** The **Cue Line** prompts to select the horizontal reference (needed since a plane of the WCS was not selected). Horizontal reference determines how XC-YC is oriented on the screen, so select an edge that is in the direction of normal XC.
- **4.9.** Ensure the arrow that appears is pointing to the right. If it isn't, then select Reverse Direction from the dialog.

The view should jump to place the datum plane flat on the screen. Adjust the geometry so the place where the sketch is to be located is in the middle of the screen. You may need to Zoom Out a bit as well.

- **4.10.** Visually determine approximately where the sketch would be located relative to the solid body.
- **4.11.** Choose **Basic Curves** from the **Sketch Tools** dialog.
- **4.12.** Ensure the **String Mode** is turned **ON**.
- **4.13.** Ensure **Line** is selected.
- **4.14.** Create the profile shown as close to shape as possible. Let's walk through it.

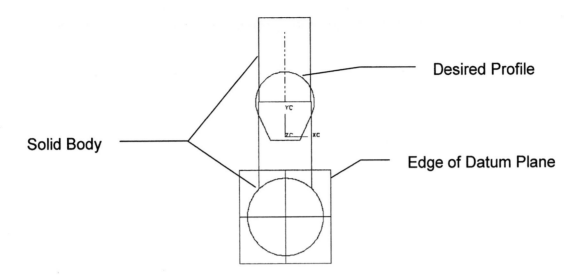

Desired Profile

Solid Body

Edge of Datum Plane

The lines are a little difficult to separate on this picture but will be easier in Unigraphics because the colors will be different.

 4.15. Once you are comfortable with the position of the sketch you may turn off the solid body and the datum planes using **Blank** or make the layers invisible.

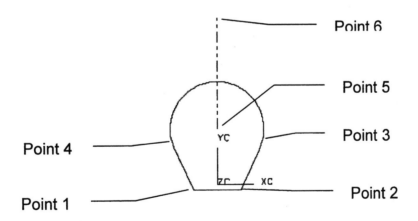

Point 6

Point 5

Point 3

Point 4

Point 2

Point 1

The following steps will use this figure and points to guide our path.

 4.16. With the **Basic Curves** dialog active, and the **Line** icon chosen, select Point 1 approximately where shown.

 4.17. Select the end point approximately at Point 2 keeping the line between Point 1 and Point 2 horizontal.

4.18. Select the end point approximately at Point 3 insuring the line is at an angle as shown.

4.19. An arc is needed so choose the **Arc** icon from the dialog. Another dialog appears and the **Cue Line** prompts for an end point, so select approximately where Point 4 is located. The **Cue Line** now prompts for a point on the arc so select as shown below to give the arc direction.

This method of placing an arc asks for the start point (in this case the end of the previous line), the end point of the arc, and then an intermediate point that will be on the arc to define direction of the arc and radius.

4.20. Choose the **Line** icon again and close the sketch by selecting Point 1 again.

4.21. Cancel the **Basic Curves** dialog.

The curve creation is now complete and some constraints need to be checked. We know that we want a line to be horizontal and end points should be coincident. These geometric characteristics are the first things to verify and to fix if they are not.

Step 5. Interrogate the sketch to view the constraint status.

Choose the Geometric constraints icon.

5.1. Choose the **Show/Remove Constraints** icon.

5.2. Toggle the **All in Active Sketch** button to **ON**.

5.3. Verify that the bottom line is horizontal and end points are coincident. **Cancel** the dialog.

The constraints that are not correct we should correct now.

Step 6. Apply **Geometric** constraints where needed.

6.1. Choose the **Constraints** icon and choose **Geometric** constraint icon.

6.2. Select the line from Point 1 – 2 and choose **Horizontal** in the window and choose **Apply**. Note here and the curves to follow that you should select the object line or arc, and not any points.

6.3. Select the line 2 - 3 and arc 3 – 4 and choose **Tangent** and **Apply**.

6.4. Select arc 4 – 3 and line 4 – 1 and choose **Tangent** and **Apply**.

Step 7. Apply **Dimensional** Constraints

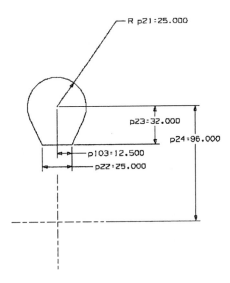

7.1. Add the **Horizontal** dimension for the bottom line and the **Radius** dimension.

Most of these dimension constraints are straightforward, like dimensioning a part in drafting. However, there is some technique involved you may not be familiar with. The next steps will walk through some of those techniques.

7.2. Add the **vertical** dimension from the arc center to the bottom line of the sketch.

In order to select the arc centers to create dimensions to the center requires some technique. To get the center of the arc, put your cursor over the arc but don't select it. Notice the arc highlights and notice points associated to the arc highlight as well: the two end points of the arc and the center point. Without selecting anything yet, slide the cursor over the center point and select the center point. Watch for visual verification in the correct point selected because the asterisk marker will appear at the point actually selected.

Another different dimension is the relational dimension at p103 = p22/2. This type of expression is used to ensure that the arcs stay centered over the flat bottom part of the sketch. Please review Chapter 6 to get a fuller description of expressions. If the dimension letters are too small or large, change accordingly the value of "Text Height" field at the bottom of the Constraint dialogue.

7.3. The relational dimension is created by selecting the **Horizontal** dimension type, then selecting the arc center and selecting the end point of the line 1-2.

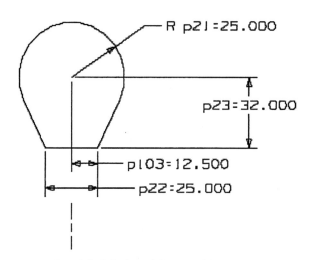

7.4. With the expression highlighted in the Value window, type in p22/2 and hit carriage return, or choose **OK**.

When the dimensional and geometric constraints are complete, the positioning constraints need to be added to locate the feature correctly with the solid body. The sketch will be located using the arc centers and edges of the datum planes with dimensional constraints.

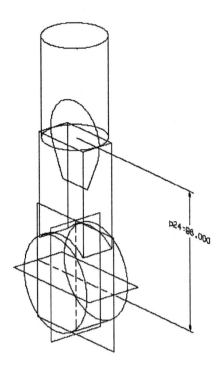

The figure above represents the sketch with the sketch dimensions **Blank**ed out for clarity. The positioning dimension is shown as applied.

Step 8. Apply **Position** Constraints

8.1. Ensure the **Constraints** icon is chosen and the **Dimensional** dialog is selected.

8.2. Choose the **Vertical** dimension icon.

8.3. To create the constraint corresponding to the 96 mm dimension, select the **arc center** of the cylinder and choose the datum plane or axis that is horizontal and located at the center of the cylinder on the bottom. Then place the dimension. That locates the sketch vertically from the arc center of the cylinder at the bottom of the solid body.

8.4. To create the constraint to center the sketch in the body, choose the **Geometric** icon and select the edge of the vertical datum plane that we see as an edge and the center point of the arc in the sketch, and then place the dimension. That constraint locates the sketch in the center of the body

The sketch should be fully constrained now.

Step 9. Extrude the sketch.

9.1. Close or cancel all the sketch dialogs.

9.2. Replace the sketch view with the Trimetric if the system didn't.

9.3. Choose **Insert → Form Features → Extrude**.

9.4. The **Cue Line** prompts to select the curves to extrude. Select one of the curves in the sketch and notice that all the curves are highlighted and selected. This is a characteristic because the sketch curves form a group.

9.5. Choose **OK**

9.6. Continue to extrude the sketch using the drawing dimensions and using positive and negative dimensions.

The solid body looks like this after these operations.

We now need to create the extrusion extending on top of the extrusion we just did. This portion looks like the figure below.

We will accomplish this portion of the body by extruding a line in both the normal extruding directions, but also the offset directions. We create the line we require first in the same sketch. We created this line after we created the previous extrusion, so it would not be swept with the previous extrusion.

Step 10. Create the vertical line. Re-enter the sketch and **Activate** the sketch.

   10.1. Choose the **Basic Curve** icon from the **Sketch Tools** dialog.

   10.2. Choose **Line** icon, toggle off **String Mode**, and construct a line from the arc center vertically to above the radius of the arc. **Cancel** the dialog.

   10.3. Choose the **Constraints** dialog and ensure the line is **Vertical**.

   10.4. Add a **Vertical** dimension to the line, and then edit the line to be 58 mm long (44 mm + 14 mm).

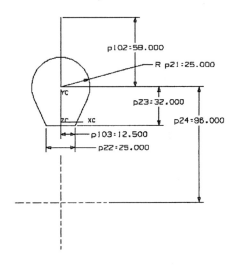

Step 11. Extrude the line to create the upper portion of the flat area of the feature.

    11.1. Choose **OK** to exit out of the sketch menu and change to the Trimetric view.

    11.2. Choose the **Extrude** icon and select the vertical line we just created. Choose **OK** the end the selection.

    11.3. Choose the **Direction_Distance** option.

    11.4. Change the direction of the sweep to be in the **+YC** direction.

    11.5. Enter into the dialog the dimensions we want to sweep the line.

    11.6. Choose **OK** and then Unite to complete the sweep.

Step 12. Blend the ends of the sweep to create the round at the top.

Now for considerations of future editing of the sketch we recommend converting the vertical line to reference for storage purposes.

Step 13. Convert Vertical line to Reference

    12.1. From the **Sketch Tools** dialog, choose the **Convert To/From Reference** icon .

This is the **Convert** dialog and it is selected now to convert sketch curves to **Reference** curves. A reference curve may be used for construction in a sketch, but it is not part of the sketch curves and will not be selected in the sweep options.

12.2. The **Cue Line** is prompting to choose the curve to be converted so select the vertical line.

12.3. Choose **OK.** The line is converted and changes colors and line font. Note now the vertical line is part of the same sketch, but when we extrude this sketch we desire to different results: 1), an extrusion of the curved closed portion of the sketch, and 2) the straight line only extruded with offsets. To carry out the first extrusion, the line must be reference. To carry out the second extrusion the line must be active. It will be necessary to change the status of the line depending on the edit you are going to do.

Step 13. Create the **Boss** on the side of the body.

Extruded Sketch

Boss to be created

Select this plane as the base for the boss

13.1. Choose the **Boss** icon.

13.2. Select the planar placement face to be the datum plane indicated above.

13.3. Ensure the direction arrow is pointed to the right.

13.4. Enter the parameters for the boss.

13.5. Use the positioning dimensions to locate the boss in the proper location relative to the solid body using the dimensions on the drawing.

Step 13. Add the holes to the solid body as indicated on the drawing. Choose the **Hole** icon and create and place the holes per the drawing.

Step 14. Create and place the keyway in the body.

We chose that the **Rectangular Slot** (alternatively, Rectangular Pocket works) would be used to create the keyway because it allows the **Thru** faces to be selected and associated to the faces in case of editing later on. A datum plane will need to be created at the location of the hole through the extruded sketch. The datum plane is then used as the planar placement face for the slot.

14.1. Choose the **Datum Plane** icon.

14.2. Several ways may be used to create the plane, but the easiest and quickest is to offset it from the plane at the bottom that is already created and in the correct orientation.

14.3. Select the bottom datum plane and enter the offset distance of 96 mm.

14.4. Choose the **Slot** icon, the Thru option, the **Rectangular** option and select the datum plane as the placement plane. Enter the rest of the information for the slot and create the slot.

Step 15. Create the remaining holes in the part.

This completes the construction of the rotator arm.

Project 10-1. Fixture

It is a relatively simple design that could be built with primitives but your
assignment is to build it with a sketch(es). Primitives are not allowed.
The part is in mm. Save this file as ***_project10-1.prt.

Project 10-2. Adaptor Block

Model this part using sketches and form features only—no primitives. The part is in mm. Save this file as ***_project10-2.prt.

You can use either one or two sketches with some other form features.

Exercise Problems

10.1   What is a sketch?

10.2   Why would you use a sketch?

10.3   Are sketches the fastest way to model a part?

10.4   What functionality is used in conjunction with a sketch, but after the sketch?

10.5   What are the basic building blocks of a sketch?

10.6   Which kinds of objects are used to build sketches?

10.7   What is the purpose for constraining a sketch?

10.8   Do sketches have to be constrained?

10.9   What are the types of constraints?

10.10   Are constraints able to be changed or deleted?

Chapter 11. Instance, Trim Body, and Thread Features

This chapter introduces feature operations that are useful to create complex geometries. These feature operations include Instance, Trim Body, and Thread. With Instance, you can quickly create copies (instances) of desired existing feature(s), obviating repeatedly creating each of them. With Trim Body, you can create a complex solid body by cutting away portion of the solid determined by the shape of a face or plane. Thread facilitates creation of any object with threads such as bolts, nuts, etc. Sections 11.1 to 11.3 discuss these three features in order.

11.1 Instance

An *instance* is a shape-linked feature, similar to a copy. You can create one or more instances of a feature, or group of features. Since all instances of a feature are associated, you can edit the parameters of the feature and those changes are reflected in every instance of the feature. Thus, this feature allows you to quickly create a number of similar features and add them to the model in one step and to edit all instanced features in one step.

As the instances are created, the Boolean operation is defined by that of each of the features that was selected for instancing. For example, if you select a boss and a hole, the instance of the boss is added and the instance of the hole subtracted, from the solid body to which they are attached.

Four Instance Options:

There are five instance options for this feature. These are available by choosing **Insert → Feature Operation → Instance** or the Instance Feature icon

Rectangular Array	To create a linear array of instances from one or more selected features.
Circular Array	To create a circular array of instances from one or more selected features.
Mirror Body	To mirror an entire body about a datum plane.
Mirror Feature	To mirror one or more features through a datum plane or planar face.
Pattern Face	Opens the Pattern Face dialog under **Direct Modeling**, to let you make copies of a face set. (This is out of scope of class.)

Instance Array Types

You can create three types of rectangular and circular instance arrays:

General	Creates an instance array from existing features and validates all geometry. An instance of a General array is allowed to cross an edge of the face. Also, instances in a General array can cross over from one face to another. This is the default type.
Simple	Similar to a General instance array, but it speeds up the instance array creation by eliminating excessive data validation and optimizing operations.
Identical	The fastest way to create an instance array; it does the least amount of validation, then copies and translates all the faces and edges of the master feature. Each instance is an *exact* copy of the original. No checking is done for invalid geometry. You can use this method when you have a great many instances, and you are sure they are all exactly the same.

The figure below illustrates a case where a General array has been created where one instance crosses the edge of the body. The Simple and Identical arrays look the same, but the Identical array is created faster, since the least amount of validation is done.

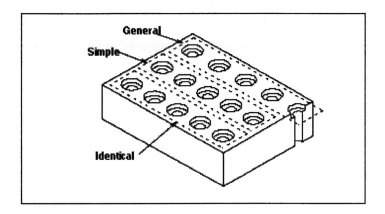

The next figure shows a part with a master feature. It also illustrates a valid Simple array, and shows how an Identical array could not be created in this situation.

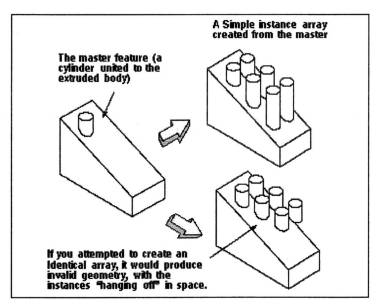

General Guidelines

- If you create a blend or chamfer on an instance after the instance set is created, the **Blend All Instances** (in the blend creation dialogue) or **Chamfer all instances** options allow you to add the blend or chamfer to all the *current* instances in that set. These options have no effect on instances created after the blend or chamfer

- You cannot instance the following objects: hollows, blends, chamfers, trimmed features, datums, instance sets, taper features, free form features, offset sheets, trimmed sheet bodies,

- The feature you select to instance is replaced by the instance array. For example, if you select a hole and specify a rectangular array of 3 x 4, the resulting instance array contains 12 instances, one of which is the original selected hole.

- You can create an instance array from an existing feature or an existing instance.

- Features that are instanced must reside within the target body. In the event you are instancing the target body itself, the created instances must intersect as each is created. You cannot instance a feature in relation to another target solid.

- Before creating the instance or array, the system temporarily displays the position of the instances based on the parameters you input. (If you selected multiple features to instance, only one of them is displayed, to save time.) At this point, you can accept these results and create the instance by choosing Yes, or respecify the positioning before the system adds the feature to the model by choosing No.

- You can edit an instance using the **Edit →Feature → Parameters** option. To edit the size parameters of a set of feature instances (height, depth, width, etc.), choose the **Feature Dialog** option. To edit the parameters of an instance array (number of instances, distance, angle, reference point, etc.) choose the **Instance Array Dialog** option.

- Use the **Edit → Feature → Move** option to translate instances. If the feature selected is a member of an instance array, the system moves the entire instance array.

- Use the **Edit → Feature → Delete** option to delete instances. If you choose a feature, which is a member of an instance array, the system deletes the entire array. The original feature, however, is not deleted.

11.1.1 Rectangular Array

This option lets you create a linear array of instances from one or more selected features. Rectangular instance arrays can be either two-dimensional in XC and YC (several rows of features) or one-dimensional in XC or YC (one row of features). These instance arrays are generated parallel to the XC and/or YC axes based on the number and offset distance you enter. You can change the orientation of the WCS (the XC and YC directions) using **WCS → Origin**, **Rotate**, or **Orient** as discussed in Chapter 3.

After you select the desired features to instance a rectangular array, the following parameter dialogue appears:

Number Along XC defines the total number of instances to be generated parallel to the XC axis of the WCS. This number includes the existing feature you are instancing. XC Offset defines the spacing for the instances along the XC axis. This spacing is measured from a point on one instance to the same point on the next instance along the XC axis. Negative values position the instances in a negative direction along the axis. Number Along YC works the same as Number Along XC (except YC in place of XC). This is true for YC Offset as well. As an example, to create a one-dimensional array in the XC direction, set the XC value to the number required and set the YC value to one.

The figure below shows a 3 by 4 rectangular array of 12 instances. Each instance is spaced .75 in the XC direction and 1.0 in the YC direction.

Rectangular Instance Array

1.00

Hole selected
for instance

Y

Z —— X

.75

Parameter Settings:

Total no. of instances in XC = 3
Offset value in XC = .75
Total no. of instances in YC = 4
Offset value in YC = 1.00

Activity 11-1. Creating a rectangular array of instances

In this activity, you will create a row of five hole instances 7 inches apart between any two adjacent holes.

Before   After

Step 1. **Open activity11-1.prt** and save it as *****_ activity11-1.prt**.

Step 2. At the **Modeling** application, choose **Insert →Feature Operation →Instance** or the **Instance** icon .

Step 3. Choose the **Rectangular Array** option.

Step 4. Choose **SIMPLE_HOLE(2)** listed in the dialog as the feature to instance and then **OK**.

Step 5. The instance parameter dialogue appears. Key in the following values:

> **Number Along XC** = 5
>
> **XC Offset** = 7
>
> **Number Along YC** = 1
>
> **YC Offset** = 0

Choose **OK**. A temporary display of the elongated hole locations are displayed in the graphics area.

Step 6. Verify the hole instances are created. Because these holes are located where you need them, you can complete the instance array by choosing **Yes** on the **Create Instance** dialog.

Step 7. **Save and close** this file.

11.1.2 Mirror Body

Mirror Body lets you mirror an entire body about a datum plane. You can use this, for example, to form the other hand of a lefthand or righthand part. When you use this option, the system creates a feature whose name is Mirror.

The following statements describe the Mirror feature and its relationship to the original body and the datum plane:

- When you mirror a body, the Mirror feature is associative to the original body - it has no editable parameters of its own. If you change the parameters of a feature in the original body, causing the original body to change, those changes are reflected in the mirrored body.

- If you edit the parameters of the associated datum plane, the mirrored body changes accordingly.

- If you delete the original body or datum plane, the mirrored body is also deleted. If you move the original body, the mirrored body also moves.

- You can add features to the mirrored body. However, be sure that you do not reorder these features, such that they would occur before the Mirror feature.

- You can combine the original and mirrored bodies, using the **Unite** option, to create a symmetrical model, as shown in the figure below.

Activity 11-2. Creating a mirror body

In this activity, you will use the Mirror Body option to create the left half of this part. The results are two solid bodies. Because these two solids will have coincidental faces at the datum plane, they can be united.

Before   After

Step 1. **Open ***_activity11-1.prt** that you created in the last activity, and save it as *****_ activity11-2.prt**.

Step 2. At the **Modeling** application, change the work layer to **61** and create a datum plane coincident on the face depicted above (i.e., offset value 0).

Step 3. Change the work layer to **1** and choose **Insert →Feature Operation →Instance** or the **Instance** icon

Step 4. Choose the **Mirror Body** option

Step 5. A **Class Selection** dialog displays to help in your selection. Select the green solid body and choose **OK**.

Step 6. Select the datum plane. The mirrored body is created as shown above.

Step 7. Unite the two bodies.

    7.1. Choose **Insert → Feature Operation → Unite.**

    7.2. Select the solid on the right side for the target body.

    7.3. Select the solid on the left side for the tool body and choose **OK**.

Step 8. Delete the **Rectangular Array** feature and observe the change in the mirrored body.

Step 9. Change the value of the expression **p10** from 10 to 30. In this part, the extrusion was created from a sketch and sketch dimension **p10** controls the height of the vertical face.

    9.1. Choose **Tools → Expression**.

    9.2. Highlight the expression **p10=10** in the list of expressions in the dialogue.

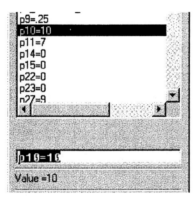

    9.3. In the value field beneath the list of expressions, change it to read **p10=30** and choose **OK**.

The two previous steps illustrates that the mirrored body is associative to the original body. If you delete the original body or datum plane associated with a mirrored body, the system deletes the mirrored body.

Step 10. **Save and close** this file.

11.1.3 Mirror Feature

This option lets you create symmetrical models by mirroring *selected features* through a datum plane or planar face. To create a simple mirrored body you would normally use the **Mirror Body** option. **Mirror Feature**, however, lets you mirror features within a body. Output from this option is a feature named MIRROR_SET. During edit of a MIRROR_SET feature, you can redefine the mirror plane and add and remove features to it.

The Mirror Feature dialogue displays as follows:

Mirror Feature Procedure

1. From the Mirror Feature dialog, click the **Feature to Mirror** selection step option if necessary.

2. If necessary, use the **Filter** field to limit the features shown in the Features in Part listing.

3. If desired, turn on the **Add Dependencies** option, to include feature dependencies of the selected features that are to be mirrored.

4. If desired, turn on the **All in Body** option, to mirror all features present in the body.

5. Highlight the features in the **Features in Part** listing that you wish to mirror, and use the **Add** button to add them to the **Features in Mirror**

11-13

listing. You can make multiple selections by highlighting multiple items in the Features in Part listing and clicking the Add button once. You can remove features in the Features in Mirror listing by highlighting them and clicking the **Remove** button. (Note that you can also add features to the Features in Mirror list by clicking on them in the graphics window with the mouse cursor. Similarly, you can remove features from the Features in Mirror list by Shift/clicking <Shift><MB1> on them in the graphics window.)

6. Click the **Mirror Plane** selection step option. Move the cursor to the graphics window and select the datum plane or planar face to be used to reflect the feature during the mirror operation.

7. Click **OK** or **Apply**. The features in the Features in Mirror listing are mirrored across the mirror plane. The result is a separate body composed of a single MIRROR_SET feature. If desired, you can use **Unite** to join the new body with the other solid body in the part file.

Activity 11-3. Creating a mirror feature

In this activity, you will use the Mirror Feature option to create the left half of this part with selected features.

Before   After

Step 1. **Open activity11-3.prt** and save it as *****_ activity11-3.prt**.

Step 2. At the **Modeling** application, choose

Insert → Feature Operation → Instance.

Step 3. Choose the **Mirror Feature** option. The **Mirror Feature** dialogue appears.

Step 4. Turn off the **Add Dependencies** and **All in Body** options if necessary.

Step 5. Select the features to mirror.

> **5.1.** Highlight the following three features from the **Features in Part** listing:
>
>> EXTRUDED(0),
>>
>> INSTANCE[0](1)/SIMPLE_HOLE(1),
>>
>> INSTANCE[0](6)/RECTANGULAR_SLOT.

When you highlight more than one feature, hold down the **Ctrl** key and click features to mirror. To deselect a highlighted feature, do the same.

> **5.2.** Choose the **Add** button to add them to the **Features in Mirror** listing.
>
> **5.3.** Choose **OK**.

The mirrored features are created as shown above.

Step 6. Unite the two bodies.

> **6.1.** Choose **Insert → Feature Operation → Unite.**

6.2. Select the solid on the right side for the target body.

6.3. Select the solid on the left side for the tool body.

6.4. Choose **OK**.

Step 7. **Save and close** this file.

11.1.4 Circular Array

This option lets you create a circular array of instances from one or more selected features. The procedure to create a circular array is as follows:

1. Select the features you want to instance.

2. In the Enter Parameters dialog, specify the array method (**General**, **Simple**, or **Identical**), the total **Number** of instances (including the original feature) and the **Angle** between instances. Then, choose **OK**.

3. Choose **Point_Direction** or **Datum Axis** to establish the rotation axis.

If you choose Point_Direction, use the *Vector Constructor* to establish a direction and the *Point Constructor* to establish a reference point. If you define the axis using the *Vector Constructor*, you can change it to a datum axis later using **Edit → Feature → Parameters** and selecting the instance. An example for this option is depicted below.

Parameter Settings:
Total number   = 8
Angle   = 45°
Rotation axis   = +ZC
Reference point = arc center

If you choose Datum Axis, select a datum axis. The radius of the array is calculated as the distance from the datum axis to the local origin of the first feature you selected. The rotation axis of the array will be associative to the geometry used to define the datum axis.

4. A highlighted representation of the array is displayed. Choose **Yes** to create the instance array, or **No** to return to the Enter Parameters dialog.

Activity 11-4. Create a circular array of instances

In this activity, you will create instances of some features using a circular array to quickly model a desired part as shown below.

Before

After

Step 1. **Open activity11-4.prt**, and save it as *****_ activity11-4.prt**.

Step 2. Create a datum axis that will be used as the rotation axis for the circular array.

    2.1. Change the work layer to 62.

    2.2. Select the cylinder face such that the datum axis goes through the axis of the long cylinder face.

Step 3. Change the work layer to **1** and choose **Insert → Feature Operation →Instance**.

Step 4. Choose the **Circular Array** option. The following **Instance** dialogue appears, displaying features for which you can create instances.

Note that the Chamfer feature is not listed in this dialogue since it is one of the features that cannot be instanced.

Step 5. Select three features that you want to instance.

    5.1. Select the EXTRUDED(0), BOSS(8), and SIMPLE_HOLE(9).

To select multiple features, press the Ctrl key and select features that you want to add to instance. Notice that as you add them, they are highlighted in screen in red.

    5.2. Choose **OK**.

Step 6. Enter the following instance parameter values:

    Number = 3 and **Angle = 360/3**.

    Choose **OK**.

Step 7. The cue line prompts you to select a rotation axis. Choose the **Datum Axis** button.

Step 8. Select **Datum_Axis(12)** or pick the datum axis from the graphic screen. Choose **OK**.

Step 9. A highlighted representation of the array is displayed as shown below.

9.1. Choose **Yes** to create the instance array.

9.2. Choose **Cancel** to close the instance dialogue.

Step 10. Create a single-offset chamfer with offset distance=3 to the circle edges of the two instanced bosses. Select one circle edge (either one). The following dialogue appears:

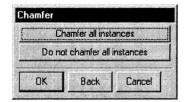

10.1. Choose the first button saying **Chamfer all instances**.

You have completed the part.

Step 11. Now edit this instance feature to make **6** instances instead of **3**.

11.1. Open the **Model Navigator (MN)** window by clicking icon   .

11.2. Move your cursor over the feature **INSTANCE[0](8)/BOSS(8)** in the **MN** window and click the right mouse button once. The following submenu appears.

11.3. Move your cursor over **Editing Parameter** and click the left mouse button once. The following dialog appears. .

11.4. Choose the **Instance Array Dialog** button

Now the circular array dimension dialogue is displayed.

11.5. Enter **Number=6** and **Angle =360/6** and choose **OK** twice.

The part is completed.

Step 12. **Save and close** your part file.

11.2 Trim Body

This feature operation trims one or more target bodies using a face, datum plane or other geometry. You select which portion of the bodies you want to keep, and the trimmed bodies take the shape of the trimming geometry.

We give the general procedure below to follow for Trim Body. Detail descriptions follow the steps.

1. Choose **Insert→Feature Operation→Trim** or the Trim Body icon ⬚.

2. Select at least one target body and click OK.

3. Select a face or datum plane, or define other geometry to trim the target bodies.

4. A vector is displayed. The portion of the target bodies in the direction of the vector will be removed. Choose to accept the direction of the vector or reverse it.

For step 3, the system is defaulted to the selection of a face or datum plane as the trimming surface, but you could choose from items listed in the Trim Body dialog that displays.

- Define Plane lets you define a plane for the trimming object by using the Plane Subfunction dialog.
- Define Cylinder lets you define a cylinder for the trimming object, by using a diameter or arc/circle.
- Define Sphere lets you define a sphere for the trimming object, by using a center and diameter.

- Define Cone lets you define a cone for the trimming object, by using two coaxial arcs, diameters and height, or diameter and half angle.
- Define Torus lets you define a torus as a trimming object and you would have to enter the positive major and minor radius values and define the torus axis.

One important point to remember is the associativity issue. If you intend to maintain associativity of the trim to the solid body, you need to use for the trimming object relative datum planes or features created through the use of the Geometry Linker (will be discussed in Assembly Modeling in Chapter 12). The above five options to define the trimming object do not maintain the associativity. For these options, the change of a solid body does not affect the trimming object.

For Step 4, the direction of the normal vector determines which portion of target bodies is kept. The vector points away from the body portion that will be kept. This is illustrated by the below figures in which the trimming object is defined by a cylinder face. The system provides an option to change the direction of the vector.

The Trim Body operation can fail under certain conditions. When you trim a body using a face, the face must be large enough to cut through the body completely. If it does not, the following error message is displayed: Non-Manifold Solid. Also the trim operation may fail if

- A face of the trimming sheet is tangent to the face of the solid body.
- The selected trimming geometries are faces from different solid bodies.
- The selected trimming geometries are disjoint (i.e., unconnected) faces from a solid body.

Away From Axis

Normal points away from the axis of the cylinder

Cylinder axis

Trimming surface

Result

Towards Axis

Normal points towards the axis of the cylinder

Cylinder axis

Trimming surface

Result

Activity 11-5. Trimming a Solid Body

This part, shown below, is a pin with an angled thru hole. There are four datum planes and one datum axis that are used to create the hole. You are going to trim this pin with the angled datum plane.

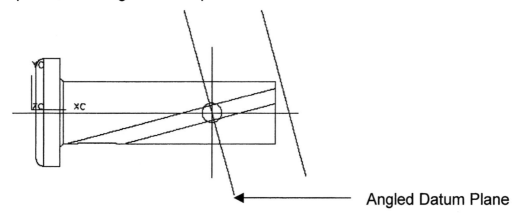

Angled Datum Plane

Step 1. **Open activity11-5.prt** and save it as *****_activity11-5.prt**.

Step 2. At the **Modeling** application, choose **Insert→Feature Operation→Trim** or the **Trim Body** icon .

Step 3. Specify the target body by selecting the pin solid body. You must select the target body even though there is only one possible target displayed. Choose **OK**.

Step 4. Specify the trim body by selecting the angled datum plane that was indicated above. The trim direction vector appears.

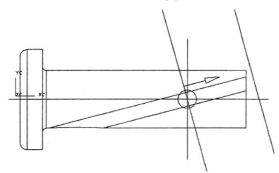

Step 5. Choose **OK** to accept the default trim direction. The resulting model looks like the below figure. Click **Cancel** to exit the trim operation.

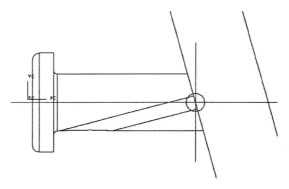

Step 6. Edit the trim body (the angled datum plane) by changing its angle from –15 to –45.

    6.1. Choose **Edit →Feature → Parameters** and select in the feature list **Datum_Plane (8)**, which is the trim body. (Alternatively, you can select it in the graphic screen).

    6.2. Choose **OK.** The **Datum Plane** dialogue appears. Key in **–45** in the **Angle** field.

    6.3. Choose **OK** twice. The trim body has been updated, which affects the trimmed solid pin because of the associativity between the angled datum plane for the trim body and the pin for the target body.

Step 7. Save and close the file.

11.3 Thread

This feature operation creates threads on features with cylindrical faces. These features include holes, cylinders, bosses, and subtractive or additive sweeps of circular curves. Some key parameters of threads are shown in the following figure.

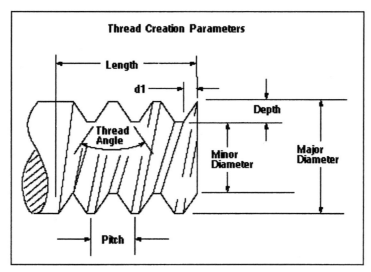

Threads can be right-handed or left-handed. A right-handed thread winds in a clockwise while a left-handed thread winds in a counterclockwise direction. This is illustrated by the following figure.

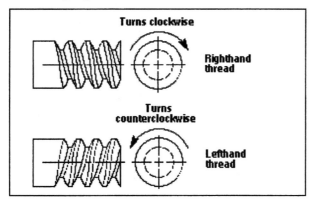

This feature operation can create two different types of threads: symbolic and detailed. Symbolic threads are displayed as a dashed circle on the face or faces that will be threaded. Symbolic threads use external thread table files, which you can customize for your specific thread requirements, to determine default parameters. Symbolic threads cannot be copied or instanced once created, but you can create multiple and instanced copies at creation time. See the figure below for examples of symbolic threads.

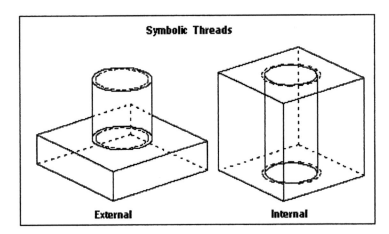

Symbolic Threads

External   Internal

Detailed threads look more realistic but also take considerably longer to create and update because of their complex geometry and display. Detailed threads use embedded tables for the default parameters. The tables that are provided in the thd_english.dat and thd_metric.dat files are from one industry standard: Machinery's Handbook, 25th edition, 1996, published by Industrial Press Inc. There are other industry standards[1] and you can modify these tables as required. Detailed threads must be created one at a time, but can be copied or instanced after creation. Detailed threads are fully associative; if the feature is modified, its thread updates accordingly. This is not true for symbolic threads. See the figure below for an example.

Detailed Thread

There are certain guidelines to follow for creation of threads.

- You can only create threads on previously unthreaded cylindrical faces.

---

[1] Engineering Design Communication by S.D. Lockhart and C.M. Johnson, 2000, Prentice Hall, Inc.

- If the cylindrical face has only one available planar end, it will be used as the start of the thread.

- If a cylindrical face has two planar (flat) ends that could be the start of the thread, your pick location will indicate the starting location and direction of the thread as illustrated below.

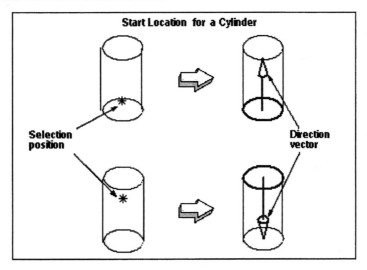

- If the selected cylinder has been united to a larger body, a non-united end is the start for the thread (see the figure below). If the other body is smaller than the selected cylinder, the end closest to the selection position will be the start face.

- The selected cylinder must have planar ends. If the system cannot find a planar end to be used as the start face of the thread, you must select a start face that is planar (for example, a datum plane).

Procedure to create threads

At the Modeling application, choose **Insert→Feature Operation→Thread** or the Thread icon . The thread creation dialogue appears. Different options are available depending on whether you choose a Symbolic or Detailed thread.

To create symbolic threads:

1. Choose **Symbolic** at the top of the dialogue.
2. Choose the thread manufacturing **Method**. Four manufacturing methods are available. They are Cut, Rolled, Ground, and Milled.
3. Choose the **Form** for the thread. This determines which lookup table is used to obtain the parameter defaults. Examples of Form options are Unified, Metric, and Acme.

4. Select one or more cylindrical placement faces. Based on Form and on the first selected face, default values for **Major Diameter**, **Minor Diameter**, **Pitch**, **Angle**, **Length**, and **Shaft Size** (for external threads) or **Tapped Drill Size** (for internal threads) appear. Most of the parameters that were grayed out are now active. If you do not want default values to be supplied from a lookup table, choose **Manual Input** and enter the parameters. **Number of Starts** specifies whether this is a single thread or multiple threads.

5. Modify the parameters as desired. (Some parameters, such as Callout, cannot be modified directly.)

6. **Callout** references the thread table entry that provides the default values. **Choose from Table** lets you choose a different entry (and, therefore, a different set of default values). If you edit the parameters manually, Callout grays out to indicate that the current parameters do not come directly from a table.

7. Choose **Tapered** if you want the thread to be tapered.

8. If you want the thread to update when the cylinder changes, choose **Full Thread**. (**Length** grays out.)

9. If a selected face belongs to an instance array, you can apply the thread to the other instances by choosing **Include Instances**.

10. Decide how you want the **rotation** of the thread to be, either a **Right Hand** or a **Left Hand** thread.

11. Choose **Select Start** if you want to specify a new **starting location** for the thread, and select a planar face on a solid body, or a datum plane.

12. Choose **OK or Apply**. With **Apply** you can continue to create more threads.

To create detailed threads:

1. Choose **Detailed** for the Thread Type. The following shortened dialogue appears.

2. Select a cylindrical placement face. Default parameter values appear, based on the diameter of the face.

3. Modify the parameters if required.

4. Choose **OK or Apply**.

Activity 11-6. Creating a thread

In this activity, you will practice creating two threads.

Step 1. **Open activity11-6.prt** and save it as *****_activity11-6.prt**.

Step 2. At the **Modeling** application, choose **Insert → Feature Operation→Thread** or the **Thread** icon . The thread dialogue opens.

Step 3. Choose **Detailed** for the thread type.

Step 4. Select the cylindrical face of the pin shaft. Default values of thread parameters appear with the thread direction vector.

Choose **OK** to create a thread on the entire pin shaft.

Step 5. **Undo** Step 4 by pressing two keys Ctrl + z at the same time.

Step 6. Choose **Insert → Feature Operation → Thread** or the **Thread** icon . Select the same cylindrical face of the pin shaft. Default parameter values appear.

Step 7. Specify a new start face that will be used to create a thread on the partial cylindrical face of the pin shaft.

    7.1. Choose button "**Select Start**" at the bottom of the thread dialogue.

    7.2. Select the datum plane indicated below.

    7.3. Choose **OK** to accept the default thread axis direction.

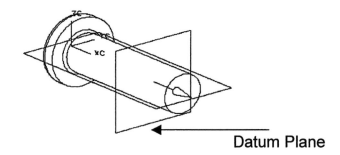

Datum Plane

7.4. Choose **OK** to create the thread.

Step 8. Edit the datum plane used in Step 7 to change the offset distance, and observe how the thread feature changes. This changes only the thread starting location, but not the length of the thread. If you want to change the length of the thread, you need to edit its parameter value on the thread dialogue.

Step 9. **Save and close** the file.

Project 11-1. Ratchet

Model the ratchet part using the drawings (in inches) below and save it as
***_project11-1.prt in your directory.

Hint: You may start with a cylinder. In order to create a gear tooth, you can create a sketch, extrude it, and subtract it from the cylinder. And then you can instance it to create all the gear teeth.

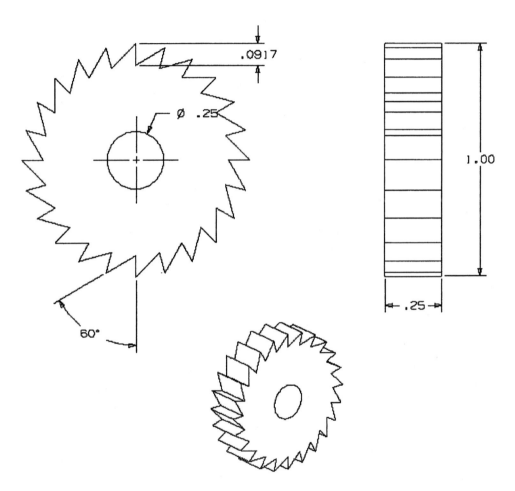

Project 11-2. Protector

Model the protector part using the drawings (in inches) below and save it as

***_project11-2.prt** in your directory.

Hint: You may find it useful to use features like rectangular array and mirror body.

Project 11-3. Shelf Stud

Model the shelf stud part using the drawings (in inches) below and save it as
***_project11-3.prt** in your directory.

Hint: You may find it useful to use features like trim body and circular instance.

Project 11-4. Flat Screw

Model the flat screw part shown below. The flat screw consists of two parts, head and shaft. The screw head has a cross-shaped slot for a tool. As you model it, capture the following design intent into your model:

Top diameter of screw head = base diameter of screw head + .75

Shaft diameter = base diameter of screw head

Shaft height (including the non-threaded angled tip)

= 5 times height of screw head

The slots are centered on the screw head and its dimensions are

Length = base diameter of screw head

Width = length / 5

Depth = height of screw head / 2

The initial dimensions of the screw are given as shown in the drawings (in inches) below. As for the parameter values for the detailed thread, use the default values provided by the system. After you finish modeling the part, change the values of the key design variables such as screw head diameter (its current value shown as 2) and observe the model update to confirm if the design intent is met. Save the part file as ***_project11-4.prt in your directory.

Hint: Create expressions with meaningful names to capture the design intent. You may need to create a datum plane to indicate the start face for the thread.

Ø 2.750

2.000

.400

R .050
for all corner and floor radii

2.000

.375

.750

use default parameter
values for thread

90°

11-41

Exercise Problems

11.1 What are the advantages of using Instance?

11.2 Give four options of Instance.

11.3 What is the major difference between Mirror Body and Mirror Feature?

11.4 Rectangular Array Instance can create instances of a feature in XC and YC directions. What coordinate system is used for this purpose?

11.5 In creating Circular Array Instance, there are two options Point & Direction or Datum Axis to establish the rotation axis. What is a major difference between the two?

11.6 When do you use Trim Body?

11.7 What is the advantage of using datum planes as a trimming object over other options such as define plane?

11.8 Describe differences between symbolic and detailed threads.

Chapter 12. Introduction to Assembly Modeling

In this chapter, we will present an introduction to the Unigraphics assembly modeling. Assembly modeling has significant importance in using Unigraphics to fully and efficiently get the most out of Unigraphics' capability. The fundamentals of assembly modeling included in this chapter are discussed in the seven sections. Sections 12.1 and 12.2 provide an overview and definitions of the assembly modeling and terms. Section 12.3 teaches how to build the assembly using the Bottom Up method. Section 12.4 introduces the Assembly Navigator Tool. Section 12.5 teaches how to build an assembly using the Top Down method, along with how to design in context. Also introduced in Section 12.5 are Interpart Modeling and the Wave Geometry Linker to associate a part in the assembly to another part in the assembly using geometry. Section 12.6 refines the assembly process by using reference sets to filter out objects that are not wanted in the assembly.   Section 12.7 introduces Mating Conditions tools to allow associating parts in the assembly in a way to insure that parts that mate together stay together.

12.1   What is Unigraphics Assemblies?

Assemblies are what you see in every day life, that you use in every day life, which someone puts together so we can use it. They include a bicycle, an electric razor, a car, a telephone, and computers, etc. All these products have in common that they are made up of parts that someone designed, fit together, manufactured and put on the market for sale. An important aspect of this is that the individual piece parts have to fit together very well and work together. The designer, or designers, that create the parts have to coordinate individual parts so that all parts fit and function together.

Unigraphics assemblies is a part file that contains the individual piece parts added to the part file in such a way that the parts are virtual in the assembly and linked to the original part. All parts are selectable and able to be used in the design process for information and mating to insure a perfect fit as intended by the designers. We will elaborate this concept in this chapter.

Unigraphics assembly modeling is the tool that allows and facilitates the collaboration among designers, draftsmen, analysis people, manufacturing people, and others, to insure their assembly works together. This enables individuals in different disciplines to work concurrently, resulting in faster delivery to market for products. This concept is related to master modeling that will be discussed in detail in Chapter 13.

12.2   Unigraphics Assemblies Definitions and Terminology

Assemblies introduce several new terms, a few of which are defined below. It is recommended that you become familiar with these terms as you continue in this chapter.

Unigraphics Assembly

A Unigraphics part file containing virtual copies of piece parts and sub-assemblies represented by pointers to the original parts. These pointers are called component objects.

Component Objects

A component object is the pointer residing in the assembly part file that links to the original part file. The pointer contains the information of the part file name, location in the assembly space and its orientation in assembly space.

Component Part

A component part is the name given to the original part file. This is to distinguish the component object that resides in the assembly part file from the original part that resides in a file outside the assembly. When Master Model methods are implemented (Chapter 13), the component part will also be the master model part.

Sub-Assembly

This is a unique Unigraphics part file in that it is a component object when it resides in an assembly part file, but it is also a part file itself because it contains component objects that reside in it. A sub-assembly resides both in an assembly part file and outside the assembly part file.

The following diagram illustrates the concepts of an assembly part file, a sub-assembly part, and five component parts. Note that five component parts are represented outside the sub-assembly and assembly part files, corresponding to the leaves of the hierarchy tree. The component objects reside in the sub-assembly and assembly part files. The assembly part file corresponds to the root of the tree.

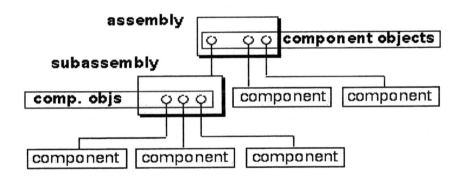

Top-Down Modeling

The assembly part file is created first and component objects and component parts are created in the assembly part file. This type of modeling is useful in new design.

Bottom-Up Modeling

The components parts are created first in the traditional way and then added to the assembly part file. This technique is particularly useful when parts already exist from the previous designs and are being re-used.

Work Part

The work part is the component part where all creating and editing of geometry is stored. The header of the graphics window displays the part file name that is the work part.

Displayed Part

The displayed part is the part(s) that is seen (visible) in the graphics window. In the case of a component part file, the displayed part and the work part will be the same part. In the case of an assembly part file, the displayed part and the work part may or may not be the same. The assembly part file when opened typically becomes both the displayed part and the work part. When top-down modeling is used to create a component part, the work part is changed to the component so that all creation is stored in the component part. In general, whenever creating or editing is done on a component in the assembly, the work part must be changed to the component being worked on.

Design in Context

The ability to make a component of an assembly the work part while leaving the assembly itself as the displayed part allows the assembly to be designed in context. All new geometry that is created is added to the work part. Edits can be made to the features and expressions that reside within the work part while all the assembly is displayed in the graphic window.

Mating Condition

Mating conditions are a set of constraints between component objects that describe how the objects fit together (i.e., mate together). Collectively, they describe a position of an object in space relative to another object as defined by the designer.

Reference Set

A reference set is a filter created and stored in a part file that determines which geometry is displayed in a higher-level assembly part file. A common use is to create a filter such that only the solid body is added to the assembly part file and all sketches and datum remain solely in the component part file. However, reference sets may be created in any part file.

Bottom Up Design

A Bottom-Up assembly modeling approach starts by identifying the lowest level piece parts that will make up your assembly, and by creating component parts and subassemblies as you move up the assembly level hierarchy.

The component parts are designed and modeled separately from an assembly level part file.

support base—component part   **support angle—component part**

wheel support assembly

The support base and the support angle were created first and then added to the wheel support assembly. Notice the second support angle had to be repositioned when it was added. Later components to be added are bolts, nuts and the wheel mechanism.

Bottom-Up Modeling--Add a Component

After entering the Assemblies application, to add component parts to an assembly use the Assembly pull-down menu and choose Components, which then brings up the cascade menu shown.

This menu is used to create, edit, and manipulate the assembly structure.

To create an assembly by the bottom-up method, choose the Add Existing command from cascade menu. This starts the Select Part dialog to select the component part to be added to the assembly.

The Select Part dialog allows you to select a part that has already been loaded as shown by the parts listed in the open window; or, you may browse for a part in a directory by selecting Choose Part File. With click of OK after selecting a part, you will be prompted with Add Existing Part dialog to allow the setting of several parameters about the component object.

- The component object may be named. It defaults to the component part name.
- The reference set may be chosen to bring to the assembly. We'll discuss this option later.
- Multiple copies of the part may be added by using an array or chain selecting thus speeding the placement of many components.
- How to position the component objects may be chosen now with available choices:
  - Reposition – place and orient the parts in one prompting sequence
  - Mate – Use Mating Conditions to locate parts relative to each other in a locked relationship
  - Absolute – Locate at the Absolute Coordinate System
- The layer of the assembly part file on which the component object resides may be chosen: Work Layer (current work layer of the assembly part file), Original layer (the same layers used in the component part file), or a layer to be specified by a user.

For this discussion you accept the default settings of these options except positioning the component object with the repositioning option. The system asks for a location point to be selected from the Point Constructor dialog and the part is placed in the graphic area at the point selected. Then the Reposition Component dialog comes up.

Choose the reposition method and orient the part exactly where you want it using one or a combination of the five Transformation options that are available.

Once the part is placed exactly where you want it you end the repositioning with OK and UG prompts to Add another component object of the same component part. If done, then choose Cancel.

Repositioning a Component

There are six repositioning methods on the dialog. One will be used later in the lesson and discussed in detail. Here is a brief description of each.

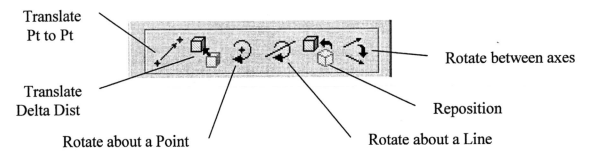

Translate Pt to Pt

Translate Delta Dist

Rotate about a Point

Rotate about a Line

Reposition

Rotate between axes

Translate—Allows movement of the component from one point to another. The orientation of the part stays the same. The points may be defined by selecting a Reference Point and a Destination Point, or by entering Delta distances in the XC, YC, and/or ZC direction.

Rotate about a Point—Allows rotation about a single point in the XC-YC plane. The ZC axis is parallel to the axis of rotation. The direction of rotation follows the right-hand rule—counterclockwise.

Rotate about a Line—Allows rotation about a line that you select. Line may be in any orientation. The line may be chosen from an existing line, edge, two points, or a point and vector. The direction of rotation follows the right-hand rule about the end point of the line chosen.

Reposition—Allows free relocation of the part from a Reference orientation to a Destination orientation with complete freedom of orientation and location.

Rotate between Axes—Allows rotation about a selected point with the angle of rotation defined by selecting two axes.

Activity 12-1. Creating an Assembly Bottom-Up

This activity helps to practice building an assembly bottom-up. You will complete the assembly from the previous picture

by adding the wheel and axle parts and the bolts and nuts.

shoulder_screw.prt   washer.prt   hex_nut.prt

bushing.prt   hex_screw.prt   wheel.prt

Step 1. To create the assembly bottom-up design, open the assembly **wheel_support_assm.prt** and save it as **xxx_wheel_support_assm.prt.** Start the Modeling Application then start the Assemblies Application.

Step 2. Add the 4 hex_screws to the assembly.

    2.1.   Choose **Assemblies → Components → Add Existing**.

The **Select Part** dialog comes up.

    2.2.   Select the **Choose Part File** button.

    2.3.   Choose the **hex_screw.prt** from the **Part Name** window and choose **OK**. The next window to come up is the **Add Existing Part** dialog.

    2.4.   Change the **Positioning** to **Reposition** and the **Layer Options** to **Work**.

    2.5.   Choose **OK**. The **Point Constructor** window comes up, asking for a point to locate the placement of the screw.

    2.6.   Choose a point in space close to the assembly.

The screw is drawn on the screen. Note it is oriented wrong to go into the holes in the angle and base. We must reposition the screw so it is oriented vertically. The **Reposition Component** dialog now comes up ready for you to choose a reposition method to locate the screw into the bolt hole in the angle.

    2.7.   Choose the fifth option **Reposition** because we want the base of the hex head to lie on the top face of the support angle. Next the CSYS Constructor dialog appears. Unigraphics prompts first to select the object to define the "from csys". A from" position plane is required to be selected. We want to move "from" the current position of the current screw location to the "to" plane resting on the angle.

    2.8.   Choose the option **CSYS of Object** for the "from" CSYS.

    2.9.   Choose the arc edge at the base of the hex head as the **"from CSYS"** and choose **OK**.

    2.10.   The Cue Line is prompting now to select the "to csys. Use the option **CSYS of Object** for the "to CSYS" and choose the top circle edge of one of the holes in the angle that mates the base. Choose **OK**.

As soon as the "to" circle is chosen, the screw moves to the hole in the angle. See the figure below for the proper circles to be chosen. Choose **OK** to confirm.

Reference Arc plane   Destination Arc plane

The Add Existing Part dialog returns now to allow the adding of additional screw components.

    2.11. **Add** the additional screws (total four hex screws) to the assembly.

Step 3. **Save** the file.

Project 12-1. Bottom-Up Assembly Modeling

Open **xxx_wheel_support_assm.prt** that you created and saved in Activity 12-1, if it is not open. Using the similar procedure of adding a component to an assembly part file as in Activity 12.1, finish the assembly that looks like below. To do so, you need to add two bushings, two washers, one hex_nut, one shoulder_screw, and one wheel. Refer to p.12-10 for the drawings of these parts. Save your file as xxx_project12-1.prt.

Hint: In order to position the wheel correctly, i.e., center it between the two walls of the support angle part, you may have to use **Analysis → Distance**.

12.4 The Assembly Navigator Tool

The Assembly Navigator Tool provides a graphical display of the assembly structure (hierarchy) of the components within an assembly, and a quick and easy method to manipulate the components in an assembly.

The Assembly Navigator window for the Wheel Support Assembly is shown below.

The window comes up as a stand-alone window and stays up until dismissed. The graphical display shows the current assembly as the work part with the hierarchy of component objects shown indented in a list below it—the assembly tree. There is an item in the list for each component, including multiple copies of the same component, displayed as a node in the assembly tree structure.

To open the Assembly Navigation Tool (ANT), choose the Assembly Navigator icon or choose from the pull-down menu **View → Assembly Navigator**.

The ANT is useful as a shortcut for many component operations without going through the menu structure. With ANT, you can also verify the assembly structure and the presence of components.

By selecting one of the components, several options are available. First, the component selected will be highlighted in the graphic view for quick identification of the component visually. In addition, using MB3 mouse button will bring up the pop-up menu with additional options and operations that may be done. We will just highlight some options here. The pop-up menu looks like this.

Notice some of the operations available on the pop-up, which are also available elsewhere in the menus.

Blank—the usual Blank, same as **Edit → Blank → Blank**.

Make Work Part—Changes the component to the Work part so creating and designing of additional geometry can be stored in the component part. The other parts in the assembly will still be visible and selectable, but grayed out as in the background. This is the configuration for how Design in Context would be done.

Make Displayed Part—Changes the component to the Work Part and the Displayed part. It is the same as working in the component part file with no surrounding parts.

Display Parent—Changes the displayed part to any part files that are parent assemblies of the component. It is the way to return to the assembly if the Make Displayed Part had been invoked.

Replace Reference Set—Changes the reference set displayed in the assembly. We will discuss reference sets in a later section.

Open/Close—Allows the opening or closing of part files, same as the File → Open/Close menu does.

Properties—This option supplies component related information related to non-graphical attributes and physical attributes.

12.5   Top-Down Design

In Top-Down design, you create an assembly at the top level of the hierarchy and move down the hierarchy, creating subassemblies and component parts. Thus, Top-Down assembly modeling presupposes that you will be "designing in context", creating new component parts relative to other components, i.e., building parts around other parts.

An "assembly" part file is just another Unigraphics part file. One main difference between regular part files and assembly part files are that component objects reside in assembly part files. But Unigraphics does not treat an assembly file as a different kind of part file but as just a regular part file. So creating and editing done in the assembly part file may be done as in any part file. The Work Part and Displayed Part become even more important when creating and editing of geometry, and creating component objects because all creating still goes into the Work Part whether the Work Part is the assembly or a component part.

There are two basic methods used to create a component object top-down.

Method One:

Create component objects first (Work Part is the assembly).

Make a component object the Work Part.

Create geometry in the component part that is now the work part.

Method Two

Create geometry in the assembly part (Work Part is the assembly).

Create a new component and add the geometry to it.

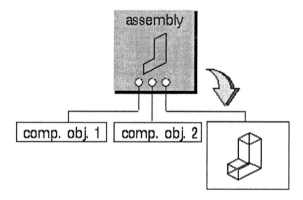

Note that for both methods described above, both geometry and the component object must be created. It makes no difference which is done first; and the methods may be mixed depending on the design needs, what information you have available for the design criteria and design intent, and other constraints you may have.

In practice, the Top-Down and Bottom-Up approaches will be mixed as you use existing parts and new parts in order to meet your design needs.

Creating a New Component

The steps to create a new component will be shown here and then an activity to practice to reinforce the concepts will follow. We will create the component object and then add geometry to it by working in the context of the assembly and using surrounding parts.

Select the pull down dialog **Assemblies → Components → Create New**

Choosing the Create New button creates a new component. Note that the current Work Part is the assembly part file.

The **Class Selection** dialog comes up to allow the selection of geometry to be added to the new component when created (Method Two). If Method One is being used and geometry will be created in the component with the component as the work part, then accept the class selection dialog without picking any geometry by choosing OK.

The **Part Name** dialog comes up to name the component part file, so type in a name. After the component part file name has been defined, you may define information related to the new component object in the **Create New Component** dialog.

Similar to the Bottom-Up method, you have the opportunity to specify some parameters of the component object: component name, a reference set, what layer the geometry will be created on, and the orientation and location in space of the component part geometry.

Enter the appropriate information in this dialog, or leave the default values, and when complete choose **OK**. If using Method One, then the normal procedure would be to make the new component the work part and start constructing geometry. An activity follows below to practice these concepts.

Activity 12-2. Creating an Assembly Top-Down

In this activity, you will add an existing component to the assembly. You will then create a new component in the assembly and add geometry to it by working in context of the assembly.

Note: You will be unable to complete this section unless interpart modeling is turned on in the customer defaults file. If you have problems, see your instructor or system administrator.

Step 1. Create a new file **xxx_fix_assm.prt** and save it in your specified directory. This empty part will be used as the assembly. Several components will be added to this assembly.

Step 2. Add the part **fix_baseplate.prt** from the **fixture** subdirectory to the origin of the assembly.

Hint: Choose **Assemblies → Component → Add Existing**.

Assembly Navigator Tool

The first method to create components in an assembly is to create the empty component part then add the geometry to it.

Step 3. Choose **Create New** in the Components cascade menu.

Next the **Class Selection** dialog displays. This is where you are prompted to select the geometry you want to add to the new component.

Step 4. Choose **OK** to create the component without adding any geometry to it. The **Part Name** dialog prompts you to enter the directory path and the component part filename that will be used when the component is saved. Specify the directory path and enter **xxx_fix_locpin** as the new component part name.

Step 5. The **Create New Component** dialog comes up to name the component, create a reference set, positioning and layer to create the part on.

Choose Work layer and choose **OK**.

Creating Linked Components

The next step is to create the geometry in the new component. There are two ways you can do this: if you want unlinked geometry, you can simply model new geometry in the new component. On the other hand, if you want the new component linked to geometry in some other component, you can link geometry from one component to the other.

There are complications to the creating of geometry within the assembly. That is, that not all creation methods are available directly. You can create a primitive and create the size of the primitive by selecting points on other parts within the assembly; however, you cannot extrude a solid by picking edges, curves or sketches on other parts.

The implications of this are that for unlinked geometry you create the component completely within itself without referencing other geometry. The component is the work part and all objects and features are within it. If you want to create geometry that references geometry on other parts (i.e., an outline as a sketch of another part, a hole of another part as the diameter of a new hole of the current work part, or a hole of another part as the positioning location for a new hole) then you <u>must</u> link the new geometry of the current work part to the existing geometry of other parts that you want to reference.   The **Wave Geometry Linker** is the tool that is used to create the link between existing geometry and the new geometry in the work part that is to be created.

To use the WAVE Geometry Linker, **Assemblies_AllowInterPart: yes** must be set in the customer default files **UG_english.def** and **UG_metric.def**. If you cannot access the Geometry Linker, contact your instructor or system administrator.

The link that is created using the Geometry Linker is a feature of the work part. The linked geometry is associative to the parent geometry from which they were selected so that when the parent geometry is changed the linked geometry will be updated and be changed also. In turn, the solid that was made from the linked geometry will be updated and changed also.

Interpart Modeling

Interpart Modeling is another term given to describe the designing in context in an assembly when modeling in a work part and selecting geometry in other parts to use as reference for creating and positioning new geometry.

Different types of objects may be selected to use as linked geometry: points, curves, sketches, datums, faces, regions of faces, bodies, and mirrored bodies. We will only include a few of these for illustration.

There are some considerations and caveats to consider when choosing to use the Geometry Linker:

- Consider the permanence of the geometry chosen, like selecting a single curve versus selecting a whole sketch. A single curve might be deleted and break the link, but a curve in a sketch could be deleted, replace with another curve and the link and updating would still be intact.

- The Geometry Linker should only be used when the parts have a strong physical constraint relative to an adjoining part and the parts will be used in the same assembly. This means that you really need parts to be related such that if a parent changes, the children need to update.
- The Geometry Linker should not be used just because you can. The link creates another level of complication and could have downstream impacts.

We will now go back to our activity and create the geometry for the locator pin using the Geometry Linker. Be sure to pay attention to the steps and the reason for each step as the pin and subsequent parts are created.

Activity 12-2. (continued)

In the previous step we created the component **xxx_fix_locpin** with no geometry in it. Now with Linking discussed we will create geometry in **xxx_fix_locpin** using a hole from the baseplate as reference. Here are the steps to do it.

Step 6. Using the **ANT** window, highlight **xxx_fix_locpin** from the list of parts, and punch **MB3** and slide down to and choose **Make Work Part**. This makes **xxx_fix_locpin** the work part. Confirm this by reading the banner line of UG window above the menu line, which should say "Displayed Part: **xxx_fix_assm.prt** Work Part: **xxx_fix_locpin.prt**". Also notice that the currently displayed part, the baseplate geometry, turned gray.

Below is a picture of our goal in designing the pin.

.50

2.0

.750

Circle in <u>baseplate</u> will be used to create bottom part of the locator pin.

Determined by hole in baseplate

The first step is to create the link with the geometry that will be needed.

Step 7. Choose **Assemblies → Wave Geometry Linker**
The Geometry Linker dialog appears with the options for selecting the type of objects to be selected at the top of the dialog.

We will use an arc in the baseplate to create the link, therefore the Curves option (the second icon of the first row) is used to create our pin.

Step 8. Select the top edge of the hole highlighted in the previous picture of the baseplate. Choose **OK**.

Step 9. Construct the lower part of the locator pin.

    9.1. Choose the **Extrude** icon.

    9.2. Choose the **Curve** option on the dialog.

    9.3. Select the top curve of the hole again, and then **OK** to accept the selection.

    9.4. **OK** to close out the selection list dialog.

    9.5. Choose the Direction_Distance option.

    9.6. Use Flip Default Direction, if necessary, to make sure that the directional vector points down (**-ZC**). Choose **OK** to accept the direction.

    9.7. Key in .75 for the **End Distance**, then **OK**. Cancel the Extrude dialog.

Step 10. That completes the bottom portion of the pin, now put a top on it.

    10.1. Choose the **boss** icon.

    10.2. Choose the top face of the pin just created as the placement face.

    10.3. Enter the Diameter to .5 and the Height to 2, then **OK**.

    10.4. Position the boss with point onto point using the arc center of the hole.

    10.5. **Cancel** from the dialog.

The locator pin is created and its lower diameter is linked to the hole in the baseplate.

Step 12. The entire assembly must be saved to save the creation in the assembly and to save the component part file in the directory. Change the work part to **xxx_fix_assm.prt** by choosing **Assemblies** → **Change Work Part** and select **xxx_fix_assm,** and then save the file.

That completes this activity.

Activity 12-3. Checking Linkage between components

In this activity, we will check the linkage between the two components added in the assembly file, **xxx_fix_assm.prt**. We will do so by changing the diameter of the hole in the baseplate and observing its effect on the location pin.

Step 1. Change the baseplate to be the Work Part.

Step 2. Choose **Edit → Feature → Parameter...** from the main menu.

   or

   Choose the **Edit Feature Parameters** icon .

The Edit Parameters dialog comes up with the list of features in the work part.

Step 3. Choose **Simple Hole(1)** from the list or select it from the graphics area, then **OK** to accept.

Step 4. The **Edit Parameters** dialog changes to show a list of options, select the **Feature Dialog** option.

Step 5. The **Edit Parameters** dialog changes again to show the current diameter of 0.375. Key in 0.1 in the dialog, and then **OK** to accept the new diameter.

Choose **OK** again to accept the options dialog.

Finally, choose **Apply** in the **Edit Parameters** dialog with the list of features.

Note that we choose Apply in this case because we want to keep this dialog here so we can use it again to change the diameter back to its original value.

Notice that both the hole (baseplate) and the lower cylinder of the locator pin are modified. This is because of the linkage between the baseplate hole and the locator pin.

Step 6. Use the **Edit Parameters** procedure again to change the diameter of the hole back to .375.

Notice now that the hole in the baseplate and the diameter of the pin went back to their original design. If you are not sure, then use **Information→ Object** and pick the hole to verify the sizes.

Project 12-2. Add Another Locator Pin

Add the second locator pin as shown in the below figure. You can do this by taking two approaches and we suggest you to try both. The first approach is to add it using the already existing part, **xxx_fix_locpin.prt.** The second approach is to create a new component **xxx_fix_locpin2.prt** and add necessary geometry to it using the Wave Geometry Linker. Name the resulting two assembly files **xxx_project12-2_assm.prt** and **xxx_project12-2_assm2.prt**.

12.6   Reference Sets

A reference set is a tool used to control what portions of a component part are loaded into an assembly. The reference set is a named grouping of objects and features contained in the component part file that will be loaded into the assembly part file. Objects not in the reference set are not loaded to the assembly.

When the Add Existing component command is used in an assembly from the cascade menu, it implies to load the component part entirely into the assembly— every piece of the component. A reference set is a method to filter out the unwanted features and objects.

Examples of the unwanted features and objects in a component part are the datum planes, datum axes, sketches, and other construction geometry that may have been created first in order to create solid body representing the part.   We will use the previous example of the wheel support assembly for illustration.

The earlier figures of the wheel support assembly showed only the solid models because we had manipulated the layers so that all the non-solid objects do not appear in the assembly. However, on a large assembly with many parts this might be very difficult to do and the assembly part file would be much larger as well. Changing layers would require finding all non-solid objects and making their layers invisible so that only the solid is visible. The reference set is an easier and more flexible method than layer manipulation in controlling visibility of objects of various components in the assembly. A reference set is created in the component part file and contains only the geometry that is desired in the assembly file such that the part looks like this.

Operations of Reference Sets

Choose **Assemblies → Reference Sets...**

The **Reference Sets** dialog has options for Create, Delete, Rename, Edit Attributes, and Information of reference sets in the current work part. The dialog also contains options to Add and Remove objects to the reference set. And the reference set may contain Attribute information also. The list of reference sets is shown in the window.

A reference set may contain the following data:

- Name, Orientation, and Origin
- Geometry, Datum Planes and Axes, Coordinate Systems and Component Objects
- Attributes (non-geometric data used for a parts list)

In the assembly, every component contains two reference sets by default:

- **Empty** (no geometry, component part is not visible in the assembly)
- **Entire Part** (this is the default condition, contains all geometry, datums, sketches, etc)

Creating Reference Sets

There are three situations where the reference set can be created:

- In the component part file
- In the assembly when the component is the work part
- In the assembly at the time the component part is created

Which one to use is your choice depending on the design circumstances.

The name of the reference set must follow these rules:

- It must be 30 characters or less; characters after 30 will be truncated
- It must have no imbedded spaces
- The name is not case sensitive. All names are converted to upper case no matter what is entered in typing.

Activity 12-4. Creating Reference Sets

In this activity we will create a reference set called Body to represent just a solid body and filter out non-solid objects. We will use the completed **Wheel Support Assembly** to illustrate how to create reference sets in some of the components in the assembly and then how to replace the existing **Entire Part** reference set with the **BODY** reference set.

Step 1. Open Support_Assembly.prt from the Support directory and save it as **xxx_activity12-4.prt**. Start the **Modeling** application and start **Assemblies** application.

Step 2. Open the **Assembly Navigation Tool.** Drag the window to a location where the geometry is visible.

Step 3. Create a reference set in the support_angle.

  3.1. In the **ANT**, select the support_angle, use **MB3** and choose **Make Displayed Part** from the pop-up window.

Note that the assembly disappears from the graphic area and the angle becomes the displayed part. In fact, notice it also becomes the work part.

  3.2. Choose **Assemblies → Reference Sets…**
  3.3. Choose **Create** button in the **Reference Set** dialog.

3.4. Type **body** as the reference set name and choose **OK**

3.5. Select the solid body of the angle in the graphics area, and choose **OK** to complete the selection of objects in this reference set and to dismiss the Class Selection menu. (Insure the selection by reading the status line, which must say "Solid Body selected".)

3.6. Choose **Cancel** from the **Reference Set** dialog window to dismiss the window because we are not creating another reference set in this component.

Verify the reference set was created.

3.7. Choose **Information → Assemblies → Reference Set**

3.8. The reference set name **BODY** is displayed in the window and may be selected to obtain more information about the reference set.

3.9. Choose **Save** from the main menu to save the reference set in the part.

3.10. In the **ANT**, select the support_angle, use **MB3** to pop-up the window and select **Display Parent** and choose the **xxx_activity12-4**. (You may or may not change the Work Part at this time—not necessary.)

Note the displayed assembly does not reflect the new reference set immediately. We must replace the reference set in the angle.

Step 4. Replace the Reference Set in the assembly

4.1. In the **ANT**, select the support_angle in which you created the reference set.

4.2. Using **MB3** on the mouse, choose **Replace Reference Set** and slide to the **BODY** reference set listed. Release the button and the reference set in the assembly is replaced with the new **BODY** reference set.

4.3. The display is immediately updated to reflect the change. The datum planes and axes disappear and a sketch disappears.

Select the other angle component, and check its Reference Set:

MB3 → **Replace Reference Set** → **BODY**

Because the other component uses the same component part file, it added the new reference set **BODY** to both components. The other component still must be updated in the assembly.

Step 5. Create a new Reference Set in the hex_screw.

    5.1. In the **ANT**, select the hex_screw, use **MB3** and choose **Make Displayed Part** from the pop-up window.

    5.2. Choose **Assemblies** → **Reference Sets…**

    5.3. Choose **Create** button in the Create Reference Set dialog.

    5.4. Type **body** as the reference set name and choose **OK**

    5.5. Select the solid body of the screw in the graphics area, and choose **OK**.

    5.6. Choose **Cancel** from the **Reference Set** dialog.

Verify the reference set was created using same method as before.

Step 6. Replace Reference Set to **BODY** in the hex_screw and **Save** part.

Step 7. Save the assembly.

Step 8. Create body reference sets in all other components and Replace Reference Sets with **BODY** and **Save** each part..

Step 9. **Save** the assembly when complete.

Other Benefits of Using Reference Sets

There are other uses for reference sets other than the one demonstrated here. These will be discussed in this section.

1. Representing Components with Simpler Geometry. Create a reference set called SIMPLE and place in it a simplified solid, or some wireframe representing the outline, or the centerline of tubing.

2. Components whose shape in the design state is different in the installed state. An example of this is a spring, which is designed in a nominal condition, then when installed it is either extended or compressed.

3. Right Hand and Left Hand Parts. Reference Sets may be used to control the use of left- and right-handed parts in an assembly. The solid is created in one configuration in a component part file, then use the Mirror Body command to create its mirror image. Therefore, left- and right-handed solids are created. Two reference sets are created: one named LH-BODY, with the appropriate solid added to it, and the other reference set named RH-BODY with its appropriate solid added to it.
The Mirror Body command is found in this sequence:
Insert → Feature Operations → Instance → Mirror Body

4. Taking forward particular geometry and data pertaining to a particular discipline, i.e., for Manufacturing, carrying forward the process planning sheets to cut a part starting with the raw stock and the intermediate stages to the finished product.

From this time on now it is expected that reference sets be used in any component in an assembly when appropriate.

12.7   Mating Conditions

At the heart of good, efficient assembly modeling is the ability to relate components in an assembly to each other in a parametric manner. The functionality of Mating Conditions allows the designer to relate components by location and orientation to each other.

By applying mating conditions to components in an assembly, you establish parametric, positional relationships between objects or features of two components. These relationships are called mating constraints. A set of constraints is established relating features of components together. We call this set of constraints a mating condition. Thus, a mating condition is made up of one or more mating constraints.

The method that we have used so far to locate components within an assembly is the Reposition option. This method generates a good-looking assembly, but it has limitations.

For example, in the Wheel Support Assembly, the screws that hold the angle to the base are merely positioned there. If the holes in the base were to be relocated, then the holes in the angles and the screws would no longer go through the holes in the base—a misalignment. By creating mating constraints between the holes in both parts and the screw, then any change in location of the holes in the base would move the other holes and screws accordingly.

Mating Conditions differ from the Interpart Modeling which we did earlier using the Wave Geometry Linker to link geometry in one component to geometry in another component. The purpose for the Geometry Linker is to define the size of geometry and to link that size in a component to the size in another component so that if the size changes in the first component, the size will change in the other component as well. It is true that with the Geometry Linker some mating has taken place, but it has limitations in defining relative position between components. Applying mating conditions allows more flexibility and handling of complex assemblies in this regard.

In general then,

1. We can say that the Geometry Linker is used to link geometry between components to define the size of geometry, and,
2. Mating Conditions are used to define the positioning of components relative to each other.

General Concepts of Mating Constraints

Mating constraints are applied to components when the positional relationship between the components is important and needs to be maintained even though changes are made to the components. So when a component in an assembly is moved to another location, then other components around it will move along accordingly in order to maintain the positional relationship imposed by mating constraints.

There are eight mating constraints that are available:

- Mate—planar objects selected to mate will be coplanar and face opposite each other, or a line that lies in a plane.

- Align—planar objects selected to align will be coplanar but planes will be in the same direction; centerlines of cylindrical objects will be in line with each other

- Angle—the objects chosen will have an angle constant between them.

- Parallel—objects selected will be parallel to each other

- Perpendicular—objects selected will be perpendicular to each other

- Center—objects will be centered between other objects, i.e., locating a cylinder along a slot and centering the cylinder in the slot

- Distance—establishing a +/- distance between two objects

- Tangent—establish a tangent relationship between two objects, one of which is curved: a free form surface, a circle, a sphere, a cylinder

These eight all have in common that they will control the movement and degrees of freedom of the component being moved in relation to another component. They will all use the terminology of moving a component FROM its current location to a destination TO position of another component that is stationary. Watch the Cue line for prompting about which state the system is ready to do.

When an object is selected in any of these constraints, the system is looking at the normal of the object: a planar object has a normal, a circle has a normal, and cylinders have a normal. Planar faces have normals, which point in the directions shown. When using the Mate constraint option, the faces would mate coplanar with the normals opposite each other. Notice that the highlighted planes are coplanar, the blocks are opposite each other and facing each other.

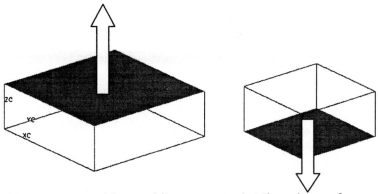

When the blocks are mated in an Align constraint the planar face normals are aligned in the same direction as noted in the figure below.

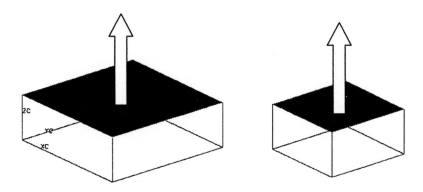

When the Align command is used for mating cylindrical shapes, select the cylindrical face. For example, select the faces of screw and bushing as shown below.

The outside face of the screw is aligned with the inside face of the bushing and the centerline vectors point in the same direction. This is analogous to aligning the centerlines of the two cylinders.

Mating Condition Dialog

This is the dialog to be used to establish mating conditions.

Mating constraints may be assigned using one of two available methods:

- Assignment on existing components within an assembly that is already configured. This is analogous to a bottom-up approach to assembly modeling.
- Assignment on components as they are added to an assembly. This is analogous to a top-down approach to assembly modeling.

You will be introduced to both methods. The instructional example in this lesson is an assembly that has some of the parts already assembled, but not mated and a few parts that need to be added to the assembly and mated at the same time.

The procedure to assign mating constraints is the same for all of the constraint types:

1. From the dialog, choose the type of constraint you want to apply.
2. From the dialog, choose the object selection filter type (optional).
3. UG prompts in the Cue line to select in the graphic area, an object in the component to be the FROM component (the component that is "moving").
4. UG prompts in the Cue line to select in the graphic area, an object in the component to the TO component (the component that is "stationary").
5. Choose Preview to see the component move in response to your constraint.
6. If satisfied, then choose Apply to actually apply the constraint.
7. If more constraints are to be added, then repeat steps 1-6.
8. When mating constraints are complete, choose OK to dismiss the dialog.

Activity 12-5. Create Mating Conditions

In this activity you will add a new component and mate that component as we add it to the assembly. You will use the same fixture assembly that you have already added two components into in the previous activity.

Step 1. Open part file **xxx_project12-2_assm.prt** from your directory and save it as **xxx_activity12-5.prt**.

To complete this simple assembly we need to add the locator blocks.

This component is not yet in the assembly, but resides as a piece part in the Fixture directory. As mentioned earlier, you can add the components to the assembly and constrain them with appropriate mating conditions at the same time. Note that the assembly should be the displayed part and the work part when the component is added to the assembly and when mating conditions are applied.

You will use the following mating constraints:

- Mate using the top face of the baseplate and bottom face of the locator
- Align using the holes in each part
- Align using the outside faces of the baseplate and the locator

The assembly should look like the figure below when you complete these steps.

Step 2. Choose **Assemblies → Components → Add Existing**.

Step 3. Click "Choose Part File" from the **Select Part** dialog and choose **locator.prt**, and select **OK**. The **Add Existing Part** dialog appears.

The **Add Existing Part** dialog now specifies the following:

- **Component name**: The component's name within the assembly will be 'LOCATOR'. The default assumes that the component's name will be the same as the part file name (note upper case), but it does not have to be!

- **Ref. Set**: All reference sets of locator are being added with the Entire Part as the default reference set. You can change the default by selecting **Change Ref. Set...**

- **Multiple add**: `Unchecked' is the default and since you are not adding multiple locators, this is appropriate.

- **Positioning**: This is where you will specify that you want to mate the component as it comes in. **Absolute** is the default, which brings in a component using absolute coordinates.

- **Layer options**: You may determine which layer of the assembly to bring in the part, or bring it on its Original layers as created.

Step 4. From the **Positioning** pulldown, choose **Mate** then choose **OK** to accept the options in the dialog.

The **Point Constructor** dialog appears. This is for specifying the location of the in-coming component in your assembly.

Step 5. Choose the **Cursor Location** icon (the second icon of the first row) and indicate a position for the new component away from the assembly in an empty place in the graphics area.

Note that the **Mating Conditions** dialog appears, ready for you to specify a mating constraint. First, you want to constrain the locator to the top face of the baseplate.

Step 6. Choose the **Mate** icon as the first mating constraint.

Step 7. Select the **Filter** pulldown and choose the Face option if necessary.

Although it is not necessary to specify a filter, it is a good habit since this makes it easy to select your intended type of geometry.

Notice that the From icon is activated on the Selection Steps menu and the Cue Line is prompting to select a FROM component.

Step 8. The **FROM** object is the locator so select the bottom face of the locator. If you have trouble selecting, wait for the select options cursor and identify your selection using the select options box.

Notice after the **FROM** selection, the system automatically is ready for the **TO** selection: the Selection Steps dialogue has progressed to the **TO** icon and the Cue Line is prompting for the **TO** component object to be selected.

Select the top face of the baseplate.

You will notice several indicators that come up now in the graphic window:

- Constraint indicator arrows, indicating the remaining degrees of freedom,
- The Status line says "Three degrees of freedom remaining".
- The planar vectors are pointing in opposite directions, indicating the Mating constraint.
- The designated constraint is listed in the window in the top part of the Mating Conditions dialog.

Step 9. Choose the **Preview** button to have a look at the response to the constraint you added. The change is not permanent until you choose **OK** or **Apply.**

To correct an improperly specified constraint, choose **Unpreview** from the Mating selection dialog, and then re-specify the constraint.

Step 10. If the constraint is correct, select Apply to accept the constraint so that more constraints may be added.

Now we will use the Align constraint to insure the locator is oriented in the correct way.

Step 11. Choose **Align** icon as the second mating constraint.

The Cue Line is prompting to select the **FROM** object.

Step 12. Choose the cylindrical face of the small hole in the locator as the **FROM** position.

The Cue Line is prompting to select the **TO** object.

Step 13. Choose the cylindrical face of the small hole in the baseplate.

Step 14. Visually note that the correct objects were chosen and if so, choose the **Preview** button to watch the component jump to the mating condition.

Step 15. If it looks fine, choose **Apply** to make the constraint permanent.

The Status line still says there is one degree of freedom remaining —and the arrows indicate it is rotation. Another constraint is required to prevent the locator from rotating out of position. There are choices about which object to constrain. In this case you might Align the other bolt holes together, or you might Align the outside planar faces of the locator and the baseplate—the ones that line up anyway.

Step 16. The **Align** icon is already chosen so apply either of the constraints mentioned in the above paragraph—your choice. After you apply this Align constraint, the Status line will say "Mating condition is fully constrained" since the degree of freedom remaining is zero.

Step 17. **Save** your assembly file and continue to Project 12-3.

Project 12-3. Adding Components and Mating Conditions

This is continuation of the previous activity. Add the locator to the other three corners of the baseplate and to add mating conditions as you add the locator to each corner. The fixture assembly should look like below when completed.

Save the completed part as **xxx_project12-3_assm.prt**. This completes the section on Mating Conditions. Important issues when applying Mating Conditions is to decide which constraints are most appropriate for your design intent. You need watch your selections closely, monitoring the Cue Line to make sure of where you are in the process, and then watching to make sure you obtain the results you want. The mating constraint is not permanent until you choose Apply or OK.

Project 12-4. Caster Assembly

The project shown below allows you to practice the assemblies and mating condition operations covered in this chapter. All piece parts already exist under directory Chapter12-partfiles/fixture. So this will be a bottom-up assembly modeling exercise. The part files needed are listed in the Assembly Navigator and are found in the Caster subdirectory.

Start by creating your own assembly part file, name it **xxx_project12-4_assm**, and then add the parts as component objects. When mating the wheel and the axle, center them between the forks.

There are more projects in the appendix to practice assemblies.

Exercise Problems

12.1 List and discuss the advantages of using Assemblies.

12.2 Define an assembly.

12.3 Define a Unigraphics assembly.

12.4 What is the name of the object that resides in the assembly part file that establishes the associative link to the piece part file?

12.5 How does Unigraphics identify an assembly part file?

12.6 Discuss difference between component object and component part file.

12.7 What parameters of the part file does the component object define?

12.8 Define Bottom-Up modeling approach.

12.9 Define Top-Down modeling approach.

12.10 Discuss the practical application of the Bottom-Up and Top-Down approaches.

12.11 What functionality is used to link the position of a component to another component?

12.12 What functionality is used to link geometry of a component to geometry in another component?

12.13 What purpose do Reference Sets perform in Assemblies?

12.14 Explain the difference in using Reference Set versus Layer Control to accomplish the purpose for Reference Sets.

12.15 What is the functionality that must be enabled by the system manager before the Wave Geometry Linker may be used?

12.16 Which sets of commands are used to create an assembly Bottom-Up?

12.17 Which sets of commands are used to create an assembly Top-Down?

12.18 Describe briefly how to apply Mating Conditions.

12.19 Contrast the differences in using Mating Conditions vs. Reposition to locate components relative to each other in an assembly.

12.20 What unique characteristics does a sub-assembly have?

Chapter 13. Master Model

In this chapter, we will introduce the concept and purposes of the Master Model method of assisting the design process from initial design through manufacturing of a part in a company. This concept centers on the individual model part created by a designer. To understand the benefits of the Master Model method in the design process, it is helpful to review the traditional approach to the design process. We will compare the traditional method to the Master Model method by following a part from initial design through the production of a part.

Section 13.1 will review the traditional and master model methods in the design process. Section 13.2 will discuss the benefits of using Master Model. Section 13.3 will describe how Master Model is accomplished. Section 13.4 will put Master Model into practice by doing two activities.

13.1 The Master Model Concept

The product design process was described in detail in Chapter 1 so please refer back to Product Design Process section if that is a bit hazy. That process identified six steps that are needed to bring an idea through to a product design ready for manufacturing.

In a quick summary, let us look a little deeper look at the design process. The designer is given a need for a product and a set of criteria and parameters that the product must satisfy to meet that need. The designer creates a design part, hands off to a draftsman to complete a drawing of the part, back to the designer who hands off to the analysis groups, back to the designer to refine the design even more, and also handing the design off to other groups that may need to see the design part as well (sales, marketing, customers, material planners). As stated in Chapter 1, it is an iterative process involving a cross-functional team of the company.

In traditional engineering and manufacturing companies the design process described above is a serial process where each functional discipline does its portion in turn after other disciplines have completed their portion. In utilizing the Master Model method in the design process, the cross-functional team can begin doing their portion of the design process at the same time (concurrently) as the other members of the team are doing theirs. Team members can actually see the digital model while the designer is still creating and designing, and see updates as the design progresses, and all may start doing their portion of the process much sooner than in the serial type process. Another statement in Chapter 1 was that computers don't change the "nature of design process", but computers do improve efficiency and productivity. Master Model methods enhance those factors even more enabling products to come to market much faster than the traditional method.

Master Model is enabled by the assembly modeling functionality in creating a copy of the designer's part as a component in an assembly, and then doing each team members part of the process in their own assembly part file. Therefore, drafting is done on the model in a part file that is a copy of the original; likewise, any CAE analysis, NC programming, documentation, and others, is done on separate copies of the original model. More importantly, the copy is made before the design is completed and the work of other disciplines may begin before completion of the design. This process is no longer serial but is concurrent.

This is the fundamental concept behind Master Model: all downstream disciplines that utilize the original designer's model must use a copy of the model as a component in an assembly to perform their disciplines; and all work is done concurrently and in cooperation with the original designer.

Graphically, the Master Model concept is visualized as below.

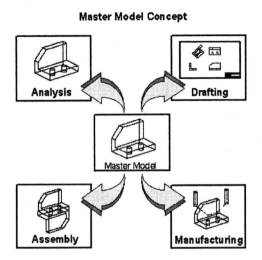

The original model created by the designer becomes the "Master Model" from which all copies are made for other disciplines. In assembly modeling terminology, the Master Model is the component part file and a component object in many other assemblies.

13.2 Benefits of the Master Model

Why use Master Model methods? In addition to the concurrent engineering benefits discussed above, there are several benefits that all contribute to bringing a better-designed part to market faster.

- The original model retains the integrity of the designer's intentions and cannot be corrupted by downstream operations or other designers, draftsmen, or other disciplines by not letting others change the original model. The original designer maintains full control of the design without sacrificing the ability of others to aid in the process to bring a part to production.

- Many disciplines may begin work and planning on a part before the part is completely designed and released for final production. Other disciplines may copy and see the part as it progresses through the design stage and begin planning what operations need to be done to perform the tasks of their discipline.

- For example, manufacturing operations require a considerable amount of planning and setup work before a part may actually be put on a machine and cut. The planning and setup work include tooling, fixture design, NC programming and etc. By allowing a look at the preliminary outline of a part, and subsequent looks as the design develops, manufacturing planners can begin the initial planning necessary to set up to cut the part.

- CAE analysis engineers may begin deciding what analysis may be needed on this part and also provide a part designer with useful feedback at the early design stage for possible design upgrade.

- When a particular part is used in conjunction with other parts to build an assembly of parts to be used in a product, then Master Model allows many designers to concurrently create models of the various parts in an assembly and to share those parts in an assembly maintained by yet another designer. All designers will have access to use other designers' Master Models for their design to ensure that parts that mate together will indeed fit together. Thus, accuracy and quality of the finished parts is enhanced, and time to market is reduced.

- In assembly modeling, the copy of the Master Model is not a duplicate of the original part but in reality a virtual copy. That is, the Master Model is not duplicated onto the disk of other users, but remains on the disk of the master model designer thus taking up no additional disk space. Each other designer has a virtual "copy" to use as background for mating and designing their parts. Thus, total usage of storage disk space in Master Modeling is reduced over the traditional method, which may use several duplicates, causing redundancies and potential inconsistencies.

The Master Model method, with the usage of assembly modeling, facilitates the industry goal of concurrent engineering, helping the various disciplines working together concurrently. Concurrent engineering greatly reduces the time to market from initial concept through manufacturing with minimal effort to update design changes.

13.3   How is Master Model Accomplished?

As mentioned above, Master Model is accomplished using the tool in Unigraphics called Assembly Modeling and components to create copies of the original design. It is a powerful tool that allows virtual copies to be made of the parts and still retain a link to the original model. The link allows the original to be changed as the design progresses and the copies to be updated so other disciplines always have the most up-to-date model from which to work.

The process to accomplish Master Model is as follows:
- Each discipline creates an assembly part file using their naming convention, and
- Adds the Master Model part to its assembly Bottom Up as a component object as discussed in Chapter 12 Assembly Modeling. The usual command sequence **Assemblies → Components → Add Existing** is used to add the designer's part file.

That's all there is to it. The component in the assembly part file may be drafted, or analyzed, or NC programmed by other disciplines. Each discipline has the ability to save the objects created in conjunction with their discipline; but they do not have the ability to make changes to the original model and save those changes because they don't have write privilege to the Master Model.

In the previous diagram, each of the part files shown around the Master Model part file is a separate assembly part file. When the Master Model part is revised, its component objects in those assembly part files can be updated with minimal or no associativity loss. For instance, when the master model has been drafted and annotated, the update to the master model will update the views on the drawing of the master model, but will also update all the associated dimensions and other annotations.

A word of caution is advisable however, in using Master Model in situations where the assembly being created is large and multiple designers are concurrently involved in designing and creating the components of that assembly. The caution is two-fold:

- With many designers utilizing many directories, perhaps multiple computer network servers and over a large network, the ability of the assembly to find and load the parts can get difficult.

- Because of the above difficulties, it may be recommended that a company utilize the WAVE technology to help keep track of the parts and their directories, and many other things, to help in complex assemblies. Refer to the UG on-line documentation for the WAVE description.

It is recommended that before setting up the Master Model processes on any assemblies of more than just a few parts, with no more than just a few people involved, more study and learning of assemblies techniques take place. However, the simple Master Model technique of one assembly with one master model component is not a problem.

13.4 Master Model in Practice

This section illustrates the Master Model in practice using an example. Drafting is chosen as our other discipline for the illustration. In the following example, a Master Model part was already created by a designer, and the Drafting department created from the Master Model another file to make drawings for a Master Model part. The designer will make a design change in the Master Model part and we will see how the change in the Master Model will be reflected in the drawing file in the Drafting department.

Activity 13-1. Exploring the Benefits of Master Model

Step 1. Open part file **shoulder_screw_dwg.prt** from the directory Chapter 12-partfiles\Support.

Step 2. Choose **Application → Drafting**.

Step 3. Inspect the shoulder screw for its dimensional values, particularly the length of the threaded portion of the shaft. **(3.250 – 2.500 = .750)**

This looks like a normal detail of a piece part, but examining it closely as in the following step will reveal that it is a component object in the assembly file showing drafting information.

Step 4. Choose Assemblies → Reports → List Components

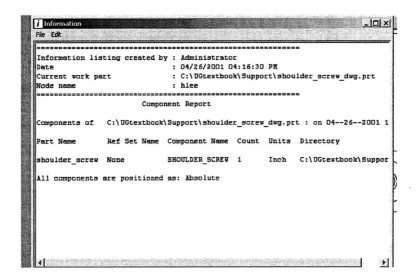

```
i Information                                          _|□| x|
File  Edit
================================================================
Information listing created by : Administrator
Date                           : 04/26/2001 04:16:30 PM
Current work part             : C:\UGtextbook\Support\shoulder_screw_dwg.prt
Node name                      : hlee
================================================================
                    Component Report

Components of    C:\UGtextbook\Support\shoulder_screw_dwg.prt : on 04--26--2001 1

Part Name       Ref Set Name  Component Name  Count  Units  Directory

shoulder_screw  None          SHOULDER_SCREW  1      Inch   C:\UGtextbook\Suppor

All components are positioned as: Absolute
```

The Information window appears showing the assembly file structure for the file
shoulder_screw_dwg.prt containing one component object named
shoulder_screw.prt. This part contains the Master Model definition.

Dismiss the Information window.

Step 5. Retrieve the Master Model file.

    5.1. Choose **File → Open** and select **shoulder_screw.prt** from the list of
the files in the same directory.

Step 6. Enter the **Modeling** application.

Step 7. Edit the length of the threaded shaft on the screw.

    7.1. Choose **Edit→ Feature → Parameters** and select **BOSS(2)** from the
list, select **Feature Dialog** and edit the height of the boss to 1.0.

    7.2. Choose **OK** three times and the screw updates.

Step 8. Change the displayed part to the drawing.

    8.1. From the main pulldown menu **Window**, select
shoulder_screw_dwg.prt from the list.

Step 9. Choose the **Drafting** application.

The drawing of the shoulder screw comes up and notice that the bottom left corner next to the drawing name reads **(OUT-OF-DATE).** This is notification to the Draftsman that something has changed and the drawing needs to be updated.

Step 10. Update the drawing.

    10.1. Choose **Drawing → Update Views**, and select **All**, choose **OK**.

Step 11. Watch the views update and notice the dimensions update to reflect the longer shaft.

Step 12. Retrieve the support assembly and see the update to the shoulder screw in the assembly. The shoulder screw was changed at the component part file level, so the assembly should be updated as well.

    12.1. Start the **Modeling** Application. Open Support_Assembly.prt from the same directory. In case you have a difficulty in loading components of this assembly, change the file loading option by choosing **File → Options → Load Options** and then choosing an option either "From Directory" or "As Saved" for the Load Method. Usually one of these options works, depending on where the component parts of the assembly are located.

    12.2. Verify the shoulder_screw has been updated.

Step 13. Choose **File → Close → All Parts**.

Activity 13-2. Creating a Master Model Assembly for Drafting

This activity will demonstrate the Master Model method by creating an assembly file to be used by the Drafting department.

Step 1. Create a **New** part file **xxx_locator_dwg** where **xxx** represents your initials. Start **Modeling** and **Assemblies** applications.

Step 2. Using **Assemblies** add **locator.prt** to this part file to create an assembly. This part is under directory Chapter 12/partfiles/fixture.

2.1. Choose **Assemblies → Components**.

2.2. Choose **Add Existing**.

2.3. Choose the **Choose Part File** button to browse directories.

2.4. Choose **locator.prt** from directory Chapter 12/partfiles/Fixture.

2.5. On the **Add Existing Part** dialog set the **Layer Options** to **Original** and **Positioning** to **Absolute** (if not already).

2.6. Choose **OK**.

2.7. On the **Point Constructor** dialog make sure the **XC**, **YC**, and **ZC** are all 0, 0, 0. If not, choose the **Reset** button.

2.8. Choose **OK** to place the locator component at 0, 0, 0.

2.9. After the locator part is on the screen, **Cancel** the dialog.

Step 3. Save and close the assembly with **File → Close → Save and Close**.

The Master Model part, **locator.prt**, was copied into the assembly file, **xxx_locator_dwg.prt**, as a component object to it. In the next chapter, Chapter 14 Introduction to Drafting, we will continue to use this assembly file and add the drawing information into the assembly file.

Exercise Problems

13.1 List and discuss the benefits of using Master Model in the design process.

13.2 List and discuss the traditional method of the design process.

13.3 What other disciplines will benefit from using Master Model and discuss the benefits.

13.4 What is the basic Unigraphics capability used to implement Master Model?

13.5 Which part file in the assembly hierarchy is the "Master Model"?

Chapter 14. Introduction to Drafting

In this chapter, we will introduce the Unigraphics Drafting application. The goal will be to give the designer/draftsman enough knowledge of drafting tools to create a basic drawing of their simple design including placing of views, dimensioning, and other annotation.

This chapter consists of 7 sections. Section 14.1 gives an overview of the Drafting application. Section 14.2 introduces creating drawings and adding views. Section 14.3 shows you how to add dimensions to the drawing. Section 14.4 discusses customizations to the drawing to meet company standards and preferences. Section 14.5 shows you how to add notes and labels to the drawing. Section 14.6 addresses how to make more modifications to the drawing for more customization. Section 14.7 adds the additional functionality of Utility Symbols to make the drawing look more professional.

14.1 Introduction to the Drafting Application

The Drafting application is based on creating views from a solid model. The views will be treated and handled as if they are 2D, but they are in fact still 3D; however, don't let this bother you that the views are 3D. All views will respond like 2D—i.e., selecting a back edge of a part for dimensioning will still project to the drawing plane and give correct dimensions.

This way of handling views makes for a very fast creation of a drawing with orthographic views, section views, imported views, auxiliary views, dimensions and other annotations added easily and quickly. The Preferences pull-down dialog allows for extensive customization of annotation and views.

Some useful features of the Drafting application and using solids are:

- Tell Unigraphics what view type you want, and then views may be added just by indicating the location with the cursor.

- As orthographic views are added, they will automatically be aligned with the parent view.

- Every view is associated with the solid. Thus, when the solid is changed, the drawing will be updated, including views and dimensions.
- Drafting annotations (dimensions, labels, and symbols with leaders) are place directly on the drawing.
- Drafting annotations (see above) are associated with the solid geometry that was selected and will update automatically if the geometry is changed.
- Fully associative view boundaries automatically calculated and sized when the drawing is updated.

In this chapter we will learn how to create a drawing, add orthographic views, dimensions, other annotations, and edit and customize all of the aforementioned.

We will assume you know how to do drafting; our goal is to teach you how to do drafting using Unigraphics.

14.2 Creating Drawings and Adding Views

We will begin by creating a drawing with views to get a quick start to this topic.

Activity 14-1. Create a Drawing

We will use the master model part file we created in Chapter 13.

Step 1. Open part file **xxx_locator_dwg.prt**.

Step 2. Verify the locator part is a component in the part file just opened.

   2.1. Choose **Assemblies → Reports → List Components**

Step 3. Choose **Application → Drafting**

Notice several changes to the Unigraphics interface—some obvious, some subtle.

- The graphic window changed to show a blank window, with a dashed line rectangle in it and the view name **SH1 (DWG) WORK** in the bottom, left corner of the graphic window. The dashed line rectangle represents the outline of the "sheet of paper" that will be the drawing. It is defaulted to an English E size drawing.

- The main menu toolbar shifted and added a new heading titled **Drawing** between the **Tool** and **Assemblies** options.

- The various modeling and creation commands are grayed out or disappeared because they are no longer valid in the Drafting application.

Step 4. Modify the Drawing size

Since the default drawing size is an E size we need to make the size a little smaller to fit our part onto the drawing a little neater.

   4.1. Choose **Drawing** from the main menu.

The dialog comes up--choose **Edit...**

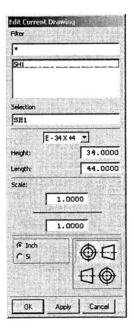

The **Edit Current Drawing** dialog comes up and several characteristics may be changed if desired.

4.2. Choose Pull-down arrow in the middle of the dialog where it shows the drawing size: **E – 34 X 44**

4.2. Choose another drawing size--the **B** size. The **B** size should be large enough for our part.

4.2. Note that the drawing scale may be changed as well, but we'll leave as is.

4.2. Choose **OK**, the dialog dismisses and the graphic area and dashed rectangle may flitter a little, but usually nothing very visual is noticed.

Step 5. Add views to the drawing.

5.1. Choose **Drawing** pull-down menu.

5.2. Choose **Add View**. The **Add View** dialog comes up.

Add View Icons–
11 View Types

Select the view to Add

Notice The Top View
Is Defaulted to Select

The first view placed on the drawing must be the Import View type. Notice that it is the default selection and does not have to be chosen. The Top view is the default view to be placed. The cursor shows a rectangular outline of the Top view and Unigraphics is ready for you to place the view on the drawing.

5.3. Select the location on the drawing surface to place the view.

> The rectangular outline placed on your cursor is a rough outline of the size of the view to be placed. If you have selected the Top view, and you intend to place Front and Right views, then select a location in the upper, left corner of the drawing surface remembering to leave room for dimensions and other anticipated annotation.

The selection remains active to place more Imported views on the drawing.

The figure illustrates the placing of the Top view and the cursor ready to place another Imported view.

5.4. Select the **Orthographic View** icon from the **Add View** dialog.

5.5. Watch the Cue Line, you are prompted to select a Parent view. This is the view that the orthographic projection will be taken from. Select the Top view as the parent view.

5.6. Another rectangular outline appears on the cursor and you may slide the rectangle up and down in a vertical line from the **Top** view, or horizontally from the **Top** view--in other words, an orthographic projection.

See the figure below for a graphic of the vertical and horizontal corridor available.

5.7. Select a position below the **Top** view, again leaving room for dimensions and other annotations.

5.8. The selection remains active to add another projection by selecting another parent view, so select the **Front** view, and slide to the right along the horizontal corridor to add the **Right** view.

5.9. It is helpful now to add a **TFR-TRI** view to the upper right corner to help identify the part for other people to aid in visualizing the part.

5.10. Therefore, choose the Import View icon again, choose **TFR-TRI** from the window and place the "Trimetric" in the upper right corner of the drawing.

The drawing should look something like this when complete.

See how easy that was! Views can be placed on a drawing very quickly, and with a little practice and with knowing the size of your part, can be placed on the drawing very accurately.

14.3 Creating Dimensions

The next step we will put on some dimensions. The **Dimension** menu is found in the **Insert** pulldown menu. Notice the **Insert** dialog changed when we entered the Drafting application.

All of the dimension types are listed on this menu and may be selected to do your dimensioning. However, it may be cumbersome to go through the Insert →
Dimension → (dimension type) each time you want to change dimensions. Instead, it is suggested that the toolbars be utilized to quickly choose the dimension types you wish to use.

From the Dimension toolbar, each dimension type may be selected to bring up a dialog for that dimension type.   Each dialog for the dimension types is defaulted to allow quick creation of dimensions and placement to quickly annotate a drawing. This can facilitate quick referencing by other disciplines to start planning for their involvement in the design process. We have shown the complete toolbar with all dimension types shown; however, you may want to **Customize** your toolbar with the dimension types you use.

Activity 14-2. Dimensioning the Part

The Dimension toolbar is up and ready to select the dimension types on it.

Step 1. Choose the **Horizontal** dimension type .

This dialog prompts you through the selection of objects to dimension and it also contains the formatting of a dimension. It is defaulted such that dimensioning may begin without worrying about the setups for now.

The **Cue Line** is prompting to select the first object or a dimension to edit. Let's dimension the overall length of the part in the **Top** view.

    1.1. Select a vertical line on the left side of the part and then select a vertical line on the right side of the part—all in the **Top** view.

Notice the dimension is placed on the cursor and you may drag it up and down on the dimension lines to select a place to locate it. Also, the dimension may be located above the part or below the part.

    1.2. Select a location and place the dimension.

The system is ready to create another horizontal dimension. All you have to do is select the geometry you want to dimension.

    1.3. Select additional geometry and place horizontal dimensions on the views to dimension the part correctly.

Note that if you make a wrong selection at any time before actually selecting the location on the drawing you want to place the dimension, you may start over by selecting the first object icon again and re-selecting the objects again.
(You will notice after you select that first object icon that the current dimension you were about to place still is on the cursor, but the Cue Line is prompting to select the first object so go ahead and select that first object and the old dimension will disappear and the graphic will show the current new selection.)

Step 2. Choose the **Vertical** dimension type .

This dimension type works exactly the same way as the horizontal type.

    2.1. Select geometry as appropriate to place vertical dimensions on the views. Your choice as what to dimension.

When finished your drawing should look something like this.

Next, we'll add some diameter and radius dimensions.

Step 3. Choose a **Hole** Dimension type .

3.1. Choose the hole in the lower corner of the part. The origin of the dimension is on your cursor and you can locate it around the hole.

Notice that the **Hole** dimension allowed you only to rotate the origin of the dimension around the hole by a limited amount. Therefore, the **Hole** dimension may be placed in an odd location, so let's talk about some other options now.

Auto Placement

There are some other helpful options on the Dimension dialog that let's discuss.

The option of the dimension with the lightning bolt through it represents Automatic Placement for system control of the placement of the origin for dimensions. **Automatic** is the default for Unigraphics out of the box. It means that Unigraphics will infer the placement of the origin only allowing you limited freedom to put it where you want. It will infer the placement of the dimension arrows. This works pretty well for the distance type dimensions: horizontal, vertical, parallel, perpendicular, and cylindrical. But the diameter, radius, and angular dimensions it usually is not sufficient, so we change the option to the other choices. These are as shown.

The other two choices are:

Manual placement with arrows on the outside of the extension lines, or

Manual placement with arrows on the inside of the extension lines.

When manual placement is chosen the dimensioning and annotation becomes completely manual with no placement options assumed.

Left or Right Leaders

When you choose the **Manual** choices above you now have to pay attention to the side of the leader you want from the origin of the dimension. **Leaders From Left** and **Right** on the Dimension dialog are toggles that you switch back and forth as you use those dimensions that have a single leader.

Leader to
Left of Dim.

Leader to
Right of Dim.

We are ready to place that Hole dimension again.

Step 4. Place the **Hole** dimension again.

    4.1. First, delete the previous dimension that we didn't like the location by choosing **Edit → Delete** and then choosing the dimension and **OK**.

    4.2. Go to the **Automatic** button and choose **Manual Placement – Arrows Out**.

    4.3. Choose the leader toggle to make the leader come to the **Left** of the origin dimension. The Left or Right leader is relative to the dimension— not the geometry.

    4.4. Select the hole in the lower left corner again. Notice now you can drag the origin for the dimension anywhere you want on the drawing.

    4.5. Select a spot on the drawing below and to the right of the other dimensions to place the origin. It will look something like this.

The other hole is a counterbore and the dimensioning for that type is different, and necessarily more complicated, so we'll leave that one until we know more.

Radius Dimensions

The radius dimensions come in three types:

 Radius (not to center)

 Radius to Center

 Folded Radius

    The **Radius not to center** creates the leader from the dimension radially toward the center of the radius, but stops before it reaches the center point. Depending on how the Automatic or Manual setting is done the arrowhead may be on the outside or the inside.

    The **Radius to Center** creates the leader from the dimension, passes through the arc and ends at the center of the arc with the arrow either on the inside or outside depending on the Automatic or **Manual** selection status.

    The **Folded Radius** type creates an artificial leader from the arc to an artificial point with a fold to indicate the leader is not actual length. This is useful for a large radius that would be out of the view.

Which one you choose is up to you and your company standards.

Step 5. Add the Radius dimension types.

    5.1. Choose the **Radius** not to center type .

    5.2. Select the arc in the corner of the cutout and place the origin of the dimension in a location of your choice. Pay attention to the Left or Right leader choice.

    5.3. Choose the **Radius to Center** icon .

    5.4. Select the small arc in lower left corner of the part and place the origin of the dimension in a location of your choice. Pay attention to the Left or Right leader choice.

These will look something like this.

Step 6. Add the Counterbored hole to look like the dimension below.

This callout may not be to everyone's company standards but it will illustrate one way to do it.

    6.1. Choose the **Hole** dimension type .

    6.2. Select the inside diameter of the counterbored hole.

14-15

Notice the dimension is on your cursor ready to be placed on the drawing. But don't place it yet.

6.3. Choose the **Annotation** icon shown below to bring up the Annotation dialog to append the dimension with annotation.

This icon opens the **Annotation Editor** dialog and you may enter pretty much anything you want to add to the standard dimension type.

Enter text in this window

Choose the Text Below icon here

Referring to the figure above of the counterbored dimension, we want to add 2 lines of appended text **Below** the dimension.

6.4. Select the Below icon shown above, and then type in the text as shown in the figure above (in all capitals—it is case sensitive).

6.5. Choose **OK** to accept the text and to dismiss the dialog.

Notice the completed dimension is now on your cursor and you can drag it around the screen to place. Also notice the defaults for left justification of the text and the right or left side of the dimension for placement of the leader.

6.6. Use the mouse to place the dimension in a convenient location.

Step 7. **Save** your drawing file.

14.4 Customizing the drawing

Let's review quickly what we've accomplished so far.

- We created a drawing, changed its drawing size from E to B.
- We placed Top, Front, and Right views on the drawing, orthographically projected from each other.
- We placed a Trimetric view on the drawing to help visualize the part.
- We dimensioned the part and used the Horizontal, Vertical, Hole, and two Radius dimension types.
- We had an introduction to the Annotation Editor where we entered Appended text to handle a special case.

We did this to illustrate how quickly and easily a drawing may be created, populated with views, and may be annotated in Unigraphics.

We also did this to illustrate how much of the drawing creation process is automated and defaulted. Most of what we did has defaults built in to allow the placement of views and dimensions quickly and easily. However, the defaults may not fit your company standards, and the defaults don't fit every special case.

This section of the chapter will describe how to change some of the defaults and show you where to find the settings to customize the drawing creation process to your company standards.

Most of the common Unigraphics defaults may be set by the system manager to be permanent changes that become your company defaults and do not have to be changed every time you enter the **Drafting Application**. Then, you only change the settings to fit your special situations as they arise.

There are three methods to change the default settings on the drawing:

- The Preferences on the main menu for changes applicable to new placements
- The various dialogs that are used to create dimensions, views, etc.
- The drafting objects may be edited after they are placed on the drawing.

So let's look at these methods and discuss how to change the default settings. The first one is the **Preferences** pull-down off the main menu bar.

Preferences

There are several ways to change the defaults and customize the look of the way drafting is done:

- Change settings in the **Preferences** pull-down main menu, and
- Change settings in the dialogs

We'll look at the **Preferences** pull-down menu first. The **Preferences** menu looks like this:

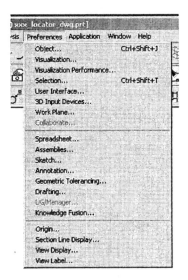

In this section we will look at **Annotation** and **View Display**, and we will look at the changes that may be made in the dialogs.

We will discuss a few general concepts first. As we mentioned earlier, Unigraphics comes with defaults built in for all the settings. You are able to override the **Preference** "factory" defaults with your own or company standards in the following ways:

- Customer Defaults file - contains settings for drafting that take effect whenever you create a new part or choose the Defaults button on a Drafting preferences dialog.   The customer defaults files are the **ug_english.def** and **ug_metric.def**.

- Part file Drafting preference settings - You can set preferences within the part file from various Drafting dialogs that affect all of the drafting objects. These settings take precedence over the Customer Defaults file for that part.

- Object specific within a part file - You can selectively change preferences on individual drafting objects from Drafting dialogs. These changes then take precedence over both the Customer Defaults file and any part file Drafting settings.

Note here the various levels of setting **Preferences** and the order they get overridden. The Customer Defaults file is valuable to set the way you want drafting defaults to be most of the time.

However, as you can see if you make changes in a part file to a drawing, to dimensions, or views, these changes override the settings in the default file. And furthermore, these changes are valid for the entire login session that you are in Unigraphics.

Merely opening a new part file and/or a new drawing do not reset the values back to default settings. There are two effective ways to reset values:

- Choose the **Default** button on the dialogs that you changed settings for.

- Exit from UG and log back in when you want to change part files.

Let's start with the **Annotation** settings from the main menu, choose **Annotation** from the Preferences menu.

Note that these settings are global to the entire drawing and part file and will be applied the next time the setting is used. They are also applied for the entire Unigraphics logon session. The dialog for Dimensions looks like:

The top two lines of buttons are the preference that may be set and the lower portion of the dialog changes to reflect the values of the button chosen.

- **Dimensions**--Lets you set dimension preferences for arrow and line formatting, type of placement, tolerance and precision formatting, dimension text angle, and size relationships for extension line components.
- **Line/Arrow**--Lets you set preferences that apply to leaders, arrows, and extension lines for dimensions and other annotations.
- **Lettering**-- Lets you set preferences that apply to lettering for dimensions, appended text, tolerances, and general text (notes, id symbols, etc.), including lettering size, font, and color.
- **Symbols**-- Lets you set preferences that apply to ID, User Defined, Centerline, Intersection, Target, and GD&T symbols.
- **Units**-- Lets you set preferences for type of units, for the display of linear and angular dimension values as well as dual dimension format.

- **Radial**-- Lets you set preferences for the display of diameter and radius dimension symbols and format.

- **Fill/Hatch**-- Lets you set preferences for cross hatching and area fill.

The Annotation Preferences dialog will change with each annotation type selected.

We'll choose the **Dimension** button and examine it closely to see what can change. The **Dimension** button dialog is the one shown above and repeated here for convenience:

This line sets whether or not extension lines and arrows are included in a dimension. And it sets the dimension placement options in the Dimension dialog.

Determines if a tolerance is included in the dimension.

Determines how many decimal places are displayed.

Determines the alignment of a dimension value with the leader.

The **Units** button sets the unit in inches. So let's look at the **Units** button.

comma or period;
trailing zero—yes or no

Location of Tolerance:
After, Below, Above

Choose decimal or
Fraction display

Choose
Leading or Trailing
Zero on Angle

Units—Choose inches,
mm, meters, Arch Ft/in,
Engineering Ft/in

Choose
Degrees/min/sec
combination

Choose Dual Dimensions
and placement location

Annotation Preferences

| Dimensions | Line/Arrow | Lettering | Symbols |
| Units | Radial | Fill/Hatch | |

3.050 ▼   3.050 ±.005 ▼

Linear Format and Units

1.125 ▼

Inches ▼

Angular Format

45° 30' ▼   45° 30' ▼   0° 30' 0" ▼

Dual Dimension Format and Units

1.125 ▼   1.125 ▼

☐ Convert Primary Tolerance to Secondary Units

Millimeters ▼

| Inherit | Reset | Load Defaults |
| Inherit All | Reset All | Load All Defaults |

| OK | Apply | Cancel |

Both of these dialogs are typical of the changes that may be made and the look of all of them. There are too many to cover them all.

The procedure is to make the change(s) you want to make in the dialog, and then choose either **Apply** or **OK** to have the change take effect. The change will be in effect the next time you use the option.

Remember, these settings are global and stay in effect until you change them. When finished with this drawing you may want to set the changes back to the original default values and formats. This may be accomplished by choosing the **Default** button.

On the other hand, if you want to change the settings of specific dimensions instead of the global setting changes, first choose the specific dimensions in the graphic window and follow the procedure.

Let's look at the **View Display** dialog off the **Preferences** main menu.

If you desire to make a part look solid in a view by hiding hidden lines, you would change three settings in the above dialog:

- ❑ Choose **Hidden Lines** button,
- ❑ Choose **Color/Font/Width** pull-down to be **Invisible**,
- ❑ Choose **Hidden Line** toggle to put a check mark in the box.
- ❑ Choose the **Apply** button for the settings to take affect.

Then all new views added to a drawing would make the part look solid with hidden lines not visible.

In other words, the four buttons in the dialog titled: **Hidden Lines**, **Visible Lines**, **Smooth Edges**, and **Virtual Intersections**, are combined with the buttons under **Color/Font/Width** to define how those kinds of curves are displayed in a view.

Selecting the **Hidden Lines** button changes the options under **Color/Font/Width** and the settings are made for **Hidden Lines**. Then the **Visible Lines** button is chosen and the settings under **Color/Font/Width** are changed accordingly and you choose the settings for **Visible Lines**. The other buttons work in the same way.

Also insure the **Edge Hiding Edge** button is toggled with a check mark in it. This button performs the job of erasing hidden edges that are behind other edges (overlapping edges) so there are not two edges on top of each other. This action contributes to the model looking 2D on the drawing.

Activity 14-3. Applying the Hidden Lines View Display

Using the drawing that is already up and the View Display for Hidden Lines created a few pages ago, we will apply the settings to a new view.

Step 1. Choose **Preferences → View Display…**

Step 2. Create the Hidden Line solid look.

    2.1. Choose **Hidden Lines** button,

    2.2. Choose **Color/Font/Width** pull-down to be **Invisible**

    2.3. Choose **Hidden Line** toggle to put a check mark in the box

    2.4. Choose the **Apply** button for the settings to take affect.

Step 3. Add an Isometric view to the drawing.

    3.1. Choose **Drawing → Add View**.

    3.2. Select the **TFR-ISO** view from the list.

    3.3. Select an open area of the drawing to place the view and pick it.

The isometric view is placed and notice it has its hidden edges invisible so it looks solid.

Activity 14-4. Applying the Annotation Changes to Dimension

Step 1. Choose **Preferences** → **Annotation...**

Step 2. Choose the **Dimension** button, if not already chosen.

Step 3. Choose the **Automatic Placement** button and from the pull-down menu that appears choose the **Manual Placement - Arrows In** option.

Step 4. Choose **OK** to accept and dismiss the dialog.

Step 5. Choose the **Horizontal** dimension and note the differences in format and how the dimension is on the cursor.

> **6.1.** Notice that the arrow placement option in the dialog has changed to reflect the choice for Manual Placement – Arrows In.

> **6.2.** Select a feature of your choice to dimension. When we placed dimensions previously the placement option was on **Automatic Placement**.

> **6.3.** Select the geometry and note the dimension may be moved about freely to place the dimension.

This completes working with the **Preference** menu.

Modifying the Dialogs

The second method we'll discuss is modifying the dialogs to customize the drafting settings. We discussed and used several of these in Activity 14-2 when we changed the **Auto Placement** setting, the **Left** or **Right** leader selection, and the **No Appended Text** choice. All of these are on the individual dimension types dialogs.

When a dialog is changed like we did above, it is a permanent change until it is changed again. The change overrides any documents in Customer Defaults that may be set and it overrides any Preferences menu settings that have been made, and in fact some will actually change the Preference settings to agree. Also remember, changes to the dialog may be made before you make the selection on the graphic window to place the drafting object.

If you make a mistake in selecting geometry, you must reselect the drafting function you want to do before you reselect correct geometry.

Activity 14-5. Customizing the Drawing

This activity will start from the beginning on a new part and go through the process of creating a drawing and dimensioning to put this information together.

The part we will use is called a shaft support. We will use the Master Model concept to create the drawing and annotate it.

Step 1. Create a new part file and name it **xxx_shaft_support_dwg.prt**.

Step 2. Choose **Application → Modeling** and **Assemblies**.

Step 3. Change to the Trimetric however you like to do that.

Step 4. Create the assembly with the solid body part file.

    4.1. Choose **Assemblies → Components → Add Existing.**

    4.2. Select from the list of parts the **shaft_support.prt** (or browse for it by selecting Choose Part File).

    4.3. Choose the pull-down to change the **Reference Set** and select the Reference Set **BODY**.

    4.4. Change the **Layer** setting to **Original** and choose **OK** to accept the dialog.

4.5. The **Point Constructor** dialog comes up and set the coordinates to 0, 0, 0 by selecting the **Reset** button (if necessary).

4.6. Choose **OK**. **Cancel** the **Add Existing Part** dialog.

4.7. Note that we chose **Original** layer, the solid body is on Layer 10, so change the Work Layer to 10 and Fit the part in the window.

Step 5. Inspect the part and **Save**.

Step 6. Choose **Application → Drafting**.

Step 7. Modify the drawing size and add views.

7.1. Choose **Drawing → Edit**.

7.2. From the **Edit Current Drawing** dialog, choose the **E – 34 X 44** pull-down menu and choose the **C** size drawing.

7.3. Choose **OK** to accept and dismiss the dialog.

Step 8. Check the **View Preferences** to insure we get dashed hidden lines.

8.1. Choose **Preferences → View Display**.

8.2. Insure the **Hidden Lines** button is depressed, insure the **Color/Font/Width** selections are Original, dashed line symbol, Original.

8.3. Insure the **Hidden Line** toggle is checked and the **Edge Hiding Edge** toggle is checked. Otherwise, make proper changes and choose **OK**.

Step 9. Add the views.

9.1. Choose **Drawing → Add View**.

9.2. The **Add View** dialog appears and is defaulted to add an Imported View and defaulted to place the **Top** view.

9.3. The **Top** view outline is on the cursor so place the view in the upper left quadrant of the drawing.

9.4. Choose **Orthographic View** icon from the **Add View** dialog.

9.5. Select the **Parent** view, which is the **Top** view.

9.6. Place the **Front** view in the lower quadrant of the drawing.

9.7. Keep placing views by selecting the **Front** view as the **Parent** view and place the **Right** view.

Step 10. Add a solid Trimetric view.

Change the **View Display** to get **Hidden Lines** invisible.

10.1. Choose **Preferences → View Display**.

10.2. Choose **Hidden Lines** icon.

10.3. Select **Invisible** from the middle button in **Color/Font/Width** selections.

10.4. Choose **OK** to accept and dismiss the dialog.

Now back to the **Add View** dialog to add the Trimetric view.

10.5. Choose **Import View** from the **Add View** dialog and choose the **TFR-TRI** from the list of views.

10.6. Place the Trimetric in a convenient location in the upper right quadrant of the drawing.

10.7. **Cancel** the **Add View** dialog.

Step 11. You may want to turn off the view boundaries.

11.1. Choose **Preferences → Visualization**.

11.2. Choose the **Names/Borders** button.

11.3. Toggle the **Show View Borders** button to uncheck the toggle and choose **OK**.

Step 12. Start dimensioning the part.

12.1. Choose the **Horizontal** icon.

12.2. Let's start by dimensioning the hole pattern.

12.3. Select the two holes at the top of the part to dimension the distance between the holes.

With the two holes selected, before we place the dimension, let's decide we want to add an Appended Text of the word TYP to account for the two holes at the bottom of the part.

12.4. From the **Horizontal** dialog, choose the **Annotation Editor** icon, select the Below button, type in **TYP** in the text window of the Annotation Editor dialog.

12.5. Choose the **Apply** button on the dialog to accept the change.

12.6. Place the dimension on the drawing.

Now we'll add the dimension from the hole to edge of the part.

12.7. Select the left edge of the part and select the left hole.

The appended text is still active and we could place the dimension but let's have the new dimension aligned with the existing dimension.

12.8. Choose the **Origin** button at the top, right of the dialog.

A new dialog appears to select which objects you want to align with.

12.9. Select the **Align with Arrows** icon and then select the left arrow of the 4.000 dimension.

12.10. The Cue Line prompts us to indicate the origin of the placement so select a spot to the left of the part and roughly in line with the 4.000 dimension.

The dimension is placed and both dimensions are aligned with each other. But we notice that we don't want a 3-place dimension for the .50; a 2-place dimension will satisfy our design intent.

12.11. Select the .500 dimension.

12.12. From the Horizontal dialog, choose icon for decimal places. This pull-down menu comes up overlaying the Horizontal dialog.

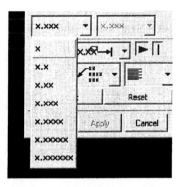

12.13. Choose the **X.XX** option from the list.

12.14. Choose **Apply** on the dialog to accept the change.

12.15. Let's add the dimension for the width of the part. Horizontal is still the active dialog, so select the left edge and the right edge of the part.

We don't need appended text so choose **Use Appended Text** and remove the check mark. Then place the dimension.

12.16. Perform similar actions with the **Vertical** dimension type to add the dimensioning for the vertical direction of the holes. Be aware of the 2- and 3-place dimensions, appended text, alignment, and leader direction.

The Top view now looks like this.

The choice of where to dimension now is pretty much discretionary, but let's choose to finish dimensioning this Top view for ease of illustrating some of the dimensioning points.

Let's add the Diameter dimensions.

12.17. Choose the Hole type .

12.18. Change the Precision to a 3-place dimension.

12.19. Choose **Preferences → Annotation → Radial**

12.20. The dialog looks like this. We want to change the diameter symbol to DIA and we want the symbol to appear after the number, i.e., .250 DIA. Choose **OK**.

Change φ 1.0 to 1.0 φ

Change φ to DIA

12.21. Select a .250-dia hole—let's choose the lower, left one.

12.22. Choose Manual Placement, Arrows In.

12.23. Add Appended Text of TYP 4 PLACES below the dimension.

12.24. Choose Leader from Right.

12.25. Place the dimension in a convenient location to the left of the part.

Now let's do the two diameters of the cylinders.

12.26. Choose the Diameter dimension type .

12.27. Select the outside diameter circle.

Notice that the previous settings are still good—3 place dimension, DIA symbol, Manual Placement, Arrows In.

12.28. We do not need Appended Text so turn that off.

12.29. We may be ready to place the dimension now—notice if leader is on the right or the left and change if necessary.

12.30. Select a spot and place the dimension.

12.31. Select the inside diameter circle and repeat the above steps.

The Top view is looking something like this now.

That completes the dimensioning of the Top view.

The Front view may be dimensioned in much the same way, only much less needs to be dimensioned. The designer needs to decide what dimensions are important and use dimensions that reflect the designer's needs.

An option a designer/draftsmen has in dimensioning diameters is to use the Cylindrical dimension type instead of the Diameter type. We will use the Cylindrical dimension type just for illustrative purposes here since we already used the Diameter dimension.

12.32. Choose the Cylindrical dimension type .

12.33. Select anywhere on the silhouette of the cylinder

12.34. Then select the other silhouette of the cylinder.

12.35. The dimension is ready to place, so select a convenient spot, paying attention to Right or Left leader direction.

And the result looks something like this.

When you have an option, we'll leave up to you and company practices which dimensioning type you use: Diameter or Cylindrical.

We'll also leave up to your discretion the rest of the dimensioning of this part. We believe we've given enough tools to complete normal dimensioning. Obviously there are a lot more options, but we believe you've been given the tools that you can locate and understand how to use the others.

14.5   Notes and Labels

Notes and labels are used to place information on the drawing such as GD&T symbols, the list of Drawing Notes, filling out the Title Block, and explanatory notes about the finishes and manufacturing details that must be passed on to NC Programming or analysis engineers.

For purposes of clarity, we will define notes as stand-alone information without a leader and labels are notes with a leader.

There is not a command titled Notes and Labels; instead they are added with the **Annotation Editor** dialog which is found under the **Insert** menu and titled **Annotation**.

Insert → Annotation… or the Annotation Editor icon .

We have already seen the Annotation Editor in Activity 14-2 when we added a dimension with Appended text: the option chosen was Annotation Editor. In Step 6 we added the dimensional information for the counterbored hole. That was easy to do, right?

Here is the Annotation Editor again and we'll examine in more detail.

Text Editing and Tool Bar

Entry or Edit Window

Preview Window

Text Preferences

Symbols to insert in text: they change to reflect which Preference button is active

Placement Option: with a leader

Placement Option: no leader

That is a brief map of the areas of this dialog.

An explanation of each of these areas follows:

- Entry or Edit Window—This is the window in which you will type your annotation and edit annotation. The text will always look the same no matter what your Preferences have been set to. The text is case sensitive so normally text on a drawing is all in capitals, so it might be handy to hit the Caps Lock key and enter capitals easily.

- Preview Window—This window will mimic the Edit Window but will accurately reflect what you will see on the drawing because it will utilize whatever Preferences have been set.

- Text Editing Buttons and Tool Bar—This area is used to perform text operations such as cut and paste, print preview, and bold, italic, underline text.

- Text Preferences—These buttons are handy copies of the Preferences menu pull-down placed to be easily available. They will change the current Preferences → Annotation settings and they affect the note or label you are creating.

- Symbols Preferences—These symbols are placed here to be easily accessible as well and may be inserted into the text by just selecting them and it will be placed where the cursor is located. They change as the Preference buttons above them are activated.

- Placement Options—When the text entry is complete and you are ready to place the note or label, then choose one of the options depending on whether you want a leader or no leader.

Please note as well that the Annotation Editor dialog may be used for creating new text and editing existing text. To edit existing text, bring up the dialog, and then select the text to be edited. The text will appear in the Editing Window and the Preview Window and you may use all of the functionality available to edit the text, including deleting all of the text out of the window and starting over with new text.

Activity 14-6. Adding a Label

The purpose of the activity is to illustrate the functionality of the Annotation Editor.

We'll use our previous part file **xxx_shaft_support_dwg.prt** and add a label to the Front view. The Front view currently looks something like this.

We want to add a fillet note that looks something like this.

Step 1. Open the **Annotation Editor** dialog.

1.1. Choose **Insert → Annotation...** or the **Annotation Editor** icon .

1.2. Type into the Edit Window: FILLETS ALL AROUND .030 R (enter capitals)

1.3. Choose the **Placement** icon with the leader.

(This one)

1.4. Another **Placement** window comes up with choices on the format and placement of the text. The window is called **Create Leader**.

This dialog contains options for different styles of leaders, left, right, or inferred leader, multiple leaders pointing to multiple sites, and then where and how to place the leader in relation to the text. The placement of the leaders and text is completely manual so all points will have to be selected.

We will leave the style of leader with the traditional arrow, but change the leader side to Inferred, and we'll leave the leader centered on the text. But we will use multiple leaders—2 in fact. Notice that the placement Labels in this manner is completely manual so all picks will have to made to locate the leader and the label.

1.5. Choose the Leader Side pull-down and select the Inferred option

1.6. The Cue Line is prompting to select the leader side end point, so select the intersection of the flange and the cylinder.

1.7. The Cue Line is prompting to select another point, so select out to the left and down a bit to establish the break point for the horizontal portion.

1.8. The Cue Line continues to prompt for a point (note that 7 intermediate break points for the leader may be done), but we don't need another point, so select New Leader up on the dialog.

1.9. The Cue Line is still prompting for a leader end point, this time select the upper side of the flange and cylinder end point.

1.10. Continue the leader to the left and a little above the flange and select a point.

1.11. Continue the leader and select a point that connects with the original leader, to look something like this when complete.

1.12. This completes the leaders we require, so now choose **OK** on the **Create Leader** dialog. This allows placement of the text.

1.13. The text box outline now comes on the cursor and you may drag it anywhere, but select a location that lines up the horizontal leader with the bottom point of the 2 leaders. It looks something like this.

1.14. **Save** the file.

Please note if you want a standard single leader label then all that is required is to pick the point where the arrow should point, and then **OK** the **Create Leader** dialog and the label will be on your cursor to place manually at a convenient location.

This completes the activity for creating Annotation.

14.6 Modifying the Drawing

In this section we will explore other modifications to the drawing that are common to do. In the first activity we did a change to the drawing in changing its size from the original E size to a C size.

This time we will change the drawing size but we will do it with views already on it, and we will change the name of the drawing.

Activity 14-7. Modify a Drawing

We will use our previous drawing to continue this activity.

Step 1. If it's not already open, **Open xxx_shaft_support_dwg.prt**.

This is the current condition of our drawing. Note the nomenclature in the bottom left corner of the drawing: **SH1 (DWG) WORK**

The first change we will make is to change the name to SHEET1.

You will want to change the drawing name to match your company standards: maybe, 53C12345-1.

Step 2. Choose **Drawing → Edit**, or choose icon

Step 3. Type in the new name SHEET1 in the box labeled Selection.

This is not case sensitive—all names will be converted to capitals.

Step 4. Choose **Apply** to accept the change. Notice the drawing name change in the lower, left corner.

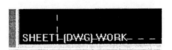

Now let's change the drawing size and see the effect.

As you may know, a C size drawing is 17 X 22, a B size is 11 X 17, and a D size is 22 X 34, etc, as shown below.

On a Unigraphics drawing, these sizes are measured from the lower left corner of the drawing. Furthermore, the views placed on the drawing have a drawing **X** coordinate and a drawing **Y** coordinate, so they are a **X,Y** distance from the drawing origin.

When the drawing size is changed the views retain the same **X,Y** coordinate value on the new drawing size. The meaning of this is that when the drawing gets smaller, some views a distance from the origin may be off the drawing—out of the boundaries of the drawing (or off the "paper"). Conversely, when a drawing gets larger there may be a whole lot of extra room on the drawing with the concentration of views in the lower left quadrant of the new drawing.

The latter condition is not bad; just means you have to move the views around some, but it leaves room for new views and other annotation to be added.

The former condition of making the drawing smaller could be bad in that it might be difficult to get the views back that are off the drawing.

Here's what our drawing would look like if we changed the drawing to a B size.

This is not a disaster—at least all the views are visible and they could be moved to be entirely on the drawing. But, obviously, this size is too small for our part.

If we make the drawing size a D size the result looks like this.

This is perfectly acceptable and probably what we wanted in the first place--to add additional views, perhaps section views, to add drawing notes, and a title block. Of course, some moving of views would be needed as well.

Let's change the drawing size.

Step 5. Choose the **C – 17 X 22** window pull-down menu and select the D size drawing from the menu.

Step 6. Choose **Apply** and watch the drawing change.

You should get the same result as the figure above.

Activity 14-8. Removing a View from the Drawing

Step 1. First let's change the drawing back to the **C** size, so repeat Step 5 and 6 above with the **C** size.

Step 2. Choose **Drawing → Remove View…**

The dialog comes up.

Step 3. Choose the **Right** view from the graphic area or choose **ORTHO@3** from the dialog.

The Right view should highlight. If it doesn't, select another view until you get the correct one. The **Reset** button may be used to unselect any views selected.

Step 4. Choose **Apply**.

The view is deleted. Note, in general, that when a view is deleted all drafting objects and view modifications associated to that view are deleted as well.

Step 5. **Save** the part file.

14.7 Creating Utility Symbols

Utility symbols are found under the **Insert** pull-down on the main menu. It looks like this.

This format of a dialog looks familiar in the layout with the selection of utility symbols on the top section, point selection choice, then the local display parameters section that defines the symbol.

For instance, the parameters that define the circle centerline that is highlighted are the dimensions of this type of centerline. The distance labeled C is the distance from the circle selected to the end of the centerline.

And why utility symbols are useful is that not only do they look good and are standard symbols on drawings, but also as you would expect, they are associative to the geometry chosen. That means they will update if the geometry changes. If the circle selected to place a Linear Centerline on the circle changes, then the Centerline changes to maintain the parameters set for it. Also utility symbols may be dimensioned to and the dimensions are associative.

Existing utility symbols may be edited on this dialog by selecting the symbol, and then editing the defining parameters. You accept the edits with Apply.

Activity 14- 9. Creating a Linear Centerline

We'll continue with our same drawing and concentrate on the cylinders in the Top view.

Step 1. Insure that the **xxx_shaft_support_dwg.prt** is the current drawing.

Step 2. Choose **Insert → Utility Symbols...** or the icon

Step 3. Choose the **Linear Centerline** icon on the dialog.

Step 4. Choose the outer diameter edge of the cylinder.

Step 5. Choose **Apply**.

The centerline goes on the **Top** view with the centerlines extending past the outer circular edge.

Next we show how to dimension using the centerlines.

Step 7. Choose the **Horizontal** dimension type.

Step 8. Select an edge of the flange and select the vertical leg of the centerline and place the dimension.

I want to place a **Vertical** dimension now but the other dimensions are too close so I need to move some dimensions first to make room. The 5.00 and the 4.000 Horizontal dimensions need to be moved up and to the right a bit.

Step 9. Place your cursor over the **5.00** dimension and it is highlighted. The cursor appears with an arrow pointing out at a 45-degree angle. This means that the dimension may be relocated, so select it with MB1, hold MB1 down and drag the cursor to move up a bit and select a new location out to the right. When the dimension is located where you want it release MB1 and the dimension is moved.

Step 10. Now I select the **4.000** dimension and move it up and to the right some also.

Now there's room for the new dimension.

Step 11. Choose the **Vertical** dimension.

Step 12. Select the centerline and select the edge of the flange and place the dimension somewhere convenient.

Step 13. Save the part file.

The Top view looks something like this now.

Activity 14-10. Creating a Cylindrical Centerline

We'll create the centerline through the cylinders in the Front view as shown.

Step 1. Choose the **Utility Symbol** dialog

Step 2. Choose the **Cylindrical Centerline** icon

The **Cue Line** is prompting to select a point to define the position for the centerline. You want to select the center point of the circle.

Step 3. Select the horizontal edge at the top of the Front view. It is a circular edge and there is a control point there at the center of the arc. A star will appear at the point selected—insure it is at the center of the circle.

Step 4. Select the other horizontal edge at the bottom of the part and insure a center point is selected. The centerline is created immediately but inspect it anyway. If you have difficulty selecting the circular edge and getting the center point, then change the **Point Position** menu to select the **Center Point** option.

This method has the defaults built in to define how far past the edge of the part the centerline extends as defined on the Utility Symbol dialog. The defaults may be adjusted to fit your needs by just entering new numbers into the dialog and accepting them by choosing Apply. And you can also edit the parameters on an existing symbol by selecting the symbol and entering new numbers, and then accepting with Apply.

The Cylindrical Centerline symbol has another method to place the centerline. It is to change the Point Position option to selecting a cylindrical face rather than points. When a cylindrical face is chosen the centerline is automatically on the center axis of the cylinder, so all the system needs to know is how far do you want to extend the centerline. The Cue Line prompts for the end points of the centerline. Pick a point outside each end of the cylinder and then you will see the centerline created.

Which option you choose depends on the design intent. The first option associates the centerline to the center points of the circular edges of the cylinder and the second option associates the centerline to the cylinder face.

Note that this part is not the best candidate for this second option because two cylinders are present. By selecting only one cylinder and placing the centerline so it looks correct limits the centerline flexibility because it is associated with only one cylinder.

Step 5. **Save** the part file.

Project 14-1. Drafting Baseplate Assembly Components

In this project you will complete dimensioning of the Baseplate Assembly component parts. We have already dimensioned the locator part partially. The assignment is to complete dimensioning of the locator and to dimension the locator_pin and the fix_baseplate. These parts are found under directory Chapter14-partfiles. You may create a drawing for the assembly as well. Use the Master Model concept to create a drafting file and use the tools we have learned in this chapter, but not limited to this chapter. If other functionalities look appropriate for your intentions you are free to use them as well.

Create two new part files for the drawings of fix_baseplate and locator_pin as shown below. The naming convention should be xxx_project14-1_dwg1.prt and xxx_project14-1_dwg2, respectively, where xxx is your initials.

fix_baseplate drawing

.500 DIA

2.75

.75

.375 DIA

locator pin drawing

.200 DIA
DRILL THRU
CBORE .300 DIA X .250

2.000

.375

.100 RAD

1.625

1.250

.375

.100 RAD

2.000

.375

.375

1.250

.200 DIA

1.625

1.000

.500

locator drawing

Project 14-2. Drafting Rotator Arm

This project is similar to the previous drafting project with use of the Master Model and dimensions and annotations. The part used for this project is rotator_arm.prt under directory Chapter14-partfiles. Alternatively you can use your own part, xxx_activity10-5.prt, if you completed activity 10-5.

Sample draft drawings are given in the following page. Choose the appropriate size drawing and note that the part is in millimeters. Save your file as xxx_project14-2.prt.

rotator arm drawing

Exercise Problems

14.1. Name the benefits of using Master Model in Drafting.

14.2. Name the benefits of using a solid model for Drafting.

14.3. What name is given to the default drawing in Unigraphics?

14.4. How is the name changed?

14.5. How is the drawing size changed?

14.6. What does the dashed rectangle represent around the drafting graphic window?

14.7. What planning needs to take place before placing views on the drawing?

14.8. Does the above planning need to exhaustive and detailed?

14.9. What cautions are necessary when a drawing is made smaller?

14.10. Where is the location of 0,0,0 in the drawing coordinate systems?

14.11. What is the significance of where 0,0,0 is located? Why do we care?

14.12. What is the general procedure to add views to a drawing?

14.13. What is a good practice to verify before placing views to insure views are displayed the way you want them to, particularly if not familiar with a part file?

14.14. Generally, what's the difference in changing the customized settings in the Preferences dialog versus changing them in the dialog you are working with?

14.15. What is the difference in a Note and a Label?

14.16. What does Edges Hidden by Edges do?

14.17. What is the general procedure to modify an annotation already on the drawing?

14.18. What action do you take to cancel a selection when placing an annotation when you realize you've made a mistake in what you've picked?

APPENDIX A. Guided Student Assembly Project
Building the Geneva Cam Assembly Model

The Geneva Cam assembly consists of 9 unique component parts and total 11 components. Their names, drawings, and dimensions are given in the following pages.

The purpose of this appendix is to give students more opportunities to practice what they have learned this book. In this appendix, students will be guided to model individual parts of the Geneva Cam assembly from a scratch and to put them into the final assembly. Section 1 addresses individual part modeling. Section 2 addresses assembly modeling. Three approaches to assembly modeling are presented. They are repositioning only, using mating conditions, and using interpart modeling.

Geneva Cam Assembly[1]

BILL OF MATERIALS			
ITEM	QTY.	PART NAME	DESCRIPTION
1	1	INDEX	STEEL
2	1	INDEX PLATE	STEEL
3	1	GENEVA	STEEL
4	1	BUSHING	BRASS
5	2	WASHER	STEEL
6	1	FLAT HEX NUT	STEEL
7	1	CAP SCREW	#3 SC. HD.
8	2	SHAFT	STEEL
9	1	SET SCREW	STEEL

GENEVA CAM

---

[1][1] The drawings for this assembly are taken from Technical Graphics Communication by Bertoline and et al. (1997) (reprinted with permission from the publisher McGraw-Hill)

Key Components of Geneva Cam Assembly

PART NAME: INDEX PLATE

PART NAME: INDEX

PART NAME: SHAFT

PART NAME: BUSHING

PART NAME: WASHER

PART NAME: GENEVA

Section 1. Modeling Individual Parts

In this section, you will create individual component pars of the Geneva assembly. Create a new subdirectory (or folder), xxx_AppendixA_Proj1, where xxx is your three-letter name initials. Save these part files under this directory. It is helpful to change the components to different colors to distinguish them easier in the assembly, so we will assign colors as we create the parts as well. Since white is the system color we will avoid our objects being white.

Section 1-1

Creating the Index

Step 1 – A new part file

Create a new file (using inches) named xxx_Geneva_index.prt and start the modeling application, where xxx is your three-letter name initials. If it is not already, change the solid color to green. The creation color is found at Preferences → Object…

Step 2 – Cylinder

Create a cylinder with diameter 2.47 and height .44-.25= .19 at WCS 0,0,0.

Step 3 – Boss

Create a .25 high, .5 diameter boss on the top face of the cylinder. Use point onto point for placement and choose the arc center of the circle edge of the cylinder.

Step 4 – Thru Hole

Create a .25 diameter through hole on the top face of the boss created in the previous step. Use point onto point placement and choose the arc center of the circle edge of the boss. The placement face should be the top face of the boss, and the thru face is the bottom face of the entire solid.

Step 5 – Datum Plane

Change the work layer to 61 and create a datum plane that goes through the axis of the boss cylindrical face. This datum plane will be used to position a slot that will be created in the next step.

Step 6 – Rectangular Slot

Change the work layer to 1 and create a rectangular slot (do not use a thru slot option). Placement face is the top face of the cylinder created in Step 1. Select the datum plane as the horizontal reference. Use the following parameter for the slot: width= .2, depth= .5 (any number larger than .19 which is the index depth, length=3 (any number larger than 2.47 which is a diameter of the index). Position it using two methods. First, use line onto line by aligning the datum plane to the center line of the slot. Second, use horizontal positioning with distance -1.25/2 between the arc center of the boss and the arc center of the slot half circle. If it is not positioned properly, you may need to change the horizontal distance to the positive number, 1.25/2.

Step 7 – Thru Hole for Circle Indentation

Create a thru hole with diameter 2 x .63 for the side circle indentation for the index. The placement face is the top face of the cylinder.

Position it using two methods. First, use point onto line by aligning the datum plane to the hole center.   Second, use horizontal position with distance 1.529 between the arc center of the boss and the hole center. For horizontal positioning, you need select the datum plane as the horizontal reference. If it is not positioned properly, you may need to change the horizontal distance to the negative number, -1.529.

Step 8 – Datum Axis

Change the work layer to 62. Create a datum axis that goes through the axis of the boss. This reference feature will be used to create an array for the next step.

Step 9 – Circular Array

In order to make the complete part, it is necessary to create circular array instances for the rectangular slot and the indented thru hole.
Click on the instance array icon. You will create a circular array of 5 instances, with the angle between being 360/5. You will instance two features, which are the rectangular slot and the thru hole for the side indentation. The rotation axis for the instance will be the datum axis.

You have now completed the index.

Section 1-2
Creating the Index Plate

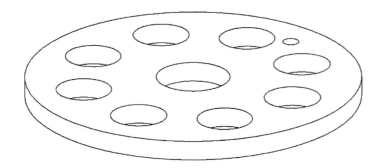

Step 1—New part file

Create a new file named xxx_Geneva_index_plate.prt. Use inches. Change the creation color to cyan.

Step 2 – Cylinder

To begin the index plate, create a 2.25 diameter, .130 high primitive cylinder.

Step 3 – Datum Planes

The next step is to change the work layer to 61 and create two datum planes. First create a datum plane that goes "through face axis" by choosing the outer cylindrical face of the cylinder. Next create a datum plane that is rotated 90° from the first plane.

Step 4 – Center Hole

Create a .5 diameter thru hole in the center of the cylinder you just created.

Step 5 – Outer Hole

The next step is to create one of the holes around the outer part of the plate. To do this first create one thru .375 diameter hole and position it with parallel distance of 1.52/2 between the arc center of the center hole and the center of the current hole and then perpendicular distance from one datum plane of .287 as shown below.

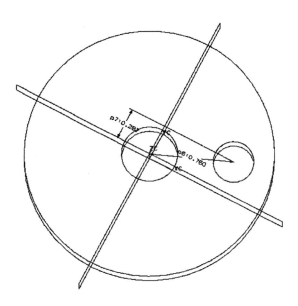

Step 6 – Circular Array

Change the work layer to 62 and create a datum axis that goes through the axis of the face of the cylinder created in Step 2.

Create a circular instance, 8 holes, angle of 360/8. The rotation axis should be the datum axis.

Step 7 – Small Hole

The final step in creating the plate is to make a simple thru hole with diameter .11.   Position it with parallel distance of 1.79/2 between the arc center of the center hole and the center of the current hole and then a horizontal distance of .35 from the arc center of one near outer hole (.375) as shown below. Note that when you pick horizontal distance for positioning, you will be prompted to specify horizontal reference. Use one datum plane that is parallel to the dimension distance being positioned.

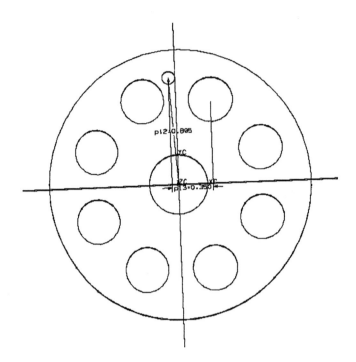

You have now completed the index plate.

Section 1-3

Creating the Geneva

Step 1—New part file

Create a new file (using inches) named xxx_Geneva_Geneva.prt. Change the creation color to red.

Step 2 –Cylinder

The part will begin with a primitive cylinder .25 high and 1.25 in diameter.

Step 3 – Boss on the top

Next, create a .5 diameter, .25 high boss in the center of the top face of the cylinder.

Step 4 – Boss on the bottom

Next, create a .5 diameter, .13 high boss in the center of the bottom face of the cylinder.

Step 5 – Hole

Now create a .25 diameter thru hole that is centered on the top face of the top boss created in Step 3 and goes through to the bottom face of the bottom boss created in Step 4.

Step 6 – Datum Planes

You will need to create three datum planes to use for reference on the next few steps.

First change the work layer to 61 and create the first datum plane DATUMP-1 that goes through the face axis of the cylinder.

Then create the second datum plane DATUMP-2 that goes also through the axis but is rotated 90° from the first plane.

Now create the third plane DATUMP-3 that is offset 1.55 inches from DATUM-1.

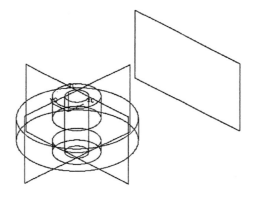

Step 7 – Indentation

You will now create the circular section indentation in the side of the Geneva. To do this, create a 2.5 inch diameter, 1 inch deep hole. Place the hole on the top face of the cylinder (not the boss) and align the center of the hole to the intersection of DATUMP-2 and DATUMP-3, using point onto line positioning.

Step 8 – Side Hole

You will create a hole in the side of the upper boss that the set_screw will go into to prevent the Geneva from spinning on the shaft when assembled.

Create a .19 diameter, 1-inch deep hole and use DATUMP-1 as the placement face. Make certain that the hole goes out in the direction opposite the indentation created in the previous step. Position the hole in the middle height of the top boss.

Step 9 – Thread

The final step in creating the Geneva is to create an internal thread on the side hole that the set_screw will fit into.

Choose Insert → Feature Operation →Thread... Choose thread type Detailed. Choose the cylindrical face of the side hole to put the thread on. Select DATUMP-1 as the start face. Choose OK to accept the default parameter values of the thread.

You have now completed the Geneva.

Section 1-4

Creating the Bushing

Step 1—New part file

Create a new part file (using inches) named xxx_Geneva_bushing.prt. Change the creation color to aquamarine.

Step 2 – Cylinder

Create a primitive cylinder .19 in diameter and .16 inches high.

Step 3 – Hole

To finish the bushing, create a thru hole .13 inches in diameter on the top face of the cylinder as the placement face. Pick the bottom face of the cylinder as the thru face. Use point-onto-point for the positioning method and choose the arc center of the circular edge of the cylinder.

You have now completed the bushing.

Section 1-5

Creating the Washer

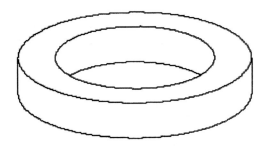

Step 1—New part file

Create a new part file (using inches) named xxx_Geneva_washer.prt. Change the creation color to yellow.

Step 2 – Cylinder

Create a primitive cylinder .19 in diameter and .03 inches high.

Step 3 – Hole

To finish the washer, create a thru hole .13 inches in diameter on the top face of the cylinder as the placement face. Pick the bottom face of the cylinder as the thru face. Use point-onto-point for the positioning method and choose the arc center of the circular edge of the cylinder.

You have now completed the washer.

Section 1-6

Creating the Nut

Step 1 – New part file

Create a new part file (using inches) named xxx_Geneva_nut.prt. Change the creation color to green.

Step 2 – Hexagon curves

Change the work layer to 41 (the default layer standard for curve is 41 to 60). Choose Insert → Curve→Polygon.... Enter the number of sides 6 and the inscribed radius .1. When the Point Constructor dialogue appears, choose the Reset button and then OK. The Hexagon curve is created at WCS 0,0,0.

Step 3 – Extrusion

Change the work layer to 1. Extrude the hexagon curves that you just created a distance of .05 inches to create the solid. To pick the curves, you can pick each of them or simply use Chain Curves.

Step 4 – Hole

First you need to create two datum planes to use for reference for positioning the hole to be created.

Change the work layer to 61 and create the first datum plane DATUMP-1 that is a center plane between two parallel side faces of the extruded body.

Create the second datum plane DATUMP-2 that is a center plane between another two parallel side faces of the extruded body.

Create a .0875-inch diameter thru hole that is in the center of the hexagon extrusion. Position it applying point onto line twice using datum planes DATUMP-1 and DATUMP-2.

Step 5 – Thread

Create an internal detailed thread. Select the inside face of the hole that was created in the last step. Accept the default parameter values.

You have now completed the nut.

Section 1-7

Creating the Cap Screw

Step 1—New part file

Create a new part file (using inches) named xxx_Geneva_cap_screw.prt.
Change the creation color to magenta.

Step 2 – Cylinder

Create a .32 high, .10 diameter cylinder.

Step 3 – Boss

On top of the cylinder you just created, add a boss that is .12 diameter and .16
high. Position it point-onto-point with the arc center of the circular edge of the
cylinder.

Step 4 – 2nd Boss

On the top of the boss you just created, make another boss that is .25 diameter,
.125 high. Place it point-onto-point with the arc center of the circular edge of the
previous boss.

Step 5 – Chamfer

Next, insert a .0125 by 30° chamfer on the top edge of the second boss.

Step 6 – Thread

Create an external thread by choosing Insert → Feature Operation →Thread…
Choose thread type Detailed. Choose the cylindrical face of the smallest cylinder
to put the thread on. Choose OK to accept the default parameter values of the
thread.

Step 7 – Rectangular Pocket

You will create a rectangular pocket at the center of the top face of the screw for
the fastening tool to grip on.

First you need to create two datum planes to use for reference for positioning the
pocket to be created.

Change the work layer to 61 and create the first datum plane DATUMP-1 that
goes through the face axis of the cylinder.

Create the second datum plane DATUMP-2 that goes also through the axis but is
rotated 90° from the first plane.

Create a rectangular pocket with the following parameters (length=width=.075,
depth=.1, corner radius=floor radius=.02). Position it using line onto line by
selecting DATUMP-1 and a centerline of the pocket. Repeat line onto line
positioning by selecting DATUMP-2 and the other centerline.

You have now completed the cap screw.

Section 1-8

Creating the Shaft

Step 1-- New part file

Create a new part files (using inches) named xxx_Geneva_shaft.prt. Change the creation color to orange.

Step 2 – Cylinder

Create a cylinder that is 2.5 inches high and .25 inches in diameter.

Step 3 – Chamfer

The only other step in creating the shaft is to chamfer the end. To do this select the Chamfer icon, and choose a single offset of .031 inches and pick the two circular edges on both ends of the part.

You have now completed the shaft.

Section 1-9

Creating the Set_screw

Step 1 – New part file

Create a new file (using inches) named xxx_Geneva_set_screw.prt. Change the creation color to brown.

Step 2 – Cylinder

Create a .19 diameter, .35 high cylinder

Step 3 – Chamfer

Create a .02 single offset chamfer on one end of the cylinder

Step 4 – Datum Planes

Change the work layer to 61 and create 2 datum planes, DATUMP_1 that is in the same plane as the unchamfered end of the cylinder and DATUMP_2 that goes through the face axis of the cylinder.   The resulting figure looks below.

Step 5 – Blend

Blend the unchamfered edge circular edge of the cylinder with a radius of .095 inches to round the top of the screw.

Step 6 – Rectangular Pocket

Now you need to create a rectangular pocket for a tool to fit into. Its parameters are X length=1, Y length =.04, and Z length =.08. Select DATUMP_2 as the horizontal reference. Position the pocket such that the long dimension is line-onto-line with DATUMP_2. You will see the status line saying "Feature position is underspecified" but it will create a desired pocket since X length is sufficiently large.

Step 7 – Thread

Create an external thread on the cylindrical face. Select the thread type Detailed. Select the cylindrical face. If prompted to select a start face, select the top face of the cylinder with a chamfered end. Accept the default parameter values.

You have now completed the set screw. This completes section one.

Section 2. Assembly Modeling

Section 2-1

<u>Assembling Parts With Repositioning only</u>

In this assembly modeling approach, components of the individual parts created in the previous section are assembled such that components do not have any association to each other. Components are just placed in space individually using WCS. Thus, when you move one component in space by choosing Assembly → Components → Reposition Components, the rest of components still remain in the same place.

Step 1 – Create a new part file

Create a new file (using inches) named xxx_Geneva_assm_repo.prt and save it under directory xxx_AppendixA_Proj1.

Step 2 – Add the index plate

The procedure to add a part will be the same for each of the components except positioning of the part in space. To add a part to the assembly, choose Assemblies → Components → Add Existing.

Click Choose Part File and locate the xxx_Geneva_index_plate.prt file, if the file is not already open. Otherwise, select it on the list of opened parts. Take the default reference set. For the multiple add option, choose no and for the positioning option, choose reposition. The layer option should be original.

Click OK for the 0,0,0 insertion point. The Reposition component window will pop up. If necessary, rotate the index_plate a little about its center point to make positioning of the index easier.

Step 3 – Add the index

Now add xxx_Geneva_index to the assembly. The distance between the center of the half-circle that is inside the slot in the index part and the center of the bolt hole in the plate should be 0. Also, the z coordinate of the bottom of the index should be the same as the z coordinate of the top of the plate.

To do this, first insert the plate at 0,4,0 in WCS. This will make it easier to see what is going on. Rotate the index if necessary so that a slot on the index should point toward the center of the index plate. Use the Reposition Component dialog to rotate the index if necessary. Now we need to move it in the y and z direction to align the hole. Choose the Point to Point icon. From the Point Construction dialog, choose the Arc Center icon. The first selection point is the From point and should be the bottom edge of the half-circle at the end of the slot that is aligned with the y-axis. The second point is the To point and should be the top edge of the small hole in the index plate. Click OK and the plate and the index should be properly aligned.

Destination Point
Arc Center

Reference Point
Arc Center

Correct Slot Orientation

Step 4 – Add the Geneva

Click Add part and place the xxx_Geneva_geneva at the point -2,0,0. The part may need to be rotated 90° about it's center to align the indented round correctly, and then translated such that the bottom face of the body of the Geneva is aligned with the top edge of the hole in the index plate to be finished. Therefore, translate Point to Point of the appropriate arc centers. After the Geneva has been moved be sure and choose OK to confirm the translate operation. The completed position of the three parts should look like below.

Step 5 – Add the two shafts

When you add xxx_Geneva_shaft, choose multiple add (or just do it twice) and the insertion point for each will be the arc center of the Geneva and of the index. The positioning in the z direction is unimportant just so they look as shown in the drawing. Be sure to choose OK to confirm the move.

Step 6 – Add the two washers

Add and position the component xxx_Geneva_washer (two units) to the assembly part. Both washers are placed on the index plate: one on top of it and one on the bottom of it. Add the first washer on the top face of the index plate and align the arc center (From point) of the bottom face of the washer with the arc center (To point) of the top edge of the smallest hole in the index plate. This washer will fit in the slot. Remember to confirm the move by choosing OK.

Add the second washer on the bottom face of the index plate and align the arc center of the top face of the washer with the arc center of the bottom edge of the smallest hole in the index plate. And again, choose OK to confirm the move.

Step 7 – Add the bushing

Add and position the component xxx_Geneva_bushing to the assembly part. Add it on the top face of the top washer and align the arc center (From point) of the bottom face of the bushing with the arc center (To point) of the top face of the washer. It too should fit into the slot, rest on top of the washer, and be flush with the top of the index. And don't forget to choose OK to confirm.

Step 8 – Add the cap screw

Add the component xxx_Geneva_cap_screw to the assembly part. The insertion point of the part can be the arc center of the slot in the index. Reposition the screw in the z direction by choosing translate and then selecting the arc center of the bottom face of the screw head and the arc center of the top edge of the bushing. Don't forget the OK.

Step 9 – Add the nut

Adding xxx_Geneva_nut is similar to adding the washer and cap screw. This time the To point for the nut center will be the arc center of the bottom face of the second washer that you added in Step 6. Don't forget the OK. The figure below illustrates the placement of the 2 washers, bushing, nut and cap screw, with the other parts suppressed for clarity. The threads have been suppressed for clarity.

Step 10 – Add the set_screw

The set_screw may be tricky because of the threads and orientation. Add the part file and place it initially at 0, -2, 0 to make placement easier. Rotate the part 90° if necessary about the –x-axis so that is oriented properly with the hole in the Geneva. Now you can translate the part so that the arc center of the threaded end of the screw is coincident with the circumference of the shaft through the Geneva. Suppressing the threads on the set_screw and the hole in the Geneva may make placement easier. It is suggested the WCS origin is relocated to be at the centerline of the set_screw hole and at the circumference of the shaft. For the Reposition translation, the From point is the center of the chamfer end on the set_screw and the To point is the WCS 0,0,0.

Note in the figure below the threads have been Suppressed for clarity and it is suggested that you suppress them for ease of selecting the edges.
Don't forget to Unsuppress when finished.

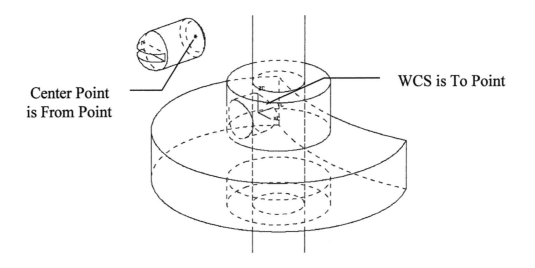

Center Point
is From Point

WCS is To Point

The completed assembly should look like the assembly shown at the beginning of this section.

This completes section 2-1.

Section 2-2

Assembling Parts with Mating Conditions

In this assembly modeling approach, we have a new design intent: components of the Geneva assembly are assembled such that they are spatially associated. This means that when one component moves to another location in space, other components move accordingly to maintain spatial relationships to the moved component. For example, the axis of a nut is "aligned" with the axis of a washer. When a nut moves in space, a washer will automatically move in order to maintain the alignment relationship to the nut.

Overview

The procedure of adding a part when using mating conditions is the same as in Section 2-1 with the exception that you will select Mate, instead of Reposition for the positioning option in the Adding Existing Part dialogue. Then, instead of repositioning the part, you will give it specific mating constraints that must be satisfied by the placement.

The process of mating parts together involves a step-by-step selection of the different type of mating constraints to be satisfied until the part is placed as needed. Particular types of mating constraints that you will mainly use in this Geneva assembly include Mate (planar objects selected to mate are coplanar and face opposite each other) and Align (centerlines of cylindrical objects will be in line with each other).

The Mating Conditions dialog displays when you select Mate as the positioning option. This dialogue shows the two parts that you are currently mating, and the mating constraints that have been specified thus far between the two parts. You can delete constraints from the list if you apply them incorrectly, as well as being able to add more constraints to other sets of parts.

Step 1 – Create a new part file

Create a new file (using inches) named xxx_Geneva_assm_mate.prt and save it under directory xxx_AppendixA_Proj1.

Step 2 – Add the index plate

This step will be identical to Step 1 of the previous section. It adds the first part into the assembly and orients it properly.

Step 3 – Add the index

Add the part just as before, but make sure to click on Mate for the Positioning option. You may need to rotate the piece 180° to make it look right. Align the centerline of the cylindrical face at the end of the slot in the index to the centerline of the cylindrical face of the small hole in the index plate. Next mate the bottom face of the index with the top face of the index plate.

Step 4 – Add the Geneva

Add the Geneva to the assembly part. Align the axis of the Geneva with the axis of the index plate and mate the bottom face of the Geneva with the top face of the index plate. Rotate the part 90° to orient it correctly.

Step 5 – Add the two shafts

Add the shaft to the assembly part. The only mating constraint necessary is to align the axis of the shaft with the axis of the hole that it is being inserted into. Reposition both shafts such that they are about centered vertically in the hole.

Step 6 – Add the two washers

Add two units of washers to the assembly part. Add the first washer with the following mating constraints: mate the bottom face of the washer with the top face of the index plate and align the axis of the washer with the axis of the smallest hole in the index plate.

Add the second washer with the following mating constraints: mate the top face of the washer with the bottom face of the index plate and align the axis of the washer with the axis of the smallest hole in the index plate.

Step 7 – Add the bushing

Add the bushing to the assembly part. Mate the bottom face of the bushing with the top face of the index plate and align the axis of the bushing with the axis of the small hole.

Step 8 – Add the cap screw

Add the cap screw part and choose Mate at the positioning. Mate the bottom surface of the screw head cylinder to the top surface of the bushing and align the axis of the screw to the axis of the bushing.

Step 9 – Add the nut

Add the nut and choose Mate at the positioning. Mate the top surface of the nut with the bottom surface of the second washer and align the axis of the nut with the axis of either the washer or the small hole in the plate.

Step 10 – Add the set_screw

Align the axis of the screw with the axis of the hole in the Geneva. Position the screw relative to the hole such that the end of the screw is just contacting to the shaft in the center of the Geneva (you can use the Tangent Constraint for this).

Step 11 – Verify the design intent

Reposition (Assembly → Components → Reposition Components) the index plate with Delta X=5, Delta Y=5, and Delta Z=3 and observe how other components react. Do other components move along?

This completes Section 2-2.

Section 2-3.

Assembling Parts with Interpart Modeling

In this assembly modeling, we have a different design intent that is more challenging than the previous ones. In addition to spatial relationships among the components as accomplished in Section 2-2 Mating Conditions, the new design intent is that components are dimensionally associated. This means that parts that fit together directly with one another should be associative to make sure that they will still fit together after a design change. For example, a change of a hole diameter will cause to change the diameter of the shaft that goes into the hole so that there is fit between two parts.

There are two methods available to accomplish this type of design intent: WAVE Geometry Linker and Interpart Expressions. These will be presented to allow you to experiment on both methods. The first method in Section 2-3 Part A was covered in the Chapter 12 on Assemblies. The second method in Part B has not been covered but included to show you the possibilities and is optional. We need to caution that Interpart Expressions is very complicated and has implications throughout the company and should not be used lightly.

A. Using Linked Geometry

A method of making an assembly interpart modeled is to use linked geometry. This means that existing geometry in an assembly is used in the subsequent creating of additional components. This can be easier and less confusing to follow than the interpart expressions method, but can only be used in a limited number of cases. This method is used when you want to create geometry from the geometry of an existing component. This will be illustrated in the example following.

Create a new directory (or Folder) xxx_AppendixA_Proj2. Create duplicates of all individual part files created in Section 1 and save them under this new directory. Repeat this for xxx_Geneva_assm_mate.prt and rename it as xxx_Geneva_assm_geolink.prt. You are going to make changes in these duplicated files, leaving the original files intact.

Step 1 – Create geometry to link from

Before you can use geometry to link, it must already exist in the assembly file.

Change the file open option by choosing File→Options →Load Options and choose the Directory option in the dialogue. Open xxx_Geneva_assm_geolink.prt.

Step 2 – Link the geometry

The first part to link will be the shaft component. First, remove one shaft component from the assembly.

Now create a new component in the assembly and save it as xxx_Geneva_shaft_geolinked_1.prt. It will initially be empty. Now make the new component part the work part. Open the wave geometry linker dialogue by choosing Assembly → Wave Geometry Linker. Click on the circular edge of one of the holes that the shaft fits into. This geometry is now listed as a linked feature in xxx_Geneva_shaft_geolinked_1.prt.

Step 3—Create the component part

Now create a shaft by extruding the linked feature (i.e., geometrically linked circle edge) using start distance –1.25 and end distance 1.25. Next chamfer the ends as before (single offset of .031 inches).

Repeat Steps 2 and 3 to create the other shaft.

Step 4—Create other parts similarly.

Create the washer in the same manner by linking to the geometry (the small hole circle edge of the index plate) and extruding with an offset.

Step 5 – Verify the design intent.

Change the diameter of the small hole of the index plate and observe if the washer hole, which is geometrically linked to the hole, also changes to still maintain fit.

B. Using Interpart Expressions

Interpart Expressions (IPE) are used when the design intent indicates that it is beneficial to relate one component to another component in an assembly. This is accomplished through creating a link between a feature expression in one component and a feature expression in another component. The linking allows the value of that expression in one component to control the value of the expression in the other component. In the case of the Geneva cam we've been working with an example would be linking the diameter of the hole in the Index part to the diameter of the Shaft that passes through it.

Note that the IPE capability is defaulted to be turned off in the ug_english.def and ug_metric.def files and it must be turned on before IPE may be used.

General Procedure to Create Interpart Expressions

1. From Design Intent identify the components and features you wish to link by expressions.
2. Make each of the affected components the work part and rename the p# for the expression you wish to use to a meaningful name
3. Make one of the components the work part, select the affected expression and create the link to appropriate expression created in Step 2.
4. That completes the linking by expression of the components. Repeat Steps 1 through 3 for each pair of components you wish to create interpart expressions.

Step 1 – Prepare Part Files

To get started we'll take the process step by step and also look at the big picture of the process. Create a new directory (or folder) xxx_AppendixA_Proj3. Create duplicates of all individual part files created in Section 1 and save them under this new directory. Copy the xxx_Geneva_assm_mate.prt and rename it as xxx_Geneva_assm_intexp.prt. Do not copy the xxx_Geneva_assm_repo.prt. You are going to make changes in these duplicated files, leaving the original files intact.

Change the file open option by choosing File → Options → Load Options and choose the From Directory option in the dialogue. Open xxx_Geneva_assm_intexp.prt. The entire Geneva cam should load into the assembly.

In general, to proceed with IPE the first step is to identify those interpart dimensional relationships between component parts that can share the same values and thus can link to the same expression names fulfilling the design intent for the fit of the parts. Below are some of such examples in our Geneva cam.

Part	-and- Part	Relationship
Index Plate	Geneva	Center hole = diameter of bottom boss
Geneva	Index	Outer radius = notch radius
Index Plate	Cap Screw	Small hole radius = thread portion radius
Index Plate	Washer	Small hole radius = inner radius
Index Plate	Nut	Small hole radius = inner diameter
Index	Bushing	Slot Width = Diameter of Bushing
Geneva	Shaft	Center Hole Diameter = Outer Diameter
Geneva	Index	Center Hole Diameter = Center Hole Diameter
Geneva	Set_screw	Side Hole Diameter = Screw Diameter

Next identify the key dimensions in the assembly that can drive interpart relationships among component parts, such as listed above. Some of the examples are listed as follows:

geneva_diameter=.63*2

index_height=.44-.25

index_plate_center_hole_dia=.50

index_plate_small_hole_dia=.11

index_plate_thickness=.13

notch_dia=2.47

set_screw_dia=.19

shaft_dia=.25

slot_width=.2

We will relate the Shaft diameter to the Index hole diameter.

Step 2 – Rename the Expressions in Each Component

At the current status of the assembly and components the names above do not exist. Instead, the components are defined by their p# numbers. The next step then is to identify the feature expressions in each component that you want to link and change the p# to a meaningful name. The names above are realistic names that may be used in their respective components.

Note that names are not an absolute requirement for creating an IPE; it is just a convenience to remember which expressions do what. Interpart Expressions may be created using p#.

The procedure is to make the component the Work Part, open the Expression dialog, identify the parameter you wish to use in the IPE and rename it from p# to a meaningful name. Repeat for affected components.

In our case of the Shaft diameter and the Index hole diameter follow these steps.

Make the Shaft the work part.

Choose the Tools → Expression, select the p# that is the diameter of the shaft, choose Rename and enter a name for the diameter, such as shaft_dia. Hit OK and then Apply.

Make the Index the work part. In the same way, change the expression for the center hole to a new name, such as center_hole. Hit OK and Apply.

Make the work part the assembly again.

Step 3 – Create the Interpart Expression to Components

The setup is complete now and ready to create the actual linked expressions.

Make the Shaft the work part.

Open the Expression dialog.

Select the diameter expression, shaft_dia, or whatever you chose to call it.

The expression will appear in the text window (where the arrow is above) and you may edit it.

Click the cursor in the window and delete out the number value, but not the name and the equal sign, =.

Choose the Create link button, select the Index from the list, hit OK and select the diameter expression we created earlier. Choose OK.

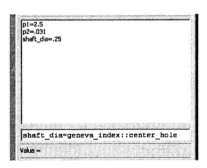

The line in the Value= window should look as shown. Hit the Enter key and the line will be accepted and become the new expression for the hole. Choose the Apply to confirm the whole procedure.

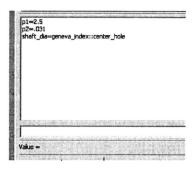

```
p1=2.5
p2=.031
shaft_dia=geneva_index::center_hole




Value =
```

Thus, the Interpart Expression has been created.

Step 4 – Verify the design intent

Make the assembly file the work part to look at the part in entirety again.

We related the parts such that the hole in the index is the driver now of the relationship. We can see if it all works properly by making the Index the work part and changing the diameter of the center hole. Change it to .2 or to .3, hit the Enter key and choose Apply. See the effect of the change on the shaft and index.

Follow-Up

Did you notice anything? There are two shafts. Both shafts changed. Now the other shaft doesn't fit the hole through the Geneva component anymore.

Another optional task is to create an interpart expression in the same manner for the Geneva component so it is related to the shaft.

This completes Section 2-3.

Appendix B. Additional Design and Assembly Projects

This appendix includes additional design projects for five assemblies[1]. Each of the assemblies consists of several components. In order to complete each assembly modeling, you need to first create a solid model for each component using various combinations of features that are covered in the first 11 chapters of this book. Then you need to assemble them using the assembly modeling and master model concepts that are addressed in Chapters 12 and 13. Chapter 12 presents three approaches to assembly modeling. They are repositioning, mating, and interpart modeling. We suggest you to practice all three approaches and compare them with respect to different levels of associative and parametric relations among different components. As a result, different approaches cause different effects of design changes to models.   You will find some non-critical dimensions, particularly on threads, missing in the drawings.   Make default standard parameter values of threads or make your best guess so that the resulting assemblies look as drawn.

Project B-1. Double Bearing Assembly

Project B-2. Double Block Assembly

Project B-3. Wheel Support Assembly

Project B-4. Shock Assembly

Project B-5. Butterfly Valve Assembly

---

[1] The drawings for these assemblies are taken from Technical Graphics Communication by Bertoline and et al. (1997) (reprinted with permission from the publisher McGraw-Hill)

Project B-1. Double Bearing Assembly

ITEM	QTY	NAME	DESCRIPTION
1	2	BUSHING	BRONZE
2	1	BASE	STEEL
3	1	CAP	STEEL
4	6	HEX HEAD BOLT	.50-13UNC X 2.00

DOUBLE BEARING

Project B-1. Continued

PART NAME: CAP

PART NAME: BUSHING

PART NAME: BASE

Project B-2. Double Block Assembly

FASTENER
2 REQ.

Ø .50 X .50

.25

Ø .13

.313 - .18 UNC X 1.75

Ø .25 X .19

BASE
1 REQ.

2.00
1.75
1.13
.87

2.75
1.25

2.75

1.88

1.50

1.25

.375 -.16 UNC
▼ .625

90°

Ø .75

.63

2.00

.25
.63

.25

1.25

2.00

R .25

2.56

4.00

2.00

.375 -.16 UNC THRU TO HOLE
⌴ Ø .50
▼

U-CLAMP
2 REQ.

.313 -.18 UNC

R .125

R .97

.82

R 1.2

2.75

1.25

.22

.63

.47

1.97

2.44

DOUBLE V-BLOCK

Project B-3. Wheel Support Assembly

SOCKET HEAD SHOULDER SCREW 5/8" DIAMETER
2.50" SHOULDER LENGTH RC1 STEEL

BUSHING
OUTER DIAMETER 1.00" FN2
INNER DIAMETER 5/8" RC1
THICKNESS 1/2"
BRONZE

WHEEL
DIAMETER 4.00"
WIDTH 1.00" BODY .50" THICK
HUB WIDTH 1.50" X .75" O.D.
GROOVE 45° AND CENTERED
CAST IRON

.50

DETAIL WHEEL

FN2 FIT

WASHER
INNER DIAMETER 5/8"
BRONZE

SUPPORT COLD
ROLLED STEEL

2.00

1.50

HEX HEAD NUT
1/2" - 13NC

.50

HEX HEAD BOLT
.500–13UNC X 1.00

R .625

Ø 3.25

4.00

R .125

1.50

1.00

2.00

4.00

4.00

4X .500-13UNC

11.50

6.50

2.50

1.00

.75

3.00

BASE
COLD ROLLED STEEL

WHEEL SUPPORT

Project B-4. Shock Assembly

WELD TO U-SUPPORT

WELD TO BRACKET

SHOCK ASSEMBLY

11	1	COTTER PIN	
10	1	CASTLE NUT	STEEL
9	1	PIVOT	STEEL
8	2	BUSHING	BRONZE
7	1	HEX HEAD BOLT	STEEL
6	1	U-SUPPORT	STEEL
5	1	SHAFT	C.R.S.
4	1	SPACER	STEEL
3	1	BRACKET	STEEL
2	1	FLAT WASHER	1.50 X .750 X .125
1	1	SELF-LOCKING NUT	.625-11UNC
ITEM	QTY	NAME	DESCRIPTION

Project B-4. Continued

PART NAME: BRACKET
ALL FILLETS R .313
ALL ROUNDS R .625

2X Ø .500

9.500
4.750 — 2.875 — 1.188
4.750
2.875
1.188
1.500
3.000
2.375
.313
1.500
Ø .750
CENTERED IN OBJECT
.313

HEIGHT OF SHAFT
DETERMINED BY USER
Ø .750
.625-11UNC X 1.00
.125 X .125
PART NAME: SHAFT

Ø 1.75
Ø 2.25
DETERMINED BY USER
PART NAME: SPACER

Ø 2.000
Ø .500
Ø 1.500
PART NAME: BUSHING
.250
1.250

2.500
1.250
.625
.75
6.500
5.000
R .500
Ø 1.500
R 1.063
4X Ø .250
.313
1.313
3.250
PART NAME: PIVOT

2X Ø .500
2X R 1.400
3.813
.313
3.500
PART NAME: U-SUPPORT
ALL FILLETS R .313
ALL ROUNDS R .625

Project B-5. Butterfly Valve Assembly

ITEM	QTY	NAME	DESCRIPTION
1	1	BODY	CAST IRON
2	2	ROUND HEAD MACHINE SCREW	#4-48UNF X .250
3	1	PLATE	ALUMINIUM
4	1	SHAFT	STEEL
5	1	WOODRUFF KEY	
6	1	RETAINER	STEEL
7	3	ROUND HEAD MACHINE SCREW	#10-32UNF X .500
8	1	ARM	STEEL
9	1	HEX HEAD NUT	.375-24UNF

ASSEMBLED SECTION

BUTTERFLY VALVE

B-8

Project B-5. Continued

PART NAME: BODY

R 1.406
6X 120°
6X Ø 1.938
1.594
6X Ø .470
R .500
Ø .562
⏀ 2.563
Ø 1.000
.313
120°
1.750
Ø .750
1.125
Ø 1.50
3.250
2.250
3X #10-32UNF
▼ .375
Ø 2.000

PART NAME: RETAINER

Ø .563
.250
120°
3X Ø .203
Ø 2.000
Ø 1.50

PART NAME: ARM

Ø 1.125
.625
.187
Ø .563
.077 X .128
KEYWAY
3.00
Ø .438
Ø .875

PART NAME: SHAFT

3.898
.240
2X #4-48UNF
.898
Ø .560
.500
.872
1.000
.03 X 45°
BOTH ENDS
.311
.375-24UNF
.472
.375
1.937
.125
Ø .560
WOODRUFF
KEYWAY
.125
Ø .560

PART NAME: PLATE
(ELLIPTICAL)

.969 1.109 1.072
.750 .949
.500 .703
.250
.000
2X Ø .125
1.000
.000
.063

Appendix C. Glossary

ABS	Absolute coordinate system.
Absolute Coordinate System	Coordinate system in which all geometry is located from a fixed or absolute zero point.
Active View	One of up to 50 views per layout in which you can directly work.
Anchor point	The intersection point of a general conic's two end tangent vectors.
Angle	In Unigraphics, an angle measured on the X-Y plane of a coordinate system is positive if the direction that it is swept is counterclockwise as viewed from the positive Z axis side of the X-Y plane. An angle swept in the opposite direction is said to be negative.
Apparent intersection	The intersection between a curve and the projection of another curve that lies in a different plane. The curves must be nonparallel and the projection occurs along the ZC axis.
Approximate Rho	Approximate Rho basically involves treating an arc or spline as if it were a conic, and then computing the rho based on that premise. This can be useful in a number of cases. For example: You may have a spline that resembles a conic, but has an inflection and a lot of data. Being able to get the rho value gives you a head start in replacing the spline with a simple conic.

	You may have a group of cross section curves and want a section surface. If you can get the rho value for the section curves you can build a law function to create a section surface with varying rho.
	Use the Information function to find the Approximate Rho for an arc or spline.
Arc	An incomplete circle; sometimes used interchangeably with the term "circle".
ASCII	American Standard Code for Information Interchange. It is a set of 8-bit binary numbers representing the alphabet, punctuation, numerals, and other special symbols used in text representation and communications protocol.
Aspect Ratio	The ratio of length to height which represents the change in size of a symbol from its original.
Assembly	A collection of piece parts and sub-assemblies representing a product. In Unigraphics, an assembly is a part file that contains components.
Assembly Part	A Unigraphics part file that is a user-defined, structured combination of sub-assemblies, components and/or objects.
Associativity	The ability to tie together (link) separate pieces of information to aid in automating the design, drafting, and manufacture of parts in Unigraphics.
Attributes	Pieces of information that can be associated with Unigraphics geometry and parts such as assigning a name to an object.
Auxiliary View	In Unigraphics, a view that shows the true size and shape of a

	part's face.
Bezier spline	A single segment B-spline.
Block Font	A Unigraphics character font that is the default font used for creating text in drafting objects and dimensions.
Boundary	A set of geometric objects that describes the containment of a part from a vantage point.
Bottom-Up Modeling	Modeling technique where component parts are designed and edited in isolation of their usage within some higher level assembly. All assemblies using the component are automatically updated when opened to reflect the geometric edits made at the piece part level. See Top-down Modeling.
Bridging Curves	A method of creating a b-curve by blending or bridging any two given curves at two specified points on the curves.
B-spline	Abbreviation of nonuniform rational B-spline. Curve created from construction points. See NURBS.
Body	Class of objects containing sheets and solids (see Solid Body and Sheet Body).
CAD/CAM	Computer Aided Design/Computer Aided Manufacturing.
Canned Layout	One of the five layouts available to the user. These include: L1 - Single View, L2 & L3 - Two Views, L4 - Four Views, and L6 - Six Views.
Canned View	One of the canned views available to the user. These include (but are not limited to) the following: TOP, FRONT, RIGHT, LEFT, BOTTOM, BACK, TFR-ISO (top-front-right isometric),

	and TFR-TRI (top-front-right trimetric).
Category, Layer	A name assigned to a layer, or subset of layers. A category, if descriptive of the type of data found on the layers to which it is assigned, will assist the user in identifying and managing data in a part file.
CGM	Computer Graphics Metafile. An ANSI standard format for picture files which can be easily moved between different operating systems and can be read by many viewing programs and plot despoolers.
Chaining	A method of selecting a sequence of curves which are joined end-to-end.
Child	A feature that depends on another for its existence. For example, a hollow cannot exist without a solid, such as a block, that the hollow can be formed in. Also called a "dependent".
Circle	A complete and closed arc, sometimes used interchangeably with the term "arc".
Class Selection	A list of options that allows the user to select objects by various methods.
CL File	Cutter Location File.
CL Point	Cutter Location Point.
Column	A single file array of points used to create a surface. Usually lined up along the V direction of the surface. See Rows and Columns for additional details.

Component	A collection of objects, similar to a group, in an assembly part. A component may be a sub-assembly consisting of other, lower level components.
Component Part	A separate Unigraphics part file that the system associates with a component object in the assembly part.
Cone Direction	Defines the cone direction using the Vector Constructor (common tool) or Constructor.
Cone Origin	Defines the base origin using the Point Constructor (common tool) or Constructor.
Conic	A conic or conic section is a curve that can be formed by intersecting a cone and a plane (parabola, hyperbola, ellipse).
Constraints	Refers to the methods you can use to refine and limit your sketch. The methods of constraining a sketch are geometric and dimensional.
Construction points	Points used to create a spline. Construction points may be used as poles (control vertices), defining points, or data points. See Poles, Defining Points, and Data Points.
Contiguous	End-to-end, as in contiguous curves.
Continuity Checks	Continuity describes the behavior of curves and surfaces at their segment boundaries. The two types of continuity usually dealt with in Unigraphics are mathematical continuity, denoted Cn, where n is some integer, and geometric continuity, denoted Gn. Within Unigraphics these can be loosely defined by the following: Gn indicates the true degree of continuity between two

geometric objects. For example, G0 means the two objects are connected; G1 means they are smoothly connected up to one differentiation, or are tangency continuous. G2 means they are smoothly connected by up to two differentiations, or are curvature continuous; etc. Gn continuities are representation (parameterization) independent.

Cn indicates the degree of continuity between two segments of a b-curve or a b-surface in the NURB representation. Generically, C0 means the two segments are G0 connected. C1 means they are G1 connected; etc. But, C0 does not mean the two segments are just G0 connected -- they could actually be G1 or G2 connected, and so on.

The key point is that Gn is for real physical continuity, while Cn is one mathematical representation of it, which may not be faithful. Since NURB is an industry standard for freeform geometry, Unigraphics uses it. But we always try to have Cn represent the same degree of continuity as Gn, to avoid cases where a curve is G1, but has C0 junction, etc.

Quoting from the ICAD Surface Designer Reference manual: "C0 continuity implies that a common point exists between two adjacent segments (i.e., the segments are touching). C1 implies that there is a common point and the first derivatives of the polynomials (i.e., the tangent vectors) are the same. C2 implies that the first and second derivatives are the same. Geometric continuity is less strict than mathematical continuity. G0 and C0 are equivalent, that is, the segments are positionally continuous. G1 implies that the tangent vectors are equal in direction, but not magnitude. G2 implies the curvature is the same, but the second derivatives are not."

Control Point	A position on existing geometry. Control points are: existing points, endpoints of conics, endpoints and midpoints of open arcs, centers of circles, midpoints and endpoints of lines, and endpoints of splines. The control point for a closed circle is its center, while the control points for an open arc are its end and midpoints. A spline has a control point at each knot point.
Control Polygon	A polygon associated with a spline, which can be used to control the shape of the spline.
Control Vertex	A vertex of the control polygon of a spline.
Coordinate System	A system of axes used in specifying positions (CSYS).
Coordinate System Tool	A group of options used for defining coordinate systems in a variety of different ways. This subfunction is also used to change the work coordinate system and to rotate the part.
Counterclockwise	The right-hand rule determines the counter- clockwise direction. If the thumb is aligned with the ZC axis and pointing in the positive direction, counterclockwise is defined as the direction the fingers would move from the positive XC axis to the positive YC axis.
Current Layout	The layout currently displayed on the screen.
Cross Splines	This is specified when creating a b-surface using the Cubic Fit method. Internal cross splines are not displayed by the system and are not selectable Unigraphics objects; rather, the system uses cross splines internally to help in the construction of b-surfaces.

Cubic Fit Surface	A b-surface creation technique in which a sequence of curves running in a roughly parallel direction is selected, and the system then □fits" them with a b-cubic b-surface.
Current Layout	The layout currently displayed on the screen. Layout data is kept in an intermediate storage area until it is saved.
Curve	A geometric object; this may refer to a line, an arc, a conic, spline or b-curve.
Curve Extension	Unconstructed portion of an open arc. The part of a circle that has been cut away.
Data Base	A comprehensive collection of information referring to the objects that make up a part.
Data Points	Spline construction points for the Least Squares Fit method. A spline created with this method are fit to the points within a certain tolerance and do not necessarily pass through them.
Datum	A datum is a fixed point that anchors a sketch point to a specified location.
Default	Assumed values when they are not specifically defined.
Defining Face	A face of a solid used to create a Midsurface.
Defining Points	Spline construction points. Splines created using defining points are forced to pass through the points. These points are guaranteed to be on the spline.
Degree	A mathematical concept referring to the degree of the polynomial in the equation defining the surface or spline.

Degree-of-Freedom Arrows	Arrow-like indicators that show areas that require more information to fully constrain a sketch.
Dependent	Same as Child.
Derivative Vector	The first derivative or tangent vector to a curve at a given point.
Design in Context	The ability to directly edit component geometry as it is displayed in an assembly. Geometry from other components can be selected to aid in modeling. Also referred to as edit in place.
Detail View	In Unigraphics, a view that illustrates an enlarged section of another view (i.e., a blow-up).
Die Engineering	A separate Unigraphics module that augments the capabilities of modeling by providing a suite of tools targeted for the design of sheet metal stamping dies.
Dimensional constraint	This is a scalar value or expression which limits the measure of some geometric object such as the length of a line, the radius of an arc, or the distance between two points.
Directory	A hierarchical file organization structure which contains a list of filenames together with information for locating those files.
Display File	A file containing display data for retrieval of a part.
Displayed Part	The part currently displayed in the graphics window.
Drawing	A collection of an unlimited number of views. Stored data includes the reference point for each view.

Edit in Place	See Design in Context.
Emphasize Work Part	A color coding option that helps distinguish geometry in the work part form geometry in other parts within the same assembly.
End Point	An end point of a curve or an existing point.
Extension Surface	A tangential, normal, or angled surface created from an existing base surface using the Extension Surfaces creation method.
Expression	An arithmetic or conditional statement that has a value. Expressions are used to control dimensions and the relationships between dimensions of a model.
Face	A region on the outside of a body enclosed by edges.
FACEPAIR_DEF	The name of the Face Pair feature that is created by two opposing defining faces.
FACEPAIR_SEL	The name of the Face Pair feature that is created with a user-selected surface.
Face Pair feature	The fundamental building block of a Midsurface feature. It contains two lists of opposing faces and the resulting Midsurface.
Family member	A read-only part file created from, and associated with, a template part and family table.
Family table	A table created from a template part, in the UG spreadsheet function, that describes the various attributes of the template part that you can change when you create a family member

Fast Font	A Unigraphics character font designed to provide faster Regenerate operations.
Feature	An all-encompassing term which refers to all solids, bodies, and primitives.
File	A group or unit of logically related data which is labeled or named and associated with a specified space. In Unigraphics, parts, patterns, schematic symbols, CL and UG/Open GRIP source, GRIP intermediate, GRIP execution and Font Object data are all stored as files.
Font Box	A rectangle or □box" composed of dashed line objects. The font box defines the size, width and spacing of characters belonging to a particular font.
Fonts, Character	A set of characters designed at a certain size, width and spacing.
Font, Line	Various styles of lines and curves, such as solid, dashed, etc.
Font Object Library	A Unigraphics library containing font object files. Each file includes the necessary information for displaying a particular character font. The font object library can only be accessed through the Font Management option.
Fonts, Line	Various styles of lines and curves, such as solid, dashed, etc.
Font Table	An ordered list of font names representing the character fonts available for the current part.
Free Form Feature	A body of zero thickness. (see Body and Sheet Body)

Gateway Reset	A technique used when recording macros that assures they will always run, regardless of your location within Unigraphics when you launch them. To use Gateway Reset, simply make the first event in the recording of a macro, Application®Gateway. This cancels the current application, and places the macro at a known starting point in the user interface.
Generator Curve	A contiguous set of curves, either open or closed, that can be swept or revolved to create a body.
Geometric Constraint	A relationship between one or more geometric objects that forces a limitation. For example, two lines that are perpendicular or parallel specifies a geometric constraint.
Global Layer Mask	The global layer mask for the entire part. The layer mask defines which layers will be visible and selectable. A view can use either the global or the individual layer mask.
Grid	A rectangular array of implied points used to accurately align locations which are entered by using the □screen position" option.
Group (v.)	Grouping is a procedure for conjoining selected objects so that they can be treated as a single object.
Group (n.)	A collection of selected objects which are treated as a single object.
Guide Curve	A set of contiguous curves that define a path for a sweep operation.
Half Angle	The half vertex angle defines the angle formed by the axis of

	the cone and its side.
Hardcopy	In general, a printed copy of computer output - e.g., drawings or listings. More specifically, the output of the hard-copy unit often attached to a Unigraphics system.
Individual Layer Mask	See View Layer Mask.
Inflection	A point on a spline where the curve changes from concave to convex, or vice versa.
Information Window	The window used in listing operations, such as Information.
Interactive Step	An individual menu in a sequence of menus used in performing a Unigraphics function.
Implied intersection	Intersection formed by extending two line segments that do not touch to the position that they cross. The line segments must be nonparallel and coplanar.
Isometric View	Isometric view orientation - one where equal distances along the coordinate axes are also equal to the view plane. One of the axes is vertical.
Isoparametric Trim/Divide	An option which allows you to trim a b-surface in either the U or V isoparametric direction at a specified parameter.
Join Curve	A method of creating a b-curve in which curves (lines, arcs, conics or splines) may be selected for conversion into a b-curve.
Knot points	Points along a B-spline, representing the endpoints of each

	spline segment.
Layer	A layer is a partition of a part. Layers are analogous to the transparent material used by conventional designers. For example, the user may create all geometry on one layer, all text and dimensions on a second, and tool paths on a third.
Layout	A collection of viewports or window areas, in which views are displayed. The standard layouts in Unigraphics include one, two, four or six viewports.
Least Squares Method	This is a technique for fitting a spline to a series of construction points. The sum of the squares of all of the distances between the spline and the construction points is minimized. This method helps reduce the number of points needed to define the spline and helps ensure a certain degree of smoothness for the spline.
List Box	The usually scrolled window found in dialogs from which you select items. Referred to as a changeable window when it serves multi-purposes.
Macro	A series of interactive steps that are organized as a group and called as a unit.
Menu	A list of options from which the user makes a selection.
MIDSRF	The name of the Midsurface feature.
Midsurface	A sheet body which is created halfway between two defining faces. The points and normals of the parent faces are averaged at corresponding parameters. The properties of a midsurface are exactly the same as any other sheet body; the

	only difference being the method of creation.
Midsurface feature	A feature that gives the user the ability to create and manipulate a list of Midsurfaces and its defining Faces Pairs.
Modal	A parameter or a status is said to be modal if it retains the value assigned to it when it was last used, rather than automatically reverting back to some default value after each usage.
Model Space	The coordinate system of a newly created part. This is also referred to as the absolute coordinate system. Any other coordinate system may be thought of as a rotation and/or translation of the absolute coordinate system.
Multi-Patch Sheet	A b-surface sheet that consists of multiple segments.
Native Mode File System	The Native Mode File Management system is a part of the Common File Interface (CFI) that allows Unigraphics to interface with the native file system on your computer. The Native File Mode allows you to use standard operating system commands and directory structures to manipulate UGII files.
Name (of an expression)	The name of an expression is the single variable on the left hand side of the expression. All expression names must be unique in a part file. Each expression can have only one name. See Expression.
Neutral Point	The starting point, or zero position, of the Navigation Cursor, as specified when the Navigate option is invoked and MB1 is pressed and held down.

NURBS	Acronym standing for Non Uniform Rational B-spline, often referred to as B-spline in the documentation.
Objects	All geometric entities within the Unigraphics environment.
Offset Surface	A Unigraphics surface type created by projecting (offsetting) points along all the normals of a selected surface at a specified distance.
Ordered Point Constructor	A list of options (methods) used to select a large number of point objects using either any of the three available chaining methods or the standard Point Constructor method which allows for specification of required points in turn.
Origin	The point X = 0, Y = 0, Z = 0 for any particular coordinate system.
Orthographic Projection	Projects views from a parent view (also called `base view'). The projected views are automatically aligned and scaled to match the parent view. By choosing the projection angle you want, selecting an existing model and indicating the parent view, you can construct a drawing containing various orthogonal views by simply choosing the view to be projected and the direction of the projection.
Parallel Projection	In a parallel projection, the lines are all parallel to a specified vector. The object is projected onto the view plane by passing parallel lines through each point at the object and finding their intersections with the view plane.
Parametric design	Concept used to define and control the relationships between the features of a model. Concept where the features of the model are defined by parameters.

Parent	A feature on which one or more feature(s) depend for existence. For example, if a block has been hollowed, the block is the parent of the hollow feature.
Part or Model	A collection of Unigraphics objects which together may represent some object or structure.
Part Family	A template part and its family table and family member parts.
Part Modality	Variables that are not automatically changed by the system throughout the life of a particular part (e.g. character size and line width). These variables are filed with the part and will be in effect each time the part is retrieved from the library until explicitly modified by the user and filed with the part.
Partially Loaded Part	A component part which, for performance reasons, has not been fully loaded. Only those portions of the component part necessary to render the higher level assembly are initially loaded (the reference set).
Parts List	A rectangular array of text containing a list of an assembly's contents together with a brief description of them.
Patch	Sections of a free form sheet body. Sheets can consist of a single patch or multiple patches.
Pattern	A collection of objects from a master part file that can be placed (merged) into your current part file as many times as necessary. A pattern is a single object, both from your point of view (e.g. selection, transformations, etc.) and from the system's point of view.
Peak	A point on a spline where the local radius of curvature is

	maximum.
Perspective Projection	In a perspective projection, all lines emanate from a common point; called the center of projection. An object is projected onto the view plane by passing those lines through each point at the object and finding their intersections with the plane.
Point Set	A distribution of points on a curve between two bounding points on that curve.
Point/Slope Continuity	A method for comparing checkpoints on curves or surfaces to corresponding points on curves or surfaces.
Point Constructor	A list of options (methods) by which positions can be specified in Unigraphics. Also called Point Common Tool and Point Constructor.
Plotter	A device which typically uses a pen to draw a permanent copy of the displayed image.
Poles	Spline construction points. Splines created using poles gravitate towards the points but do not actually touch them (except at the endpoints). Poles offer better control of the curvature of the spline than do defining points. Also called control vertices.
Polynomial Cubic B-Surface	A b-surface consisting of an array of associative cube patches which can be exported to most other CAD/CAM/CAE applications.
Position continuous	Referring to a spline that has no breaks in it.
Project	A method to project certain types of geometry onto surfaces

Points/Curves	and planes. Also allows you to move or copy the object to be projected.
Read-only Part	A part for which the user does not have write access privilege.
Real Time Dynamics	Produces smooth pan, zoom, and rotation of a part, though placing great demand on the CPU.
Reference Set	A named section or partition of a Unigraphics part created in the Assemblies application.
Reference View	A view on a drawing in which you cannot directly work.
Refresh	A function which causes the system to refresh the display list on the viewing screen. This removes temporary display items and fills in holes left by Blank or Delete.
RGB	Short for red-green-blue, representing a mixing model or method of describing colors, used with light-based media (such as monitors). RGB uses the additive primaries method, mixing percentages of red, green, and blue to get the desired color. Adding no color produces black, and adding 100 percent of all three colors results in white. Interactive options exist for RGB values in the Unigraphics Color Palette and High Quality Image Output Setup options.
Right-Hand Rule, Conventional	The right-hand rule is used to determine the orientation of a coordinate system. If the origin of the coordinate system is in the palm of the right fist, with the back of the hand lying on a table, the outward extension of the index finger corresponds to the positive Y axis, the upward extension of the middle finger corresponds to the positive Z axis, and the outward extension of the thumb corresponds to the positive X axis.

Right-Hand Rule for Rotation	The right-hand rule for rotation is used to associate vectors with directions of rotation. When the thumb is extended and aligned with a given vector, the curled fingers determine the associated direction of rotation. Conversely, when the curled fingers are held so as to indicate a given direction of rotation, the extended thumb determines the associated vector.
Rho	Rho is the projective discriminant, a scalar value that controls the "fullness" of each conic section. See Approximate Rho.
Row	A single-file array of points used to create a free form sheet body. Defines the U direction of the sheet. See Rows and Columns for additional details.
Screen Cursor	A marker on the screen which the user moves around using some position indicator device. Used for indicating positions, selecting objects, etc. Takes the form of a full-screen cross.
Selection Ball	The screen cursor contains a selection ball when necessary. A portion of an object must fall within this area to be selectable. The size of the selection ball is set in Preferences. The default radius is .125 inches and is centered at the cursor.
ShapeSCAN	A Unigraphics application for reverse engineering that allows you to rapidly model physical parts based on digitized point clouds and for which the corresponding mathematical models do not exist.
Sheet body	An object consisting of one or more faces not enclosing a volume. A body with zero thickness (see Body).
Side face	A list of opposing faces found in a Face Pair.

Single-Patch Sheet	A b-surface sheet that consists of only a single segment.
Sketch	A collection of geometric objects that closely approximates the outline of a particular design. You refine your sketch with dimensional and geometric constraints until you achieve a precise representation of your design. The sketch can then be extruded or revolved to obtain a 3D object or feature.
Sketch Coordinate System (SCS)	The SCS is a coordinate system that corresponds to the plane of the sketch. When a sketch is created the WCS is changed to the SCS of the new sketch.
Slope	The slope in the X-Y plane is the ratio of the Y change in relation to the X change between two points on the line.
Smart body	All bodies created using curves including solid and sheet. A smart body will automatically update when you modify any of its creation parameters (that is, the defining curves, Rho, or the Row and Column degrees).
Solid body	An enclosed volume. A type of body (see Body).
Spline	A smooth free-form curve.
String	A contiguous series of lines and/or arcs connected at their end points.
Studio for Design	A Unigraphics module that provides tools specifically tailored for Industrial Design applications. This includes basic tools for the initial concept stages, such as the creation and visualization of virtual designs, and progresses ultimately through the production of primary and secondary surfaces.

Sub-assembly	A part that both contains components and is itself used as a component in higher-level assemblies.
Surface	The underlying geometry used to define a face on a sheet body. A surface is always a sheet but a sheet is not necessarily a surface (see Sheet Body).
Sweep of Arc	The number of degrees covered by an arc.
System	The Unigraphics system.
Tangent continuous	Indicating a smooth spline. A tangent continuous spline has no "kinks" or "folds" in it.
Template Part	A Unigraphics part file constructed in such a way as to allow a family of parts to be built based on it.
Temporary Part	An empty part that is optionally created for any component parts that cannot be found during the loading of an assembly.
Tolerance	The allowable deviation from a standard, especially the range of variation permitted in maintaining a specified dimension in machining a piece; the total permissible variation in a size or location dimension; the difference between the permitted minimum and maximum sizes of a part.
Top-down Modeling	Modeling technique where component parts can be created and edited while working at the assembly level. Geometric changes made at the assembly level are automatically reflected in the individual component part when saved. See Bottom-Up Modeling.
Trim	To shorten or extend a curve.

Trimetric View	A viewing orientation which provides you with an excellent view of the principal axes. In Unigraphics II, the trimetric view has the Z-axis vertical. The measure along the X-axis is 7/8 of the measure along Z, and the measure along the Y-axis is 3/4 of the measure along Z.
UG/Open GRIP	Graphics Interactive Programming - A high-level language that provides the user with an optional means of operating the system. Almost any operation which can be performed interactively in Unigraphics can also be performed by executing the commands of a UG/Open GRIP program. It performs mathematical computations, includes branching and looping capabilities, and allows the use of separately compiled sub-programs.
Undulations	Reversals of curvature in a spline.
Units	The unit of measure in which you may work when constructing in Unigraphics. Upon log on, you may define the unit of measure as inches or millimeters.
Upgraded Component	A component that was originally created pre-V10, but has been opened in V10 or later and been upgraded to remove duplicate geometry.
User Exits	Allows you to automatically run UG/Open GRIP programs at certain points in Unigraphics.
User Table	A list of all valid Unigraphics user numbers and passwords. When a user logs on, the user number and password will be compared to those in the table.

User Tool	Custom built dialogs from which you can launch macros and UG/Open API and GRIP programs.
Vertex	A defining point in certain geometric constructions. The vertices of a spline are the intersections of adjacent line segments forming the control polygon of the spline; the vertices of a polygon are the intersection points of adjacent sides of the polygon.
View	A particular display of the model. View parameters include view orientation matrix; center; scale; X,Y and Z clipping bounds; perspective vector; drawing reference point and scale.
View Dependent Edit	A mode in which the user can edit a part in the current work view only.
View Dependent Geometry	Geometry created within a particular view. It will only be displayed in that view.
View Dependent Modifications	Modifications to the display of geometry in a particular view. These include erase from view and modify color, font and width.
View Layer Mask	A layer mask specific to a view. The mask will determine which layers are visible for that view. Use the individual (global) mask to control layer visibility for specific (entire) views.
View of the cursor	Perspective that allows you to select positions in a three dimensional environment. Indicating a screen position with respect to the *view of the cursor* specifies a location in a plane parallel to the viewing screen. This is different than the screen position in the Point Constructor which always specifies a position in the XC-YC plane.

WCS	Work Coordinate System.
WCS, Work Plane	The work coordinate system (WCS) is the coordinate system singled out by the user for use in construction, verification, etc. The coordinates of the WCS are called work coordinates and are denoted by XC, YC, ZC. The XC-YC plane is called the work plane.
Where-Used Report	Contains a list of all part files in which a specified component part exists.
Work Layer	The layer on which geometry is being constructed. You may create objects on only one layer at a time.
Work Part	The part in which you create and edit geometry. The work part can be your displayed part or any component part that is contained in your displayed assembly part. When displaying a piece part, the work part is always the same as the displayed part.
Work View	The view in which work is being performed. When the creation mode is view dependent, any construction and view dependent editing will occur only in the current work view.
Z Clipping Planes	Front and back clipping planes parallel to the X-Y plane of the view. Geometry is clipped to these planes. Only geometry which lies between the two planes is displayed.
XC axis	X axis of the work coordinate system.
YC axis	Y axis of the work coordinate system.
ZC axis	Z axis of the work coordinate system.

Appendix D. Transition between V.16, V.17, and V.18

The Unigraphics user interface of V16 has been significantly changed from the previous versions and greatly improved. Unigraphics V16 is fully Windows compliant and uses native Windows user interface technology to provide a familiar operating environment for Windows users. These changes provide a more modern look and feel for Unigraphics, while streamlining the user interaction for increased user productivity.

We have used the Unigraphics user interface of V18 throughout the book. For all V16, 17, and 18, however, the modeling user interface is near identical for all the features used in this book, and thus this book is directly applicable for V16 and 17. We believe that this will be true for future versions unless there is a major change in the Windows user interface. In this book we present a set of essential features most commonly used in solid modeling for engineering design. We do not expect a drastic change in these essential features (user interface or functionality) in the future. Below we give a summary of some noticeable changes, although they are straight and easy to pick up.

Feature Modeling Interface Changes

V18 user interface for the modeling features described in this book is near identical to those of V16 and 17 except for the following dialogue changes.

Block, Hole, and Boss: The procedure and methods are no different, but all the steps are on a single dialog in V18 as compared to multiple dialogues in V16. We give a comparison example for Hole below.

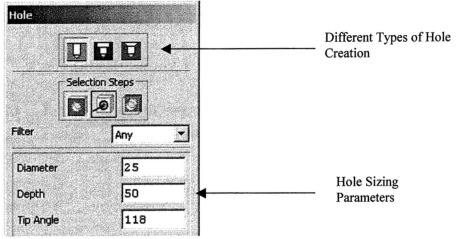

Different Types of Hole Creation

Hole Sizing Parameters

V.18 Hole Dialogue

V.16 Hole Dialogue: hole type

V.16 Hole Dialogue: placement face

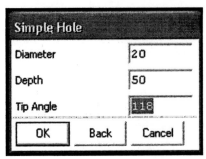

V 16 Hole Dialogue: parameters

Sketch: The appearance of the sketch tools dialog, and some of its icons have changed, but the functions remain nearly the same as shown below.

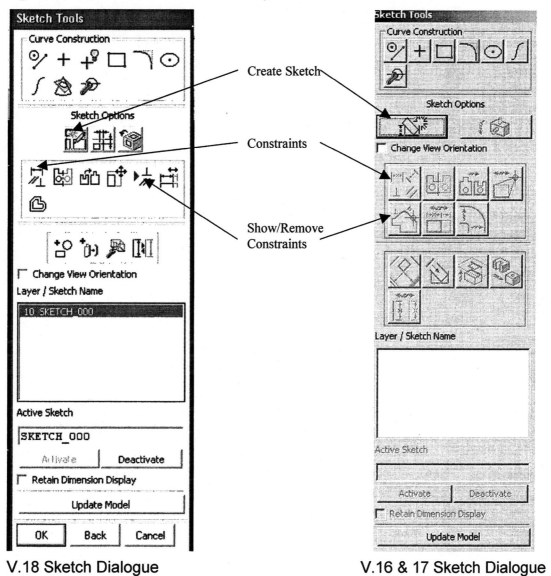

V.18 Sketch Dialogue   V.16 & 17 Sketch Dialogue

Assembly Modeling Interface Changes

In V17 and 18, Assemblies licenses are controlled by the **Assemblies** option on the Applications pulldown menu (**Applications → Assemblies**). Toggling **Assemblies** ON causes an Assemblies license to be taken, and the functions available from the Assemblies pulldown menu to expand. Most of the functions available on **Assemblies → Edit Structure** in V16 are on the **Assemblies → Components** cascade menu in V17 and 18 as shown below.

V.16 and V.17/18 Assembly User Interface Comparison

V17 and 18 provide some new functions in manipulating components of assemblies. These are available on the **Assemblies → Context Control** cascade menu as shown below.

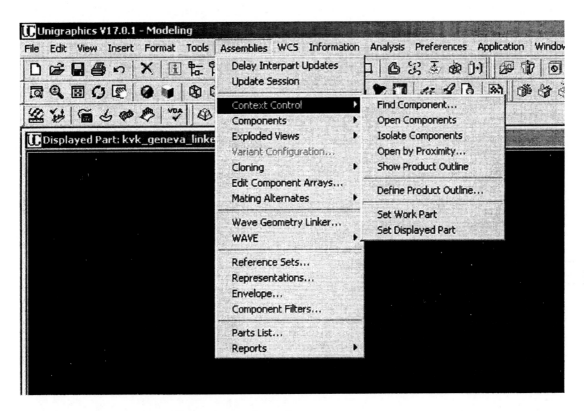

The table below describes these functions.

Context Control Menu Options	
Find Component	Lets you search for components matching defined criteria.
Open Components	Lets you open the selected components.
Isolate Components	Lets you show just the selected components. All other components are blanked.
Open by Proximity	Provides options for loading or selecting components close to the selected components.
Show Product Outline	Shows or hides an outline of the overall assemblies.
Define Product Outline	Lets you define which objects should appear in the product outline.

V17 and 18 provide the Assemblies toolbar to easily access the above assembly functions as an alternative to using the Assemblies pulldown menu. If the Assemblies toolbar is not visible, choose **View→Toolbars→Customize** or **Tools→Customize** to bring up the Customize dialog. Scroll down the **Toolbars** list on the Toolbars page, then turn ON the **Assemblies** toolbar by setting its checkbox. To find out the function description of the Assembly toolbar icons, move your cursor on each icon. Then you will see the description of the icon displayed.